Don Turner, hero of the popular television series *One by One*, is based on David Taylor. He is one of the handful of independent veterinary consultants to zoos, marinelands and safari parks. At a moment's notice he and his partner must be prepared to fly anywhere in the world to the aid of sick or injured animals. He has frequently appeared (as himself!) on radio and television programmes. His six previous books are all available in hardback from Unwin Hyman Ltd and in paperback from Unwin Paperbacks:

ZOOVET
The World of a Wildlife Vet

DOCTOR IN THE ZOO
The Making of a Zoovet

GOING WILD
More Adventures of a Zoovet

NEXT PANDA, PLEASE!
Further Adventures of a Zoovet

THE WANDERING WHALE
and other adventures from a zoovet's casebook

DRAGON DOCTOR
More adventures from a zoovet's casebook

The Complete
ONE
BY
ONE

DAVID TAYLOR

London
UNWIN PAPERBACKS
Boston   Sydney   Wellington

First published by Unwin Paperbacks,
a Division of Unwin Hyman Ltd in 1987

UNWIN® PAPERBACKS, a Division of Unwin Hyman Ltd,
40 Museum Street, London WC1A 1LU, UK

Unwin Paperbacks, a Division of Unwin Hyman Ltd,
Park Lane, Hemel Hempstead, Herts HP2 4TE

Allen & Unwin Australia Pty Ltd,
8 Napier Street, North Sydney, NSW 2060, Australia

Unwin Paperbacks, a Division of Unwin Hyman Ltd,
with the Port Nicholson Press
PO Box 11–838 Wellington, New Zealand

British Library Cataloguing in Publication Data

Taylor, David, *1934–*
    The complete one by one: the real-life
    adventures of TV's most famous zoovet.
1. Zoo veterinarians
I. Title
636.098'092'4   SF995.84
ISBN 0–04–925038–8
ISBN 0–04–925039–6 Pbk

Set in 10½ on 11½ point Palatino by
Nene Phototypesetters Ltd, Northampton
and printed in Great Britain by Biddles Ltd, Guildford, Surrey

By the same author

ZOOVET: THE WORLD OF A WILDLIFE VET

DOCTOR IN THE ZOO: THE MAKING OF
A ZOO VET

GOING WILD: ADVENTURES OF A ZOOVET

NEXT PANDA PLEASE!: FURTHER ADVENTURES
OF A WILDLIFE VET

THE WANDERING WHALE: AND OTHER
ADVENTURES FROM A ZOOVET'S CASEBOOK

DRAGON DOCTOR: MORE ADVENTURES
FROM A ZOOVET'S CASEBOOK

Chapter One

THE FIRST steps I took towards becoming a zoovet were made when I was a young schoolboy with an absorbing interest in everything which flew, swam, crept or crawled. Wandering the fields and moors of the Pennines around my home in Rochdale, near Manchester, I would find no end of creatures obviously in trouble, especially sheep. Unable to rise, often with inflamed and swollen vulvas, frequently being eaten away by blowfly maggots, these pitiful animals lay alone on windswept hillsides or at the bottom of quarries, or struggled in moorland streams. It was no use trying to find the owners of the sheep. The moors are vast and the flocks wander for miles, gathered in only once or twice a year by shepherds who miraculously know where they are likely to be. Besides, the farmers did not bother to do anything for these fallen individuals even when they came across one. ' 'Twon't do no good, lad,' they would say, turning their back on the animal's misery and trudging off. The moor was common land and the grass free food. Losing a few sheep from disease or foxes or thieves was part of the game. They still made enough to live by.

School homework would be forgotten as I crouched in the rain over yet another sodden woolly body, thumbing through a book called *Veterinary Counter Practice*. This slim volume was written to help chemists give first-aid advice in their shops to pet owners. It was illustrated by Edwardian engravings of bearded men in frock coats solemnly holding unprotesting and improbable cats with linen-draped heads over bowls belching medicated steam, and of ornately coiffed ladies using what looked like armoured gauntlets to thrust pills down dogs' throats. Certainly it was the Gospel on veterinary matters as far as I was concerned. I did not know that I was looking at sheep dying of gas-gangrene brought on by difficult lambing with livers riddled with fluke parasites or with blood-streams lethally deficient in calcium, none of which was mentioned in my book. I just covered the animals with my jacket, treated their inflamed parts with Germolene oint-ment, picked the maggots off them and forced Dad's brandy between their lips.

I do not think a single one of my sheep patients ever recovered. Once, twice, sometimes three times a day I would go out to them and sooner or later I would find them dead. On one black occasion I came across a ram that had fallen into a quarry but was still alive. The jagged ends of its shattered femur poked a full four inches through the skin, alive with industrious bluebottles. Trembling and sick with fright, I killed my first patient, suffocating him with my jacket wrapped tight round his nostrils and mouth. He took a long time to die. I walked home dizzy with remorse and did not sleep at all for two nights.

In addition to the Germolene and brandy, my box of medicaments included vitamin tonic and tincture of arnica, a stinging brown herbal preparation which was my grand-mother's cure-all. Grandmother seldom walked out on the moors with me, but was my ally, mentor, co-conspirator and assistant in all my surgical work at home on small beasts. She was a spirited, bustling woman with features the colour of pale honey and homely as an oven-bottom muffin. She knew alcohol, tobacco and cosmetics to be works of the Devil and had stormed out of church in mid-sermon when the new curate had revealed himself to be an evolutionist. Sturdily built, with grey gleaming eyes in a round face, she ate little other than a sort of unbleached tripe, a diet which she never appeared to find monotonous

2

and which she augmented on Mondays with cold fatty mutton and mint sauce. The small boys of the neighbourhood held her in great respect for the way in which, if she were so minded, she could strike a brilliant shower of sparks from the cobblestones in our back street by clipping them expertly with her iron-soled Lancashire clogs. Lots of the lads, myself included, could kick atoms of fire from the stones like this as we lounged outside on a summer evening, but none of us could approach the effortless pyrotechnic display put on by the old lady as she passed us on her way to or from the tripe shop.

There was a second reason why the small boys held her in great awe. Along with the strictly seasonal hobbies of 'swaling' (burning the dead grass on the moor edges); 'conkering' (duelling with horse chestnuts hardened and threaded onto pieces of string in which the object was to split one's opponent's nut away from its string), cricket, and whipping tops along the flagstones, we all kept mice. The problem was that getting hold of tame mice was almost impossible during the war years, and there was a serious dearth of the small rodents in the hutches, pockets and private hideaways of the boys in our street. Grandmother solved the problem. Somehow she found out that they kept mice, both white and chocolate coloured, at the Rochdale gasworks, presumably to test for gas just as canaries were used in coal mines. One Saturday morning she led a band of us down to the gasworks. We each carried some form of small container, a tin or a cardboard box. Ecstatically, we came home with mice; Grandmother knew the man who had the key to the room where the mice were kept. Normally a surly individual, he was genial in Grandmother's presence and chuckled as he put one or two of the velvety little creatures into each of the containers thrust urgently under his nose. After that breakthrough, we tried visits to the gasworks alone, but without Grandmother it never worked. They had none to spare, they did not keep any mice, the man was too busy. But for Grandmother, persuaded by a gaggle of imploring six- and seven-year-olds to make a detour from her Saturday trip to market, mice were always forthcoming.

Hardworking and practical, she was at the same time highly sentimental. She paid me threepence a week to sing for her each Sunday evening a sugary ballad entitled 'I'll Walk Beside You' while my mother accompanied me on the piano. This excruciating ritual regularly brought tears to Grandmother's eyes (and had the same effect, though for different reasons, on the rest of the household); mercifully it ceased when my voice began to change.

In her youth Grandmother had been a seamstress, and she insisted that I learn to sew and knit, arguing that the art of surgery on which my heart was firmly set was just cutting and stitching, and that neatness in weaving threads in and out of living flesh could be developed on pieces of flannel, silk and worsted. I spent hours grafting squares of cloth together under Grandmother's grey, hawk-like eyes and had my knuckles painfully rapped by one of her thick metal knitting needles whenever I grew careless. Her wisdom was confirmed years later at university when the Surgery Professor, watching the students clumsily practise their first simple operations on the chill, unbleeding bodies of already dead animals, urged us to darn our socks and sew on buttons at every opportunity. 'Less beer and wenching and more needlework, gentlemen,' he would roar as we cobbled away at the corpses.

Grandmother and I made a good team. She was adept with the only anaesthetic we had, a freezing spray of ethyl chloride. With one hand she would hold the struggling form of a thrush I had found fluttering and tumbling frantically through the undergrowth, and with the other would direct a stream of the numbing liquid onto the bird's shattered wing bone. As hoarfrost formed on the blood-stained flight feathers, she would tell me to begin splinting the limb with matchsticks and strips of sticking-plaster, her eyes following the movements of my fingers through a pair of gold-rimmed spectacles.

My parents tolerated well enough at first the toads convalescing in the bathroom cupboard, the paralysed owl that sat on top of the grandfather clock in the hall and the rabbit road-accident victims that either regained vitality or inexorably wasted away in the emergency wards I estab-

4

lished in empty zinc washing tubs. But as the number of patients grew, so did the problems. The owl on the hall clock stopped the ancient timepiece when I forgot one day to replace the sheet of newspaper on which he squatted and his droppings slipped through a gap in the wooden casing and completely clogged the brass works. With the greatest difficulty Dad cleaned them up, but the clock never worked properly again. Still, if any member of the family raised the matter of the luckless clock, Grandmother would fold her arms, heave up her bosom and tetchily remind all present that it was her clock, that it suited her very well and that it never had kept good time: a preposterous statement that all knew, but none dared say, was the very opposite of the truth. With the grumblings silenced, Grandmother would slip me a solemn wink.

When the war came, our house's old coal-cellar was converted into the family's air-raid shelter. Its ceiling was reinforced by bracing beams and pillars, and bunk beds and supplies of tinned food were put in there. In fact, Rochdale was never attacked and the family did not seem to make use of the shelter during the infrequent air-raid warnings. I soon saw how this could be turned to my advantage, for there had been more trouble with my parents over my veterinary activities. My father, going into the garden to inspect the rows of glass cloches under which he grew radishes and lettuce, had found not only that his ripe, fresh salad had been requisitioned for essential victualling of the rabbit wounded in the zinc tubs, but also that two recuperating old hedgehogs were actually bedded down within the line of cloches. Grandmother to the rescue again. She stood between my irate father and myself and defended her beloved seven-year-old grandson. 'Enough of that, Frank,' she said to my father, wagging a stern finger. 'There's a war on, you know.'

That was all she said. The power was in the way she said it. I can still remember clearly the sheer force of her words as she stood, arms akimbo, grey eyes unblinking. Nothing could have sounded less unreasonable or more obvious: with a war on it was time for every English man and

5

woman, and every English rabbit, owl and hedgehog, to stand shoulder to shoulder in the common cause.

Next day, as Grandmother replanted Dad's garden with salad seeds, I took her into my confidence and outlined my idea of putting the more contentious species of mammal and bird in the apparently unused air-raid shelter.

'Your mum won't have it, dear,' Grandmother murmured as we discussed the possibilities. 'I know we don't often use the shelter, but suppose we do, some time?'

I argued that it was most unlikely that we would and that, apart from the old lavatory in the yard, I had no alternatives. Grandmother eventually agreed to help me but suggested that I bring my patients into the room via the chute which had been the means of delivering coal from the street when the coal-cellar was being used for its original purpose. In this way I would avoid the front and back doors and the attentions of other members of the family. It was a sound idea. My accomplice waited in the big room next door to the coal-cellar, bottling fruit, squeezing clothes through the mangle in front of the high open coal fire or doing a bit of whitewashing. With my patient in a sack or wrapped in my jacket I lifted the heavy iron grate from the coal chute at pavement level and slid down into the new hospital ward. There on the bunk beds I had the boxes, tins, jars and cages that held the sick and infirm. When the coast was clear, Grandmother would slip in and we would get to work.

The air-raid shelter hospital survived a first discovery by my young sister, Vivienne, who stumbled on it one day but was bought off by Grandmother, who gave Vivienne a little locket in exchange for her silence. Shortly afterwards, however, an air raid over Manchester led to Rochdale having a long alarm call on the sirens. The sound of bombing could be distinctly heard in our house that night and my parents decided we should all sleep in the shelter. Piling through the doorway in their pyjamas, the family found the place of refuge already fully occupied by things furry, scaly and feathered. Worse, my father discovered that I had used almost the whole cache of tinned corned beef on feeding the hedgehogs, and my little sister was

bitten through her nightdress as she sleepily sat down on the bottom bunk and on the orphan fox cub to whom it belonged.

Grandmother miraculously soothed everyone's shattered nerves and fearlessly admitted opening the tins of corned beef for me, but then and there my long-suffering father decided to convert the lavatory in the yard into a recognized and approved wild animal hospital. The problem with the lavatory/hospital was that there was no room for Grandmother and me to do any actual work. That still had to be done elsewhere. Our favourite place was the kitchen. The light was good and that was essential, particularly for our regular hedgehog clinics. Together we would set about painting with chloroform the bloated blood-sucking ticks clinging to the bellies of our prickly patients. After waiting a few moments for a parasite to loosen its hold, Grandmother would stand back while I, as head surgeon, picked it off with tweezers. The trouble with hedgehogs, particularly sick ones, is that they often carry a hefty load of fleas around with them as well. The warm kitchen seemed to encourage these prodigious jumpers to leave their hosts, and on one potentially disastrous occasion my mother found scores of energetic little varmints leaping about on some pastry she was rolling out. Grandmother seized one, cracked it between finger and thumbnail and pronounced it to be a mosquito. Since it was late January, she had to add that it was an unseasonably early mosquito, but after that we began to use DDT powder on the animals before putting them into the hospital shed. Grandmother always made sure my mother was out or busy somewhere else in the house before we began hedgehog clinics. We used the kitchen table and spoke in low voices.

When things went well, Grandmother would hum gleefully and give me a hug. Just having me to herself pleased her enormously and, although she undoubtedly loved the animals we dealt with, her principal reward I think was to feel that in some way she was helping to lay the first tiny foundations of what we both wanted me to become – a veterinarian. We would never dream that I might do anything else or that I might not be able to qualify for veterinary school. 'Why,' Grandmother would tell her cronies, 'one day David's going to treat tigers.' She was dead right.

When it came to goldfish, newts and frogs with skin diseases we at first did not do very well. I painted their ulcers with creams and antiseptic lotions but the water quickly washed these away. Time after time I had to bury my failures in the garden.

'I've an idea,' Grandmother said one day, as she watched me dispose of the most recent victim, a goldfish. 'Go and get me the paste I use for my false teeth, David!'

I went upstairs for the ointment that Grandmother, locked in the bathroom, used in the mysterious ritual of her toilet each morning.

'Now,' she said when I gave her the tin of tacky grey stuff, 'next time we have a goldfish with one of those nasty sores, we'll paint on the arnica as usual but then, before putting him back in the water, we'll smear on some of this

8

denture paste. It's funny stuff; as soon as it gets wet it sets like wax. That's how I keep my teeth in, young feller. Here – try a bit.'

I took a little of the grey paste and put it on my tongue. It was tasteless but I could feel it changing its consistency and sticking tight. I ran my tongue along the top of my mouth but the paste did not come off, and it was still hanging around when I went to bed that night. When I found the paste still unpleasantly tacky on my gums the following morning I began to realize the possibilities of the stuff. Now all we needed was a suitable case.

Some weeks later a friend brought me a lovely big frog. He was green, glistening and impassive as he sat on the palm of my hand, gulping. One of his front toes was swollen and had a parboiled appearance. Serum oozed through the skin. I showed him to Grandmother. 'The false-teeth stuff,' I reminded her. 'This is our chance.'

Grandmother was enthusiastic. 'Get the paste from my room,' she instructed. 'We'll put it on over some comfrey ointment.'

Comfrey ointment was only one of the herbal preparations whose virtues Grandmother preached. As well as arnica tincture, she taught me how to use quinine, senna and ipecacuanha wine. I was supervised in applying iodine and gentian violet and sticky kaolin poultices. Sometimes we would take animals with respiratory troubles and go out to seek the municipal road-menders with their smoking tar-boilers. Grandmother would tip the wide-eyed workmen a shilling as we stood letting an armful of sniffling hedgehog breathe in the pungent vapour for a quarter of an hour. 'What's good for whooping cough in children will be good for hedgehogs,' she would say confidently.

Grandmother held the frog gently while I smeared soothing, dark-green comfrey ointment on the inflamed toe. Then I covered the whole of the delicate foot with the false-teeth paste and placed the frog in a large glass jar with a couple of inches of water and a stone to climb on. I was pleased to see the paste stick to his foot as he paddled about. Next day it was still holding the comfrey ointment in place. Grandmother seemed very pleased and patted my head. Three days later we wiped away the paste and the ointment and looked at the toe. There was no doubt about it; the swelling was going down and the toe looked healthier. I repeated the double application, returned the frog to his ward and presented him with half a dozen fat bluebottles that I had caught for him. The frog and Grandmother made veterinary history, for the toe healed completely in a week, a record for frogs attending my clinic, and we released him in the pond of a nearby park. I still use Grandmother's denture paste on dolphin and sea-lion wounds.

Grandmother also hit on a novel way of treating tortoises and similar creatures that had taken a tumble or received blows hard enough to crack their shells, exposing the soft tissues underneath. Nowadays I happily cut away great windows in tortoise and terrapin shells to do operations; the window in the shell is repaired with modern epoxy resins and glass fibre and heals perfectly in a few months. When Grandmother and I were in practice, we had no such thing as epoxy resins and plastics, but she was on the right track. I must have been about twelve years old when she came up with the notion.

'It occurs to me,' she said one day when we were surveying the septic, irregular hole in a terrapin carapace caused by the bite of a cat, 'that to protect the soft stuff underneath once you've cleaned it up, we should seal the hole in the shell properly. Get the Bulldog kit.'

My Bulldog kit for repairing punctures in the tyres of my bicycle consisted of a small tin containing sandpaper, glue, french chalk powder and discs of inner-tube rubber. I fetched it. Inner tubes, fine, I thought as I returned with the kit, but terrapins?

But there was no arguing with Grandmother. 'Now, my boy,' she said, 'cut out the diseased flesh.' She sprayed a fine stream of freezer on the spot. 'Dab on the arnica.' I did as she directed. 'And now go ahead as if the terrapin was just an ordinary tyre puncture.'

The terrapin pulled in his head with a faint hiss, apparently resigned to reincarnation as a bicycle. I sandpapered the edges of the hole in the shell, dusted them lightly with the chalk, applied the sticky glue and pressed on a rubber patch of the appropriate size. A perfect job.

Grandmother beamed. 'Now,' she said, 'judging by the size of the hole and knowing how long it takes one's fingernails to grow half an inch and allowing for the fact that terrapins are cold-blooded and likely to heal slower than mammals like us, I reckon you ought to be able to take a peek in about a month.'

The punctured terrapin, with the black patch looking like a trapdoor covering his machinery, re-extended his head and legs when he was certain that he was back in his vivarium and not likely to find himself caught up in the Tour de France. He looked unconcerned and began nibbling a tiny pond snail.

The patch held underwater, and each day I checked the edges to see they were secure. As the days went by, 'Black Spot' seemed destined to be a good deal luckier than the name I had given him. One month to the day I brought the terrapin into the kitchen. Even Grandmother held her breath as I snipped the rubber patch with her nail scissors. I peeled the rubber back and we bumped our heads as we bent for a closer look. I let out a gasp of delight; the shell had knitted together completely and healthy new carapace covered the hole. 'Black Spot' did not allow himself to get excited as Grandmother and I hugged one another and laughed with relief – we took our work very seriously and shared our occasional successes with no less intimacy than when we commiserated with one another over our frequent failures.

'Grandma,' I said, 'one day they'll award you the Nobel Prize for Medicine.'

I had total faith in Grandmother's knowledge, and only slowly did this state of affairs reverse itself. By the time I went to university she was laid low with chronic heart disease and would not take a pill or a drop of medicine prescribed by the most eminent of specialists until her grandson and one-time partner had given the OK. She was immensely proud when I made it as a veterinarian. She hung my degree scroll above her bed and lived for me to go and talk about the old days and check the latest advice of her doctor.

Some years later I tackled my first giant tortoise case, one of the massive and rare 300-pound Galapagos tortoises at Belle Vue Zoo, Manchester. Not having had experience of the immense contractile power of their hind-leg muscles, I had let the beast trap my hand securely within the shell where I had been injecting into the soft skin of the groin. I wonder what Grandmother would have to say about patching up monsters like this, I was thinking as the keepers dragged on the rapidly disappearing leg that was pinioning me. I would tell her about it when I visited her that evening, now bed-ridden but alert as ever. I could imagine her softly wrinkled golden face breaking into a wide grin as I reminded her about 'Black Spot' and compared him with his huge Galapagos relative.

The telephone rang. The head reptile keeper took the call and then came over to me.

'Dr Taylor,' he said, 'bad news, I'm afraid. Your father rang to say that your grandmother has just passed away.'

Chapter Two

T HANKS TO Grandmother's encouragement, my passion for animals stayed with me through school and university, and at university I found myself being drawn more and more towards the care of the exotic species, the wild, sometimes rare animals who, it seemed to me, demanded veterinary work of the most challenging and the most rewarding sort. After graduating in the late 'fifties I took a partnership in a veterinary practice in my home town of Rochdale, Lancashire. Rochdale is a grey, lustreless town of around 100,000 souls lying beneath the damp western slopes of the desolate and rocky Pennine moorland, with the big industrial centre of Manchester situated on the flat land twelve miles to the west and surrounded by smaller towns and villages, all of which saw their heyday in the industrial revolution and the reign of King Cotton, when the moist climate of Lancashire was so perfect for the spinning of yarn before air-conditioning and humidifiers were dreamed of. Above Rochdale's cobbled streets rose a forest of tall mill chimneys, but what sorts of animals were to be found in those drizzly streets, in the shabby smallholdings and on the bleak, windy moorlands? Certainly none of the wild, exciting creatures of which I dreamed: tigers, buffaloes or armadilloes.

A typical veterinary practice in Rochdale consisted of a mixture of household pets and farm animals, and it was on dogs involved in road accidents, sows that got into difficulties when giving birth and sheep struck down by mysterious lethal epidemics that I learned the arts of surgery, obstetrics and medicine. It was useful, rewarding experience in a general practice like hundreds of others in the north of England – but there was something else, something of vital importance to a young vet who had already developed a consuming interest in exotic species. Among the clients of the practice I had joined was the large zoo in Manchester, Belle Vue. There were other practices nearer the zoo but the connection went back to the nineteenth century, when Rochdale was the veterinary centre of that part of England. The vet in the practice who had for several years done all the work at Belle Vue was Norman Whittle, and with him I had visited cases at the zoo as a student and had first gained some idea of the problems of exotic animal medicine. Now that I was qualified, surely I could achieve my ambition and get to grips myself with the diseases of the wild animals in the zoo in Manchester. But how? The zoo director had a good working relationship with Norman Whittle and trusted him. If an elephant was sick or a python poorly, it was Whittle he sent for. What possible good could Taylor, the new boy, do? There was apparently no escape from my predicament. I could not get in to do the work because my experience was virtually nil, but unless I did achieve a breakthrough and treated some zoo animals I could not begin to get the experience.

Wednesdays began to assume an immense importance in my life, for Norman had his half-day off each week on Wednesday afternoon and I was on call for Belle Vue. This might be my chance, I thought, but for months I was disappointed. Unless the zoo needed him urgently they would leave a message asking Norman to call on the Thursday morning, and in the rare event of an emergency, Edith, our receptionist, would manage to contact him wherever he was and that was the end of his half-day relaxation. It was most frustrating; my one chance to deputize for my senior partner was if he was out of contact on a Wednesday afternoon or away, on holiday abroad for

14

instance, but on these occasions Belle Vue's animal stock seemed to be strictly on their best behaviour and paragons of blooming health and vitality, right down to the weediest chipmunk in the small mammal house.

Then it happened. It was Wednesday afternoon. Norman Whittle had gone to the coast and was not expected back until late. The zoo director, Mr Wilson, rang. Edith explained that Norman was away. Yes, OK then, was the reply, if it had to be Dr Taylor, Dr Taylor it would have to be. But hurry! One of the chimpanzees had lost a thumb. I jumped gleefully into my battered old Jowett van and set off.

It had all started over the asparagus. Each day a rich variety of fruits and vegetables was sent up to the great ape house at Belle Vue from the wholesale market in the city, depending on price, availability and what was in season. Out of the day's selection Len, the senior ape keeper, would build up a balanced and attractive diet for his collection of chimps, orang-utans and gorillas. A slim, phlegmatic individual with grey eyes blinking behind spectacles and a chirpy Manchester accent, he had to make sure that the apes received essential protein, vitamins and roughage. Whenever possible he included delicacies which his charges could enjoy for the sheer fun of eating – grapes, pomegranates or peaches. An odd case of eggplants or avocados left unsold at the end of the day would usually end up at the zoo, and on this particular day a crate stuffed with tender asparagus bunches had arrived. Len took a few bunches down to the ape house to see what his chimps would make of them.

Robert, the big male chimpanzee, shared quarters with two adoring females, Sapphire and Chloe. Robert was a highly successful chimp Casanova who had sired a number of healthy infants at Belle Vue. As his reputation for a reliable, no-nonsense approach to the business of breeding grew, he acted as surrogate husband to a number of females sent in from other zoos. Whether they were ugly or pretty, placid or cantankerous, intelligent or somewhat simple-minded, it did not matter to Robert. He accepted all comers with equal decorum, and the erstwhile barren females

15

would leave after a few weeks' amorous holiday in Manchester, indubitably and uncomplainingly pregnant. As well as being a most gallant and gentle begetter, though, Robert was also a gourmand; in fact he was downright greedy. Woe betide anybody who came between him and his victuals. If he fancied something tasty he had to have it, and none of his companions dared indicate that perhaps Robert's eyes were too big for his belly.

When Len gave a bunch of the tender white and lilac asparagus shoots to each of the three chimps who stuck their arms through the bars, it was the first time that any of them had seen this vegetable. Robert shuffled through his bundle of succulent stalks, sniffed the buds, took a bite and found them exquisite. Sapphire and Chloe were doing the same. Robert gulped down his share and craved a second helping. Sapphire's had all gone but Chloe still held a few pieces; like Gladstone, she believed in the virtue of thoroughly chewing her food. Grunting, Robert shuffled over to Chloe and imperiously thrust a hairy hand towards

16

the remaining asparagus stalks. Chloe whipped them smartly behind her back and screeched at the importunate male, her lips curled back and her white teeth chattering. For a second or two Robert was nonplussed – he was used to getting his own way without resistance. He put on one of his menacing looks and pushed his face close to Chloe's. Eyeball to eyeball, unblinking, Robert glared one of his most meaningful glares, a glare which in the past had never failed to bring mischievous adolescent chimps and timorous keepers to heel, and which had quelled many a nagging old matriarchal ape. Chloe did the unthinkable; she bit his ear, neatly punching a small but painful hole through the middle of the flap. Astounded, Robert backed off half a pace. This was too much! With a short, sharp rush he threw his 150 pounds at Chloe, bowling her over and grabbing with both hands at the stalks she was tenaciously clutching. Struggling and screaming, she refused to let go as Robert pulled her clenched fist towards his bared teeth. His enormously strong index finger could not winkle its way into her palm, nor could his conical yellow canine teeth prize open her grip. Thwarted, Robert was driven to desperate measures, and with a single easy scrunch of his jaws he bit off Chloe's thumb; it was sliced off as cleanly as a severed stalk of celery. Chloe at once released the remains of the asparagus. Robert quickly gobbled them down, then picked up the amputated thumb, sniffed indifferently at it and threw it out of the cage in the direction of Len, who had watched the drama helplessly.

Those few sticks of asparagus resulted in Chloe being maimed for life, although she learned to make do with nine instead of ten digits in no time at all. They were also the reason why I was bouncing in the Jowett through grimy streets of small terraced houses and steaming fish-and-chip shops, on my way, alone, to my very first unaided zoo case at the age of twenty-two.

The twelve-mile drive to the zoo gave me time to think. The message had said something about a thumb being lost by a female chimp. I knew little else at that stage. Still, fingers were like toes and I had treated dozens of cases of domestic animals which had lost toes or had had to have them surgically amputated. The operation was comparatively simple. Bandaging the injured zone after treatment presented no complications, and I had long ago mastered a handful of little tricks using lacquer, sticky tape, repellent aerosol sprays, leather bootees or plastic bags to protect dressings against the teeth, claws and persistent ingenuity of indignant tabby cats and frantic poodles. Yes, I reassured myself as I wound my way through the traffic, fingers were indeed like toes.

Then the snags started to occur to me. Tabby cats and poodles, even for that matter cows, were all fairly easy to anaesthetize. There was always a fond owner or burly farmer to hold the creature while I injected the anaesthetic. Dart-guns were still years in the future. Who was going to hold the chimp? Again, my arts of wound dressing had been developed in animals which had no manual dexterity. Might not a wily ape remove whatever dressing I used in little more time than I took to put it on? It dawned on me that I did not know the best dose for chimpanzees of the one anaesthetic that I might have to use: barbiturate. At the time all my other anaesthetics were either gases like ether and halothane – and I could hardly walk up to a 150-pound great ape, slap a mask on its knowing face and ask it to count backwards from one hundred – or other injectable knock-out drugs which were old-fashioned, risky or corrosive. Barbiturate, the latest anaesthetic for veterinary use at the time, was at least safer but one needed to know something about dosage. Supposing I lost my first zoo patient! I gulped. It was a prospect too awful even to contemplate. Take it easy, I told myself, what am I worrying about? Drip it into the chimp's vein a little at a time until the desired level of sleep has been achieved. That way, providing I don't rush it, I'm bound not to exceed the safety limit.

Two miles to go. I tried not to think about the anaesthetic problem; the dripping-in method would be just the thing. But hold on a minute, the slow drip into the vein is all very well, but what is the chimp going to do during the seconds or even minutes when she begins to sense the first hint of dizziness, when she sees double or the room gently begins

18

to spin? She's going to have ample time, if you don't knock her straight out, to part company with your carefully implanted intravenous needle and play havoc with any homo sapiens in the operating theatre – particularly the anaesthetist. Less than confident now, and for a fraction of a second cursing my stars for arranging that the thumb should take leave of its owner on a Wednesday, I swung into the zoo entrance. The commissionaire peered suspiciously through my side window and beckoned to me to wind it down.

'Yes, sir,' he growled, 'what can we do for you?'

I tried to shake off my apprehension and put on a professional face. 'It's the vet,' I replied loudly.

'You're not Dr Whittle.'

'No, but I am the vet.' And then, as an afterthought – it sounded rather grand – 'To see the chimpanzee, an emergency.' The gates were opened and I drove into the grounds.

As I stopped the van outside the great ape house, the face of Matt Kelly, the head keeper, peered from the door. Grabbing my bag I climbed out of the van. My heart was hammering in a mixture of excitement and dread. This was it. Another face appeared at the door as I approached. It was Mr Wilson, the zoo director. Just my luck, I thought, to have this pair of Celts to deal with on my first zoo case. I had met both of them at the zoo with Norman Whittle when I was still a student. Kelly was a tough, experienced and shrewd Irishman and Wilson an acerbic Scot with a face like a walnut. Both knew a lot about animals, were intolerant of fools and amateurs and did not seem much impressed by veterinarians in the zoo. Students, it had seemed to me, were held by both of them in some contempt, and both of them undoubtedly considered me still very much a student where exotic animals were concerned. It was true, but dammit, I had to begin somewhere. The trouble was that they knew this was my beginning, and I knew they knew. I crossed my fingers under the handle of my medical bag.

'Good afternoon, Mr Wilson, Mr Kelly,' I began, 'Dr Whittle's away and out of contact, I'm afraid, so you've got me.' I gave a rather tentative jolly laugh.

19

The two zoo men greeted me stonily. 'Yes, well, come and have a look at Chloe,' Wilson said, and led the way into a corridor flanked with a number of intricate barred gates that opened onto small cells lit solely by electric bulkhead lights. It was like walking along one of the gangways at Alcatraz. All around me the chimpanzees and orang-utans set up a deafening din, screeching, rattling and beating food dishes against the walls. One big male chimp burped as I passed him and pressed his face close to the bars. I smiled at him and put out my hand to tickle one of his knuckles clenched tight round a bar.

'Careful! Don't do that!' hissed Kelly, walking behind me. 'He'll have you arm off if ye don't watch out! That's the feller that took the thumb off this afternoon.'

I looked at Robert the maimer, inside for life. He gazed at me intently, eyes never blinking. As I continued on down the passageway, I felt a warm moist patch soaking through my trousers. Robert had urinated on me through the grille.

Chloe sat alone in her sleeping quarters, banging a stainless steel drinking dish on the floor with her good hand. The other, mutilated hand she held high above her head so that all the world could see the damage wrought by the evil Robert.

'That's it,' said Wilson, pointing. Kelly said nothing. Both men stood looking blank. They did not seem to be anxiously awaiting my words of wisdom. I looked hard through the bars. The diagnosis was clear and simple: the thumb was off. So far so good. Now for the next stage: treatment. There were some drops of blood on the floor but the hand did not seem to be actively bleeding at present. It looked as if Robert had performed his amputation rather neatly straight through the bottom knuckle joint, so there was no surgical operation for me to do, but he had left a rather irregular edge to the skin. Ought I not to straighten that up, stitch up the hole and put a dressing on? And was there not a risk of infection? Chimpanzee mouths normally contain a rich variety of nasty microbes, some of which can cause serious diseases when given the chance to invade healthy flesh. Yes, it looked as though I would have to do something.

I decided to broach diplomatically the subject of how to get to grips with Cloe. 'Hmm,' I murmured wisely and subtly. 'Hmmm.' I hoped the 'Hmmm' was of a tone, pitch and duration perfectly calculated to suggest not that I was at a loss but rather that such cases were well within my province. Wilson and Kelly said nothing and stared blankly on.

'I see,' I continued, again trying to convey optimism and confidence rather than sterile perplexity. Still they said nothing; they were forcing me to the point where I would have to make a positive suggestion for treatment. I decided to approach the nettle obliquely before grasping it. 'What's she like?' I asked. It was a suitably vague question.

Wilson frowned. 'D'you mean what's she like to handle?' he snapped.

'Er, yes,' I replied brightly.

'Can't,' said Kelly lugubriously. 'Can't.'

'Well, I think we ought to stitch up the hole if we can, dress it and give her a shot of antibiotic,' I went on. 'What would be the best way, do you think?'

A distinctly aggravated look appeared on Wilson's walnut face. 'Can't,' he said. 'There's no way of doing it.'

I had to say my piece. 'Is there no way you can hold her long enough for me to get some barbiturate into her vein?' I asked in my politest voice.

Both men broke into a burst of humourless laughter. 'Catch hold of her? Chloe? Impossible. Impossible.' Wilson's nae-nonsense Glasgow accent seemed stronger than ever. 'How do you suggest we do that?'

The ball was back in my court. 'Well, if you've no way of trapping her, and we've no way of getting a drug in by injection, the only thing is to try doping her food.'

'No chance.' This time it was Kelly's turn. 'She's fed up for today, won't take any more. Anyway, Chloe's as sharp as they come at spottin' doctored food.'

If I had to wait until the next day, and then still use the imprecise and unpredictable way of introducing barbiturate in the food, I would have lost valuable time. Infection might have set in and the stitches might not be so certain of holding. What would we have done if the animal had been haemorrhaging severely? Waited until she was so weakened by blood loss that she had no more will to resist?

I stood looking in at the wounded chimpanzee. The case was a supremely simple one, the type of therapy obvious, but there was nothing I could do. The zoo director and the head keeper knew that I would be unable to make any positive constructive contribution; they must have known it when the call had been put through to my office. With a first personal taste of gnawing impotence, I began to realize the futility of veterinary medicine as applied to zoo animals. It seemed in those days before the invention of the dart-gun that the zoo vet had only two alternatives: to inject, dose, lance and anoint only small, relatively non-violent creatures such as lizards and turtles, whose problems were obscure, unstudied and baffling to the veterinarian familiar with the workings and ways of domestic animals; or to stand at one side of the bars and guess what might be wrong with the choleric gorilla or tiger that lay on the other side, obviously ill or injured but just as obviously an ungrabbable and ungrateful patient.

Chloe was one of the latter cases. I knew that with some animals it had been possible to immobilize them for treatment by using sheer brute force, casting nets over them and then having seven or eight of your heaviest men sit on the captive until it was almost suffocated or someone was severely bitten through a gap in the rope mesh. Even if such humane barbarity worked, the effect on animals and staff was utterly demoralizing. The end result was a terrified, exhausted patient, still virtually unexaminable. No point in taking his temperature; it was roaring up in panic. No chance of feeling with one's fingers for the liver abscess or ball of cancer that might lie in the abdomen; the body wall was held hard as iron. And even if one could get the bell end of the stethoscope into the right position without it being bitten off, the galloping heart was masking much else which might be significant. I was not going to begin by treating my first zoo case that way.

There was nothing more to be done for Chloe except to give the zoo director a broad-spectrum antibiotic which could be added to her fruit drinks for a week or so. The three of us retraced our steps. Robert was still hugging the bars of his cell closely. I looked at him as I passed, keeping close to the opposite wall of the passageway in the hope of staying out of range. Was there in his gaze the merest hint of mockery? He grimaced and stuck his tongue behind the barely parted rows of yellow teeth. 'Tsk, tsk, tsk,' said Robert.

The two zoo men and I went outside and stood for a moment before I climbed back into my van.

'Well, thanks anyway for coming,' said Wilson.

'Yes, it should heal up without any trouble,' Kelly reassured me. 'Oi've seen these chimps do terrible things to one another. It's amazin' what nature can do. Healed up in no time at all. Baboons, too – wounds ye could put your hand into after fightin'. But they heal up with no bother in a couple o' weeks.'

'Well, I'd like to have sutured Chloe's hand,' I replied. 'Perhaps one day we'll have ways of doing such things easily enough.'

I still wondered why they had bothered to send for me in such a hurry in the first place, since they did not seem the slightest dismayed by my non-performance. Having just achieved my dearest ambition, my first zoo case, I found myself driving home to Rochdale in a black depression. Could it be that after all I should stick to cattle and horses?

That evening I told my wife about my uncertain debut with Chloe, Mr Wilson and Matt Kelly. Shelagh and I had met while we were both still at school and had courted for six years while she qualified as a therapy radiographer and I carried through my veterinary studies. Her green eyes and strong determination bear witness to her Irish ancestry, and she has a deep love and understanding of animals of every kind; I had seen her move earthworms from footpaths with the concern of a devout Hindu lest they be trodden upon and injured, we had wrestled together over many a dying animal brought to our doorstep, and we had worked side by side over pregnant ewes needing Caesarians in the middle of the night when I had no anaesthetist or surgical assistant available. Her optimum was unflagging and her judgement of the right approach to animal patient and owner impeccable.

'Don't worry,' she said reassuringly, 'you've not lost Chloe. There will be other times. One of these days you'll show 'em! There'll be new ways of getting at these animals and then you'll get the upper hand. Men like Kelly and Wilson have been in the business all their lives. You know the problems you've had with old-fashioned Pennine farmers in the six months since you first started in practice – they didn't want the young feller with the new-fangled ways, laughed when you sterilized the skin before injecting a cow down with milk fever, wanted you to cut the tails of tuberculous cows to get out the 'worm' that was sucking the meat of the beasts' bones – you're getting over all that with time and battling on. Same with the zoos. You've got to keep reading about exotic animals, keep going if you get the chance. One good success can make all the difference.'

Shelagh was right. It would be a long haul before I could ever move about the zoos with the same growing confidence in handling every kind of case, together with the right psychological approach to the owners, that I was developing in general practice. The idea of one day working solely with exotic animals seemed the most tenuous of dreams. Even Shelagh doubted whether we would ever be able to achieve that.

On the day after my first visit to Chloe, I also tackled Norman Whittle about the affair. Norman was a quiet, elegant individual ten years my senior, with a fair moustache and, if the term can be applied to animal doctors, a superb bedside manner.

'Why do they bother to call us at all when they know there is little we can do?' I asked him.

He smiled. 'Quite simply to cover themselves. To cover themselves for the sake of the Board. Happens to me all the time. Something ill, they fiddle about with it as best they can for a few days until it looks as if the poor sod's going to die, then they send for the vet. If there's going to be a corpse, they've got to be able to report to the Board that "the vet was called in but the animal expired". As for

Chloe, she wasn't likely to die, but the same principle applies. A high-value animal they can't get to grips with and so, just in case something goes wrong, or if a visitor reports the presence of a nine-fingered ape to the RSPCA, they've got to be able to say that the buck was passed to the vet.'

'So what you're saying is that we're professional fall guys for the zoo?'

'Yes, essentially. OK, so we supply them with drugs they can put in the food of animals with diarrhoea and vitamin syrup for things that look out of condition or down in the mouth, but basically we go so that on the monthly reports it can read something like "Despite veterinary treatment, x number of mammals, y number of birds and z number of reptiles cocked their toes." '

'Don't you feel you do some good for the zoo animals, though?'

'In a few cases, yes – calving a giraffe that's in difficulties, lancing an abscess on the occasional elephant – but they're few and far between. Mostly I haven't any way of knowing what's wrong with these creatures and they, people like Matt Kelly, know I don't know. I don't think zoos in general have much time for vets.'

'But they need us to rubber-stamp the losses?'

'Afraid so.'

Not only was Matt Kelly right about Chloe's hand – it healed perfectly without any infection or discomfort and within three weeks the skin had closed the gap completely – but I knew that Norman's analysis of the relationship between zoos and vets was basically true as well. Perhaps it was partly the profession's fault for paying too much attention in the past exclusively to domestic animals. Not many years earlier, veterinary education had concentrated almost solely on the problems of the horse. Gradually, as the automobile seemed likely to be more than a nine-day wonder, farm animals and then later the dog and cat received a more appropriate proportion of a student's time. Even today the handling, diseases and therapy of exotic creatures are squeezed into a total of one or two hours' instruction out of a five- or six-year course in some veterinary schools. When I first treated Chloe not even that amount of tuition was available.

The more I thought about Norman's remarks the more crystal clear it seemed to me that I had to have three things if I was ever going to progress in zoo medicine. First I had to look into new ways of getting drugs accurately inside the bodies of creatures too dangerous or too nervous to be injected by hand; secondly I needed powerful, compact, safe sedatives and anaesthetics for every possible class of exotic patient; and thirdly I would have to learn everything I could from old-timers like Kelly at Belle Vue about the lore of zoocraft, about moving among and handling difficult and dangerous animals. Matt Kelly might not know the exact location of the sinuses of Rokitansky-Aschoff in a rhinoceros's liver, or the dental formula of a binturong, but he knew a hell of a lot about the care of wild creatures. I must pry some of it out of him.

☆☆☆☆☆☆☆☆☆☆☆☆☆☆

Chapter
Three

☆☆☆☆☆☆☆☆☆☆☆☆☆☆

I WAS called to attend Mary the elephant at Belle Vue Zoo, who had been suffering from increasingly severe attacks of toothache. Elephants have a peculiar tooth arrangement with a system of continual replacement throughout their lifetime of the grinding molars. The teeth develop from buds at one end of a groove in the jaw, move forwards into use as they grow, and then fall out to be replaced by others coming along the groove behind them. This process sometimes hits snags. A tooth jams instead of falling out cleanly and the animal shows all the signs of tenderness and irritation in the mouth that humans would associate with an impacted wisdom tooth. Mary's problem was one stage worse than this: she had developed an abscess at the base of a tooth root in the lower jaw. The abscess enlarged and caused severe pain within the un-yielding confines of the bony jaw. Mary became irritable and grumpy. She ate little other than soft over-ripe bananas. She drooled saliva more than usual and would open her mouth for inspection only with great reluctance.

When I was first called to examine her I asked the keeper to persuade Mary to open her mouth. Eventually, after lots of soothing talk, I could put my hand inside. Feeling about in an elephant's mouth is not the least hazardous of veterinary procedures. There is not much room, and it is easy to find one's fingers being pushed by the strong muscular tongue between the grinding surfaces of the teeth, a most excruciating experience. When I tapped the infected molar with the back of my knuckle, Mary pulled back, beat me lustily about the head with her trunk and screeched like a pig. A root abscess: normally one would extract the tooth and all would be well. At least that was how things went in other animals, but in an elephant it was quite a different matter. The tooth in question was firmly embedded in the jaw and, like all elephant teeth, had multiple curved roots which sweep deep down into the jawbone and interweave intricately with the bony tissue around them. Pulling, even with giant forceps, was out of the question and so was elevating, the flicking out of a tooth by means of a lever-like instrument. I decided to try medical treatment instead, to destroy the abscess by injections of antibiotics and to relieve pain by injectable analgesics.

The snag with this course is that the trouble tends to flare up again some weeks or months later. Sure enough the injections produced rapid disappearance of all symptoms and within a day Mary was her own amenable self again. Two or three weeks later the zoo rang up to say that Mary was beginning to show the same symptoms again but this time the pain was so bad that she was banging her head against the wall. I drove down at once to Manchester and sure enough a very forlorn Mary was having trouble again with an abscess under the same tooth. The drug injections quickly put matters right and the following day the elephant had stopped the head-banging.

Over the next six months Mary had four more attacks of toothache involving the same tooth root and each attack was more severe and lasted longer than the one before. The head-banging became the principal symptom. Mary would stand for hours close to the wall of the elephant house, deliberately rocking on her ankles and crashing the affected side of her head against the brickwork with a regular, dull, horrible thud that could be heard two hundred yards away. She had knocked the paint off a large area of the wall and loosened the pointing between the bricks. The last attack was the worst. Mary refused all food

28

but stood night and day against the wall, seeking to counter the aching focus in her jaw by temporarily distracting the throbbing nerves as one ton of head jarred into the brickwork. It was terrible to listen to and unpleasant to watch: she was bruising and cutting the skin on the side of her face and she was becoming ill-tempered and unpredictable to handle. What was more, the wall was definitely no immovable object assailed by an irresistible force. It was beginning to bulge outwards, many bricks were loose, and the zoo director feared that the structure of the building was now at serious risk. We had to do something more positive. The tooth causing all the trouble would have to come out.

It was clear that the only way to remove the offending molar was to perform a major operation on the jaw. The gum along the side of the tooth root would have to be flapped up, the thick covering plate of bone would then be chipped away and the tooth with its roots intact could be teased, cajoled and manoeuvred sideways out of the jaw. This would mean a long period under general anaesthetic: a shot of local as performed by the dentist, or even a nerve block, the numbing of the nerve to the tooth by surrounding it with local anaesthetic at some point on its path back towards the brain, would not be feasible. The area of tissue involved was too large and complicated and the animal was in far too agitated a state. Anyway it would be impossible to do the necessary work unless she was lying down with her head still.

The problem was that at this time, the late fifties, there was no really suitable general anaesthetic available for the elephant. Major operations on the elephant had rarely been performed. Local anaesthetic was used for minor matters but otherwise it had been a question of tying the poor creature down with chains and hobbles and using the crudest of methods. Giving chloroform or ether was virtually impossible; barbiturates had to be given intravenously in ridiculously large doses, had a nasty knack of damaging the veins and tissues round about where they were injected and depressed breathing seriously, while chloral hydrate, the old stand-by of horse practitioners, was so disgustingly bitter when given in water that an animal would need to be stopped from drinking for three or four days before it would accept the doctored liquid. I decided to look into the possibility of using a new and promising drug which I had been using for two or three years on other exotic creatures.

Giving Mary a stiff dose of pain-killer and antibiotics to relieve the situation, I announced that we would operate on her the following day and that suitable preparations should be made. Then I went home to consider further the matter of anaesthesia in this, my first case of major surgery on the elephant.

The new drug, phencyclidine, had been the first important breakthrough in modern zoo animal anaesthesia. It was highly concentrated, formed a stable solution which had no annoying tendency to go off, and could produce its effects when given by any route including by injection under the skin, by mouth or in a flying dart. Its taste was not too bitter, so that when used to spike the fruit drinks or milk of those discerning and wide-awake customers, the great apes, it usually went down unnoticed. There were disadvantages, too. The dose was calculated on body weight, and once it was administered there was no way of neutralising its effects, which wore off gradually over a number of hours. Some animals such as polar bears were easily overdosed with the stuff, and I noticed how little phencyclidine they needed to knock them flat out compared with brown or Himalayan black bears. Wolves, the first animals on which I had ever used the chemical and the tranquillising gun, frequently developed alarming convulsions when unconscious under phencyclidine. The drug had proved to be unsuitable for horses and I had discovered to my dismay that it had serious untoward effects in zebra: instead of anaesthetising an animal which had broken out of its pen and could only be dosed by means of a flying dart containing phencyclidine, the drug produced an alarming degree of excitement and distress which persisted for hours. But in monkeys and apes, the big cats and some other carnivores it was superb. We never saw any signs of the long-lasting sexual stimulant effects or burning

30

sensations of the fingertips and toes which humans treated with the drug had reported, although big cats under phencyclidine anaesthesia do regularly extend and contract their claws.

For Mary's operation phencyclidine was the best drug I had at the time. Checking that evening through my library I found one or two reports of its previous use on elephants, but details were scanty. What was suitable as an experimental dose in the African bush where elephants were plentiful was not necessarily right for Mary, a valuable and much loved animal in a city zoo in the industrial north of England. I had to get the dose right. Another problem is estimating the weight of an animal such as Mary. My usual practice is to walk the animal or take it in a lorry to a public weighbridge, but the toothache had made Mary crotchety and unco-operative and I could not risk taking her out of the elephant house. If an animal cannot actually be weighed I take the average of three estimates made by myself and two other people accustomed to working with animals, which is what I had to do in Mary's case. With the small amount of information which I had accumulated I was able to calculate a dose for the following morning. Certain nagging problems remained: how long would the anaesthetic last and what would be the cumulative effect of any further doses once she was down? What awkward physiological changes would several hours' unconsciousness produce in the ponderous creature? How was I to ensure that she went down with her bad tooth uppermost? It is not easy to turn a four and a half ton elephant when she is collapsed unconscious like a great pile of coal.

The next morning I was up early. My first call was to the local ironmongers. Dental instruments for human or ordinary veterinary use are far too puny for the granite-hard teeth of an elephant and the thick, resilient bone in which they are embedded. What I needed was a set of high-quality, all-metal masonry chisels. The ironmonger produced exactly what I wanted, a set of tough tungsten-edged tools specially intended for punching holes in hard stone. When I explained what they were for, the shopkeeper said he would sell them to me at trademan's price.

'After all,' he said, 'you're using them for your trade, I suppose. Never thought I'd find myself selling surgical instruments!'

At the zoo I found Mary suffering considerably from the diseased tooth. The pain-killing drug had worn off and she was in a black mood. As I entered her quarters she glowered down at me and shuffled agitatedly around, whisking and flailing her trunk. It was going to be difficult keeping her still enough even for the normally simple under-skin injection of phencyclidine. I decided to leave all the instruments outside until she was anaesthetised. How she would go down and whether, during the few seconds that the anaesthetic first affected her brain cells, she would feel dizzy and become alarmed, I did not know. But I remembered having cases of horses run amok during the first stages of barbiturate dosage, with disastrous effects on the surrounding and carefully sterilised equipment, and I was not taking any chances.

Matt Kelly solved the problem of keeping Mary still for a second or two while I gave her the dope. Mary had one great weakness – an unbridled appetite for custard pies, the open, nutmeg-sprinkled, Lancashire variety. Even though the toothache had quenched her desire for more conventional foods, Matt guessed that she would still be quite unable to resist these delicacies and he sent up to the zoo restaurant for some. Sure enough, when a keeper appeared with a box full of the newly baked golden pastries, the demeanour of the miserable animal immediately changed. Her black mood became, well, charcoal-grey, she stopped roaming irritably about and proceeded with obvious enjoyment to roll the custards one after another into her mouth, carefully avoiding the offending left side of her jaw. While she was thus engaged I slapped three times on her rump with the flat of my hand and then, when she was accustomed to the contact, slapped her again with equal force but this time with a three-inch needle held between my fingers. She did not feel a thing as I connected the syringe full of anaesthetic to the needle and pressed the plunger. It was in. I had begun the general anaesthesia of my first elephant.

32

Mary continued to consume the last of the custard pies, still standing calmly as we silently watched her. The elephant's soft munching was the only sound to be heard. Now I was going to be faced with the answers to the questions with which my mind was racing. What was the effect of the drug going to be? Was my dose adequate or perhaps even too large? Had my needle squirted it deep into a layer of fat where its absorption would be greatly delayed and the effect minimised? A minute passed. Mary cleared the last flakes of pie pastry from her lips and looked at Matt for more. No signs of grogginess. At what time should I consider giving another dose, I wondered, clenching my fists. How would a second injection act in relation to the first? What would the cumulative effects be? Suppose the first effects on Mary were indeed to make her feel dizzy and alarmed. What if she ran amok while still sufficiently conscious to stay on her feet? For a moment I almost wished myself back in the everyday vet's world of anaesthetising dogs with fractured legs and ponies for castration.

Two minutes passed, then five. Suddenly, as if chilled by a gust of icy air, Mary began to tremble. Her knees buckled and she sagged down on legs of jelly. With a drowsy sigh and a boom as her leathery side hit the thick carpet of straw on the floor, she crashed over. She was flat out with the operation site and the bad tooth fortuitously uppermost. Matt and Mr Legge, the zoo director, positioned her legs and trunk as comfortably as they could and I checked her breathing and the working of the massive heart with my stethoscope. The operation was under way.

The peeling back of a large flap of gum over the root area took only a few minutes and the bleeding was very quickly controlled with forceps. Then began the slow business of chipping away the bone. It was fantastically hard. I struck the sharp chisels with a heavy metal mallet, working to a guideline painted on the bone in purple antiseptic dye. I was working naked from the waist up, as I prefer to do during prolonged large animal operations, particularly in warm animal houses. The effort was making my arms ache and the sweat streamed down my face and chest. Hordes of little red mites from the straw saw it as their duty to climb

33

aboard and stroll about my body, making me itch annoyingly. Bit by bit, but far slower than anticipated, I chipped my pathway along the jawbone. It was so hard that the jarring as the mallet and chisel rebounded from the dense tissue began to numb my hands. Mary remained perfectly unconscious. From time to time I stopped my chiselling to examine her pulse and breathing – so far all was well.

After two hours I had at last broken through the jawbone right along the line I had marked. Then, using a strong stainless steel bone 'pin' rather like a small crowbar, I levered the plate of bone off. There below it was the whole of the troublesome molar's complex root system. Like an iceberg, there was far more of the tooth below the surface than protruded above the gum, and the roots were still hideously intertwined with a lace-work of bony bridges. On and on I chipped, gradually freeing the broad, curved root branches. With my crowbar I tested my progress now and again by attempting to lever the great tooth outwards. Still it remained firmly implanted. After four hours I could at last see the inflamed area on the root that was the cause of all our problems. It was not much to look at: just a pinkish-yellow blob about the size of a pea. Another hour passed and then, as I tried levering outwards yet again, there was a loud cracking noise and the largest tooth I have ever extracted heeled over and fell out of the jaw with a thud.

From now on it was plain sailing: replace the plate of bone, fill the gaping hole in the gum (it was as big as a house brick) with a four-pound ball of sterilized dental wax, and stitch up. As I began the last lap, replacing the gum flap, I noticed that the colour of the gum was not as bright pink in colour as it had been. The colour was now distinctly tinged with lilac. I hurriedly completed the last knots in the catgut and sat back exhausted on my haunches. The colour change in the gum had diluted some of the elation in finishing the job. Now to attend to the animal's general condition and protect it from post-operative complications. Mary still lay dreaming on her side. Her reflexes were becoming a bit stronger. First I checked the heart and

34

lungs again. Her heart was thumping strongly but faster now. As I listened to her lungs, with the stethoscope placed on the uppermost part of her chest, all sounded normal.

Then, faintly, from far away, I heard the deep rumble of a new sound, a dull bubbling noise far below the healthy swoosh of air in and out of the lung nearest to me. I went round to the other side of the animal and knelt down, pushing my stethoscope hard into the tight space between the underneath side of the chest and the floor. I could not get very far in but the bubbling noise was distinct, rather like a cauldron of jam gently boiling. I knew what was beginning to happen. The immense weight of the animal pressing down on the lung nearest to the floor was interfering severely with the flow of air and blood through the vital tissues, and fluid was collecting in the underneath lung. It is something to be watched for in all animals lying on their sides under anaesthetic and it can usually be prevented by turning the animal frequently from side to side.

'Let's get her over as quickly as possible,' I said. 'I don't like the sound of the right lung.'

Matt and his keepers hurried to attach ropes to Mary's feet and to push planks as levers beneath the bulging belly. Everyone pushed or pulled. Keepers braced themselves with their feet against walls and their backs wedged beneath Mary's legs.

Gradually we raised her until she was lying on her backbone with all four feet in the air. Then we let her down gently on the other side. I gave injections of heart and lung stimulants and drugs against shock and infection. The bubbling noise was now less noticeable in the right lung but, to my horror, I detected the first sounds of it in the other lung. Mary had been down under anaesthetic for too long. Although she was beginning to rouse, she had a long way to go and I had no way of speeding up the process. The lungs were becoming fatigued. We were in trouble, Mary was beginning to drown.

Her breathing became steadily more laboured and abnormal. She was more restless and moved her legs and trunk erratically. She even tried to raise her head a few inches from the ground. The unpleasant sounds in both lungs increased and, more ominously, some areas of the lung tissue became silent: they had filled completely with liquid and there was no longer any movement of air through them. An oxygen cylinder was set up and the gas was fed by tube under a sheet placed over Mary's head. For a moment I saw again, as if in a nightmare, Chota's tarpaulin-covered body as I had seen it on my first visit to this very zoo. Although now the tube which led under the sheet carried not deadly carbon monoxide but life-giving oxygen, it was beginning to look as though the end result would be the same, for Mary's breathing was steadily weakening. If only I could have reversed the effects of the injected anaesthetic! A full return to consciousness and the ability to stand and move would soon have restored good circulation in the chest.

Mary's colour was changing for the worse. The gums were now grey-blue with only a hint of pink. The respiration was weaker and seemed more laboured. The interval between breaths became agonisingly longer.

'Stand next to me and we'll try artificial respiration,' I said to Matt, who was standing glum and tight-lipped. 'Both together we'll get on and off the chest to see if our weight can compress the ribs.'

Simultaneously we both jumped onto the rounded grey chest of the recumbent giant. The rib cage sank a little. We immediately jumped off again. There was a slight expansion of the chest, but it was impossible to tell how much air had been sucked in. We repeated the process. On, off, on, off: at five-second intervals we jumped with all our weight onto Mary's chest. We tried jumping up and down on the chest itself. Our exertions produced some wheezing as small amounts of air were forced in and out but it was not enough. I stopped and listened again with the stethoscope. The lungs were in dire trouble, with fluid building up, and the heart was beginning to fail fast. I gave more injections, more circulation stimulant and a chemical to give a kick in the pants to the centre in the brain that controls breathing. It was no good. Five minutes later Mary stopped breathing altogether and the heart-beats faded away fainter and fainter until I could hear them no longer. Mary, the most famous of Manchester Zoo's elephants and voted by schoolchildren their favourite animal in the park, was dead.

The autopsy on Mary confirmed that the long operation under phencyclidine had produced serious fluid build-up in the lungs with a resulting fatal lack of oxygen and heart failure. The zoo director and I had a meeting with the Board to report on Mary's loss. It was miserable explaining how my technique, up to date as it was, just had not been safe enough for a long operation on an elephant. I told the Board that if another elephant developed the same problem as Mary on the following day I would have to do the same again, using the same anaesthetic. It would be so until someone developed a new way of tackling anaesthesia in the elephant.

☆☆☆☆☆☆☆☆☆☆☆☆☆☆

Chapter Four

☆☆☆☆☆☆☆☆☆☆☆☆☆☆

THE WARDEN in charge of the big cats at Windsor Safari Park took another look through his binoculars and gasped loud enough to cause his assistant, who was keeping his eyes firmly fixed on a tiger that was sneaking slowly towards the electrically operated gate, to turn his head.

'What the devil?' muttered the warden. 'The cheetahs are dancing about!' He handed over the glasses and pointed to the distant cheetah reserve. 'Have a quick look and then we'll drive over. Rummest thing I ever saw. Dancing cheetahs!'

The two men climbed into the zebra-painted Land Rover and drove across the grassy parkland, avoiding the snake of visitors' cars making their way through the Berkshire bit of darkest Africa on a late Sunday afternoon in July. The cheetahs were in their favourite corner of the reserve, a quiet shaded area where Gary Smart and I had ordered the grass and weeds to be allowed to grow unchecked some years before in order to create some privacy for the mating of these shy and easily distracted cats. (It seemed to have worked; we had begun to breed cheetahs and had even had one female who presented a litter of six cubs.) When they drew close to the animals, the two wardens found their initial impressions apparently confirmed; it did look like dancing. The leggy, spotted cats that we'd imported from

south-west Africa were milling about in the most extraordinary way. It looked like some sort of feline hoe-down, everyone moving in circles or going to and fro, claws lifted abnormally high in a high-stepping gait and rumps and tails swaying to some exotic rhythm outside the range of human ears. Not only that but like African ritual dancers in a trance, they seemed unaware of the Land Rover's arrival; expressions were fixed, eyes stared into infinity and soft mewings came from half-opened mouths.

'Is it some sort of mating display like birds do?' The assistant wasn't experienced in the ways of big cats, but his boss wasn't listening. He was already calling up Francis Rendell, the park's curator, on his walkie-talkie.

'Cheetahs all haywire,' he was saying. 'Gone bonkers or food-poisoned or something. Better get the vet in fast.'

When he looked back to the weird ballet he saw that two of the animals had collapsed and were lying apparently unconscious. A third was finishing its pas de quatre with a downward-spiralling collapse onto its haunches to sit as

39

immobile as a Staffordshire china dog. That left six carrying on with the choreography. The warden looked round; there were more cheetahs somewhere. He caught sight of them lying on their sides in a patch of sunlight thirty yards away. They looked as cool and poised as ever. He walked towards them and when he got as close as they were prepared to allow they stood up, stared at him and stamped their fore-feet in warning before turning and loping fluidly away. No dancing or unconsciousness there. The warden hurried back to the unconscious cheetahs, which looked to be flat out. He pulled at the tongue of one that was threatening to choke and cursed as the furry dancers reeled round him.

I had just finished talking to Liliana in Madrid about another attack of Chang-Chang's listlessness – again it was accompanied by mucus in the droppings but again we had decided on balance not to interfere – when Francis rang. 'Can you come over right away? Looks like bad food-poisoning.' I'd worked with Francis, one of the most widely experienced of young British zoo curators and a first-class marine mammal man, for many years by then. An imperturbable character who had coped, cool as a cucumber, with innumerable alarums in the zoo world, he sounded unusually hot and bothered. Something very serious must be up.

'I'm on my way. Meanwhile brew up some very strong black coffee – about half a gallon,' I said after he'd briefly described the symptoms. 'I'll explain when I get there.'

The move to Lightwater had been advantageous in more ways than one. Now I was only twenty minutes from the Windsor park. It made more sense for me to be in the South and leave Andrew to handle the North, even though it meant that I rarely visited dear old Belle Vue. In the past I'd sometimes driven twice in one day from Rochdale to London or Windsor. The long motorway run didn't trouble me, but I had collected speeding fines with monotonous regularity, stiff necks from cat-napping in lay-bys and service stations and indigestion from hurried meals-on-wheels. With the radio-telephone in my car I'd been able to handle most distant emergencies well enough, but there's no substitute for getting to a case as fast as possible. With the best will in the world, and a police escort on occasion, it is still impossible to cover the 200-odd miles between Lancashire and London in less than two and a half hours – long enough by far for many urgent cases to pass beyond the point of no return. I'd been lucky over the years, but now our dispositions were more logical and secure. Francis's cheetahs illustrated the point perfectly.

From the telephone description I suspected poisoning, not from food but from something more sinister – malicious doping. It is not infrequent, and I see one or two cases per year in zoo carnivores. Zoos attract cranks and nutters among their visitors and they also regularly produce disgruntled staff, individuals with chips on their shoulders who become obsessed with the animals in their care, spend long hours alone communing with bird or beast, and gradually lose their sense of perspective. Grudges may be incubated against the head keeper or director who are seen as unsympathetic or downright cruel in, say, deciding to sell a particular favourite creature or refusing to supply some item of diet that is not strictly necessary but which a keeper would like to please his charges with. There are a thousand and one areas where seeds of resentment may grow in every zoo. Zoo staff are generally poorly paid in comparison to workers in other industries; many are dedicated idealists who do not share the aims and attitudes of management towards captive animals. Management often communicates poorly or not at all with the people who are actually in charge, day in and day out, of stock worth perhaps millions of pounds. The man who has to muck out the monkeys is rarely if ever consulted when the architects roll up in their limousines to sketch out the new monkey house, so it doesn't surprise you to learn that the said house, when erected in arty-crafty stainless steel and given a champagne opening by Sir Solly Zuckerman or whoever, like as not hasn't got anywhere for the monkey-man to dump his muck.

Strangely, animal staff who are dismissed for some reason and, even more strangely, animal staff who are still in employment at the zoo, may occasionally go bad and strike back for real or imagined grievances not against the directorate but against the inmates themselves: the animals. Paradoxically, the animal man rounds on his animals. I see much of this phenomenon. Giraffes deliberately terrorised at night in the darkness of their houses – four dead of shock by first light. Arson that killed a house full of parrots and nearly cost the lives of zebra and bison. Stabbings and shootings of monkeys and birds. No, I'm not referring to incidents that might have been the work of the public, of vandals breaking in after hours: these are known cases where zoo staff have lost their grip on reason. Where the culprits have tried to explain their motives, not once have I heard anything about an inexplicable hatred of the animals having arisen in their minds. The explanations, sometimes tortuous, sometimes startlingly lucid, have always outlined humans or human systems as the foe. 'Anyone who works with animals in whatever capacity must be at least a bit dotty,' says a zoo director friend. He may be right.

A further hazard, of course, is the visiting vandal who wreaks his mindless evil on the creatures within the zoo from time to time. He tends to prefer the more defenceless creatures – wallabies or penguins (only yesterday I post-mortemed another rock-hopper penguin at Chessington Zoo, the second in one week to have his skull bashed flat by some brave marauder) – or easy targets like crocodiles. After being hit on the head with a five-pound lump of rock, a fine old alligator at Belle Vue didn't eat another thing in the nineteen remaining months of his life. We raised the depressed fracture of his skull and set the shattered pieces of bone with superglue bought from Woolworths, but although the skull healed satisfactorily there was nothing we could do about the terrible damage to his little brain. And sometimes we find evidence of poisoners at work – a dolphin deliberately fed crystals of copper sulphate secreted in fish, slug-killer given to bears. Malicious doping, usually by means of barbiturates, has plagued Chester Zoo over the years and I'd had one major attack at Belle Vue. On that occasion cats of every sort – leopards, tigers, pumas and lions – had been affected, the tigers most profoundly of all. It isn't too difficult to recognise the signs of barbiturate poisoning and I'd been able to confirm the diagnosis by having blood samples analysed at Newmarket by the laboratory people who specialise in spotting 'nobbled' horses. I hadn't been certain that the poisoning was deliberate: there was always the chance that the cats had been fed meat innocently contaminated with drugs, perhaps a horse euthanased by a vet's injection and then sent to a knackerman who forgot that the horsemeat would still contain the euthanasia drug. When the Newmarket lab reported that they'd been able to pinpoint the exact kind of barbiturate, butobarbitone, I was rather disturbed. There is no sort of butobarbitone injection that a vet might use on any animal for either anaesthesia or euthanasia, but there are plenty of butobarbitone sleeping pills around prescribed for humans. How could butobarbitone pills find their way, accidentally and in high numbers, into the meat used for feeding big cats?

We never solved that question, but all the animals recovered – and that's where the strong coffee came in. Given as an enema three times a day, it had helped immensely in earlier cases. It was a safe and lasting stimulant and it combated dehydration and kidney failure; since starting what one venerable head keeper had christened my 'Nescafé-up-the-arse' therapy, I hadn't lost a single case of drug intoxication in large felines. I had a feeling as I raced through the wooded Crown Lane that lies between my home and the safari park that the Windsor cheetahs might be another case of barbiturate poisoning. I'd give them coffee till it came out of their ears. Of all the big cats, the cheetah is the most delicate and likeliest to die at the slightest excuse.

I turned into the park entrance, flashed my headlights at the girl in the cashbox and drove straight through to the cheetah reserve. With all the visitors about it would be quicker going in at the exit lock-gates to avoid the slow queue through the tiger and lion sections. As usual, drivers hooted and gesticulated wildly when they saw me going in the wrong direction against the traffic flow.

Francis met me in the corner of the reserve where three animals now lay motionless. Some 'dancers' were still on the floor and other cheetaahs walked slowly over the grass close by. Cheetahs are harmless creatures to work amongst, and even in the breeding season it isn't dangerous to walk through their big reserve or even enter one of the small inspection pens with them. There are no known cases of cheetahs attacking men and although they have big teeth, powerful jaws and long, non-retractable claws, they never use them on humans unless handled unwisely. They are nervy beasts and, I believe, suffer far more easily than do the other big cats from stress and the side-effects of stress in captivity; these delightful feline greyhounds demand space, privacy and meticulous attention to design when a zoological collection wishes to introduce them. Windsor's cheetah section is one of the best in Britain and it is even equipped with two cheery little Jack Russell terriers who guard the indoor quarters against rodent night-visitors after dark and patrol the ditches and fence-line during the day.

'They seem to fall into three groups,' said Francis as we stood and looked around us. 'The ones that are flat out, the ones doing this staggering dance and a few that are just a wee bit rocky on their hind-legs. Also there appear to be others that are completely unaffected.' He pointed to one large male racing under the beech trees in fruitless pursuit of a wood pigeon that looked likely to make it into the branches.

I knelt down by one of the unconscious animals, felt for the femoral pulse in the warm groin and peered at the eyes. The mouth looked an unpleasant lilac colour and breathing was weak and shallow. A dancing cheetah brushed my back and I turned to watch it swing away. The feline fandango was in reality a form of ataxia, partial loss of control over the limb muscles. Francis was right: the animals did display three different clinical pictures more or less, but there were differences of degree. The dilating pupils of the eyes convinced me that my earlier guess looked likely to be proved right. The animals were doped and a barbiturate was the odds-on culprit.

I called over the warden for the cheetah section. 'When were these animals last fed?' I asked him.

'About five hours ago.'

'Were they absolutely normal before then?'

'Right as ninepence. I'll bet my life on that, Doctor.'

'What kind of meat did you give them?'

'To tell the truth, I don't know.'

'Don't know. What do you mean, you don't know?' Was the man daft or blind, I thought, and the irritation showed in my voice.

'Well, I gave a group of them a whole carcass, and I'm pretty sure that these sick ones are that group.'

'Yes, yes, but what kind of bloody carcass, for God's sake?'

The warden shrugged his shoulders and puffed out his cheeks. He gave a small embarrassed laugh. 'I really don't know, Doctor. It had no head on and no skin. Just a skinned carcass, fresh delivered by the knackerman this morning.'

'How big was this mysterious corpse? Goat, donkey, carthorse, cow, Loch Ness Monster?'

He stretched out his arms. 'About so long. Good-quality meat, I thought. Around seventy pounds weight altogether.'

'Were there four legs and what were the feet like?'

The warden pondered for a while. He was certain that the carcass had consisted of four legs, a trunk and a neck, but neither he nor his assistant could remember seeing the feet. We looked over the ground where the cheetahs had been fed. Only blood smears remained on the grass and a few slivers of bone. The cats wouldn't have eaten a hoof or well-developed cow's foot, but they might have relished a pig's trotter or the soft horn of a still-born calf. My guess was that the carcass without a name probably came minus its feet. So how to identify the species now?

'There is one thing I'm pretty sure of,' said the warden as I picked up an unrecognisable bone fragment. 'This group of cheetahs fed communally like they generally do on the carcass. Yellow Tag here and Blue Tag over there – he gestured towards the two deeply unconscious cats – stood side by side eating at the neck end. I can't recall the exact

45

positions of all the others in the group but I think Clubfoot, who hardly seems affected at all, was at the opposite end of the body.'

All the cheetahs were easily identifiable. Many carried plastic eartags as part of the breeding record scheme instituted by the Smart family. Clubfoot was so named because of a distinctive enlargement of a front wrist joint that Francis and I had long ago X-rayed and found to be a chronic and incurable but apparently painless bone deformity.

If what the warden was saying was correct, it might be that the poison was concentrated or introduced into the carcass at one particular point, the neck. But even so, for so many animals to be affected the drug must have been distributed in some way throughout its tissues. I looked at the bit of bone in my hand: not only was I absolutely in the dark as to which species of animal it belonged to, I couldn't even tell what part of the skeleton it was from. It could have been a tail-tip or a bit of the skull. Putting it in my pocket, I got down to the business of trying to revive the narcotised cheetahs. 'Get those that can walk back to the night houses,' I told the warden. 'The worst ones we'll carry in the cars.'

Very soon we had all the patients indoors and I began the anti-barbiturate treatment. Francis carefully pumped the strong coffee he'd prepared into the rear end of the almost comatose animals. After taking blood for poison analysis, I squatted at their heads, giving injections of doxapram into the foreleg vein and warm saline under the skin over their ribs. The depressed breathing was causing the lilac colour of the mouth that signified cyanosis, but as soon as the doxapram circulated round to the brain things should improve. Sure enough, I saw the chest expand more strongly as the drug hit the right spot.

With deeply anaesthetised animals lying on their sides there is always the risk that the underneath lung will become congested with blood through the action of gravity on a sluggish pulmonary circulation. That had happened to me before with Mary, the Belle Vue elephant. Cheetahs being infinitely more easy to handle than elephants, I instructed one of the cheetah keepers to stay with the doped animals and turn them over every twenty minutes until, as I always say in such circumstances with big cats, 'you are in danger of getting bitten or clawed by the beast as it wakes up.' Deeply narcotised tigers may need this regular turning for up to two days and nights.

There was nothing more to be done for the moment. The injections would need repeating every six or seven hours. By tomorrow I would know if we had won.

I went with Francis to look at the other animals. None of the cheetahs which had fed separately from the affected group was showing any signs of doping, nor were any of the lions or tigers. The drugged meat was almost certainly confined to the one carcass consumed by my patients, but just to be on the safe side, I asked the keepers to use the remainder of the stock of beef, sheep and pig meat only for feeding the old male lions. If there was any more spiked food around, they were tougher, and to be honest less valuable, than the cheetahs or tigers. Francis would order more meat from the knackerman and also ask him if he could throw any light onto the mystery of the nature and origin of the headless carcass.

The regular treatment of the doped cheetahs continued. The doxapram injections, which broke through the cloud of barbiturate that was numbing the brain cells and stimulated breathing, needed topping up. The working of the kidneys needed frequent monitoring and the amount of saline injection adjusted, but by the following day the position was much improved. Only two cheetahs were still on the danger list but even they were beginning to come round. I could tell this by the way the ears would flick automatically if I dropped a little cold water into them, and by the fact that they drew their legs back ever so slightly when I nipped them on the delicate skin between a pair of toes. To my delight one cheetah even gave a feeble growl of disapproval, even though still unconscious, when I prodded its anus with a pencil-point to test the reaction of the sphincter muscle.

Francis had been in contact with the knackerman but as I feared, he couldn't give us any useful information. Many dozens of animals went through his charnel-house every day – sides of beef that hadn't passed muster for human consumption, cattle struck by lightning, ponies destroyed after road accidents, sows dying in the process of giving birth, sheep seriously worried by dogs, even the occasional zoo animal that had died of disease or old age. It wasn't possible to say what or even how many kinds of animals had made up the half-ton assignment of meat feed delivered to Windsor.

It looked as though we would never get to the bottom of the puzzle. Like some near-perfect murder case, the body had totally disappeared except that in this case the body had been the weapon or at least the vehicle of death. Then I remembered the bit of bone I had picked up on the previous day. I rooted round in my pocket and looked at it again. Still I hadn't a clue as to what animal the little splinter might have belonged to. How to identify it, if at all? I knew that a forensic laboratory could use the precipitin test to establish the specific origin of a speck of tissue or blood, so I decided to try the anatomists at Cambridge: perhaps someone in Professor Harrison's department of veterinary anatomy would be able to recognise something about the structure of the bony morsel that would give it a name. I put it in an envelope with a covering letter and sent it by the next post. Meanwhile a phone call had come in from the Newmarket laboratory – the cheetah blood was strongly positive for pentobarbitone.

As the days went by, the need for doxapram became less but the importance of fluid to combat dehydration of the doped and undrinking cheetahs increased. When the animals were compos mentis enough to cause trouble I gave their saline transfusions in the special crush-cages that are fitted to two of the 'hospital' dens in their house. Bit by bit the cats returned to normality and when they were finally steady on their feet and able to eat and drink again, Francis and his team could relax.

The Cambridge University anatomists came up trumps and coinciding with the end of the cheetah therapy came a letter with a report on the bone fragment: it was part of a bovine upper foreleg. I discussed the result with Francis

48

and our conclusions were far from satisfactory. We knew from the warden's report that the carcass had been a whole one and not very large. Now found to be bovine, it must have been a large calf. The fact that the cheetahs feeding on the neck end had been worst affected and those at the rear end least so might indicate that the barbiturate had been injected into the calf's jugular vein. If there had been a leakage around the needle injection site, a not uncommon occurrence, the drug would have accumulated in fairly high concentration in the neck tissues and remained there long enough to poison whatever fed on the calf after its death. One big query remained: why would anyone inject a calf in the jugular with a barbiturate? Dogs, cats and sometimes horses are humanely euthanised by veterinarians using intravenous barbiturates, but I have never heard of a calf being destroyed in this way. A farmer wanting to have a calf killed would take it to the slaughterhouse, where a humane killer would be used to avoid spoiling the meat.

Another possibility was that the animal had been given an intravenous shot of pentobarbitone as an anaesthetic for some operation, perhaps to correct a hernia or for castration, and had died under anaesthesia. But again this seemed highly unlikely: barbiturates had been used years before for anaesthetising cattle, but had had several disadvantages and had been superseded by much more satisfactory and efficient drugs. I couldn't imagine any veterinarian in this day and age using the fairly long-acting pentobarbitone, a drug that wasn't easily cleared from the animal's system and whose original antidote was no longer manufactured, on a calf needing surgical attention. The knackerman could not recall picking up any calves said to have succumbed during an operation, although it isn't usual for such information to reach the knackerman in any case: he simply picks up the deceased and hurries off.

The third possibility was the most worrying of all: malicious introduction of the drug into the carcass. Could someone have stuffed a handful of Nembutal sleeping capsules into the open neck-end? It would have been possible, although security in the park was at a high level and the meat store was deep within the big cat reserves. I knew all the wardens and keepers and couldn't believe that any one of them would have done such an insane thing, yet it surely could not have been an outsider unless someone had tampered with the meat before it came to the safari park.

The mystery was insoluble and so it has remained to this day. No more barbiturate poisonings have occurred at Windsor and whenever I drive through the cheetah reserve at the park and see those big cats lying elegant as sphinxes under the trees or chasing the feed-truck expectantly, I always return to wondering: how did the knock-out drug get into that one hapless calf?

☆☆☆☆☆☆☆☆☆☆☆☆☆☆

Chapter Five

☆☆☆☆☆☆☆☆☆☆☆☆☆☆

ALTHOUGH IT was now almost two years since I had joined Norman Whittle in his practice, I seemed to be no nearer the solid diet of zoo cases that I craved. Without a background of zoo-animal experience I was frequently forced into tight corners where my ignorance was nakedly exposed. It was not just the difficulty of diagnosing a whole new range of diseases in animals that figured nowhere in orthodox veterinary education – there were times when I could not even put a name to the species of creature that was borne, dragged or prodded into the consulting room. Animal owners often do not take kindly to the veterinarian working with pet cats and dogs who has forgotten the name of 'Fluffy', 'Poochie', 'Garibaldi' or whatever in the time between visits, even though these may be years apart. The position was considerably trickier when a furry brown creature about as big as a ferret and with large orange eyes with pinpoint pupils was proudly plonked down on the table and the owner said, 'Horace, this is Dr Taylor. Be a good boy now,' and then continued, 'I've brought Horace down from Carlisle, Doctor, because the zoo told me your practice could get rid of this skin disease that's been bothering him for months.'

Having travelled 110 miles with this whatever-it-was, the smiling owner of Horace would not be impressed if I started off by asking what sort of beast I was dealing with.

He was absolutely certain I knew. I looked at the Horace and the Horace gazed gently back to me. He seemed docile enough as he moved slowly around the table top. Anyway, he had to be a mammal because he was hairy.

'He's got these small bald patches on his head, Doctor,' the proud owner announced.

I looked at Horace's head; it was mongoose-like, with small ears and a pretty, damp nose about the size of a chihuahua's.

'Well, well,' I began hopefully, 'it's not often we see one of these.' The idea of this artful gambit was to lead the owner into giving me the clue I needed by agreeing that crunchlappets or flummerjacks or whatever the thing was were indeed getting rarer.

The owner of Horace did not fall into my rhetorical snare. 'No, Doctor,' he replied, 'but Mr So-and-so says that Dr Whittle's practice did wonders with his when it was sick.' Impasse.

I looked at Horace's feet; they were finger-like and reminded me of a monkey's. Although there was not much sign of anything to grab hold of I decided to stall for time by first stroking Horace and then picking him up so that I could get a better look at the diseased areas. He diffidently sniffed my fingers as I approached him. To my horror, as I stroked him I felt his backbone. Horace had a backbone like all mammals, but what chilled me as I ruffled through his fur was that the spines of his vertebrae appeared actually to be jutting out through his skin; my fingers were pressing directly on his spinal column! He seemed plump enough and there had been no talk of an accident – why on earth should Horace's owner be worrying about bald patches when there was something much more dramatically significant happening to his beloved pet's back? Perhaps I could get through the examination, diagnosis and treatment without actually knowing what Horace was. No, that was a hopeless idea. I was a fool – I should have admitted my ignorance as soon as Horace arrived.

At this juncture Horace decided to bite me. He did it once, precisely and powerfully, on the index finger which I was using to feel his spine. He then gazed gently at me once more as I jerked back my hand with a yelp and stuck the bleeding digit in my mouth.

'Oh my, Horace,' exclaimed his owner, 'that's a naughty boy. Still, I suppose you get lots of those in your job, Doctor, dealing with the likes of him.'

My finger was bleeding copiously and hurt like hell, but at least Horace had given me the chance I needed to save my ridiculous dignity. 'I'll just nip and get a Band-aid,' I said and slipped smartly out of the consulting room.

In thirty seconds I had plastered up the punctured finger and shot upstairs to my collection of zoo books. Somewhere in there, God willing, I would track down the Horace animal. Feverishly I flicked through the pages of an encyclopaedia of the animal kingdom. Horace's fingers seemed to be the crucial feature, but then I remembered his strange protruding spine. Not a monkey and yet not really like one of the small carnivores such as a stoat. There was nothing like him in the mongoose line. I turned to the raccoon family – maybe Horace was a cacomistle, whatever that looked like. I found the photograph of the cacomistle. Yes, the face was similar but the ears were too big and the clawed feet were most un-finger-like.

Hoping I would remember the appearance of a cacomistle should one ever be brought to me, I hurried hopefully on to the chapter dealing with the pro-simians, that strange bunch of individuals who lie halfway between insect-eating carnivores and monkeys. Horace certainly had some of the typical appearance of an insectivore, as well as those monkey-like fingers. Bingo! As I looked at the appealing faces of these most distant cousins of Man, the aye-aye, the tree-shrew and the rest, I suddenly found myself faced by an illustration of Horace in glorious colour. 'Long time since I was bitten by a potto,' I said gaily as I opened the door of the consulting room.

Pottos, the caption to Horace's picture stated, have horny processes on their spinal columns that project through their skin, so at least my fears about what had appeared to be Horace's exposed backbone were set at rest. He was my first pro-simian patient, though, and of pro-simian ailments I knew not a thing, but by taking scrapings and swabs of his bald patches for analysis I would try to find out what was causing the hair loss.

About a week later, Edith handed me the laboratory report on the scrapings I had taken. It started, 'Your sample from a ?dotto??? (what breed of cat is that – or is it a joke?) . . .'

I would have to become accustomed to folk thinking that I was some sort of nut addicted to practical jokes. I would learn to wait patiently while the person answering the phone at a pharmaceutical company scoffed disbelievingly when a vet from Rochdale ordered some special tropical drug for bilharzia in baboons, or when the international cable operators stopped me in mid-dictation of some urgent message containing phrases like 'Suggest your penguins have got bumblefoot' with a 'Come off it, mate, is this an April-fool thing or something?' Years later I had to threaten an operator with legal action if he did not type out my cable about a deadly serious matter which concerned not a potto, nor indeed any kind of wild animal, but a footballer. The star player of the famous Real Madrid soccer team in Spain had contracted a unique fungus infection of his knee bone; he might well never play again. The fungus infection had never previously been recorded in humans, but the Spanish doctors knew that I had been involved in treating various kinds of fungus infection in zoo animals. They contacted me via my friends, the directors of Madrid Zoo, and I cabled what information I had concerning the fungus. I suppose one can excuse the disbelief of the cable operator as I began to dictate: 'Concerning the footballer's kneecap, I know of one case of an otter in Africa and one possible hedgehog. . . .' Eventually the cable was accepted, and I like to think that the otter and the hedgehog helped that soccer star to play again.

The rest of the lab report on Horace the potto read: '. . . is positive for Trichophyton sp. – Ringworm.' I handed the report back to Edith and sighed as I wrote a prescription for Horace's owner to pick up that would in time completely clear his pet's ringworm. Even if a potto was unusual, his skin disease was anything but. Would I never be let into the zoo?

After two and a half years of treating cats and dogs, pigs and cows, with the occasional potto or python to bring me tantalizingly close to zoo work, I was all ears when Norman Whittle casually broke some news one winter's day as we both stood warming the seats of our pants in front of the gas fire in our little office. 'There's a new director been appointed at Belle Vue. Name of Legge. Got a first-class reputation as a naturalist and particularly with fish.'

Could this at last be the opportunity for me to begin doing some of the real zoo veterinary work? A new director could well mean a brand new approach to the management of the animals. The zoo had recently been taken over by an international hotel and leisure group, there were rumours of new animal houses to be built and new species to be exhibited. It sounded like the perfect chance for a young, green veterinarian to get in at the beginning of a fresh chapter. I tackled Norman about it at once.

'You know how I feel about exotic animals,' I said, 'but I

don't seem to be getting anywhere with the odds and ends, the parrots, bush babies and monkeys, that come here from time to time. I learned more when I went with you as a student to Belle Vue.'

Norman knew what I was going to ask him. 'Zoo work,' he said, screwing up his face pensively and rocking back and forth on his heels. 'Do you think there's a future in it?'

'I'm absolutely certain there is.'

'As I've told you before, we don't know much about what we're doing down there, David. Can't handle most of the animals. Guesswork, inspired guesswork, most of it. It's the know-how of keepers like Matt Kelly that counts. They call us in as a formality.'

'But it's one of the biggest zoos in Britain; there must be a vast amount of work for us. What about nutrition, preventive medicine, fertility improvement? There must be limitless scope for things that only a vet can do. And with a keen new director . . .'

'You may be right, but I don't go very often, you know. In the past they've called me only when they've got themselves into a sticky hole. We're the last resort.'

'But if they don't appreciate veterinary work in the zoo, we should get involved deeper, show them, force them to see the value. The new company and new director mean a chance for new attitudes.'

Norman sighed and slowly shook his head. 'We don't know enough about these creatures. We haven't the tools. You know how it is; if a gorilla gets a bad eye they ask some specialist in humans from the eye infirmary to look at it. He comes along if and when he can spare the time, but he's used to humans who don't break both your arms and chew the top off of your ophthalmoscope if you try shining bright lights in their sore eyes. So the specialist loses interest and the case isn't followed through. A bunch of human surgeons from the university come to take blood from the lions, and three lions die because the anaesthetist doesn't have a clue what frightening things morphine does to cats. So they try again, this time using a barbiturate, and another one never wakes up. It's rather depressing. You'd find it very hard to break into that sort of set-up.'

The story of the dead lions I had heard before. It made me angry then and the thought of it still does.

'Doctors be damned,' I said. 'It's the veterinary surgeon who should be in charge of the health of every one of those animals in Belle Vue.'

My partner laughed but there was sadness in his eyes. 'You're right, but you'll have a rugged time trying to convince some folk. Most of the time, with things like rhino and giraffe, I'm completely in the dark. The best I can do is to treat zebras like horses, giraffes and camels like cattle, lions and tigers like domestic cats.'

'But that leaves out most of the animal kingdom. What about reptiles, primates, things like tapirs and elephants and porcupines?'

Norman shrugged. 'Hobson's choice. Follow first principles.'

'And animals die.'

'Yes. And I have to admit that even at post-mortem I can't usually be sure why a creature gave up the ghost. Now and again I can do something positive, but mostly it's terribly frustrating. Anyway, remember we are a mixed farm and small-animal practice – don't you think the zoo could well be more trouble than it's worth?'

Norman's last sentence chilled me. I did not care to hear him even hinting that we might consider pulling out of zoo work. It was my only chance of penetrating the world of wildlife medicine. He – we – must not lose heart. Fearfully I asked, 'Would you seriously think of dropping the zoo?'

'Well, it's twelve miles away, the city traffic's getting worse, all the rest of our work is round Rochdale, there are practices nearer to the zoo than us.'

I felt my pulse quicken. If Norman went on in this vein his next words would surely be the renunciation of the one thing that I felt made our partnership special: the collection of strange and wonderful beasts in Belle Vue that fascinated me so powerfully. The very possibility made me shiver. I made up my mind immediately: nailing my colours to the mast with brass studs that hold firm to this day, I said, 'Let me take over the work at Belle Vue. I want to make something of exotic medicine.'

Norman smiled again and slipped on his white coat. It was time for surgery. 'OK,' he said, 'that's fine by me.'

At last I was going to do the zoo work; now all I needed was for the zoo to ring and report a sick animal. I made sure the other members of the staff understood that it would not matter whether I was on or off duty, I must be informed immediately the new zoo director called. God forbid that it should happen when I was in the middle of a difficult calving out on the moors!

A week went by. My visiting list consisted solely of dogs, cats, cows and pigs. Another week came, and another, and still whenever the telephone jangled it was the same sort of request: 'Got a heifer here with a bloated stomach that's tight as a drum,' or 'Our old bitch is drinking day and night and gone off her legs.' Just when I was beginning to wonder whether the Belle Vue stock had been given a bunch of remarkably effective amulets as well as a new director, the message I had been waiting for came in. A young camel that was being raised on the bottle was having problems with its mouth. Could the vet please attend?

I was delighted as I set off for Manchester. Here was an animal made for my opening performance: easy to handle and with few anaesthetic problems. I reckoned I knew a thing or two about mouths. Camels' teeth resembled cattle's and I had pulled out dozens of those. Tongue infections, ulcers, oral forms of cancer, foreign bodies: I had no qualms about dental work and I had covered, so I thought, the whole field in pet and farm animals as well as the odd new-world monkey with so-called South American primate disease, which deforms the facial bones and scatters the growing tooth buds in bizarre disarray. I hoped camels were not prone to some esoteric mouth complaint afflicting them and them alone, murrain of the Pyramids or Gobi Desert tooth rot or some such pestilence, about which I had not read but which was common knowledge among Egyptian camel drivers and head keepers like Matt Kelly.

The road from Rochdale to the zoo in Manchester ran past an unbroken succession of terraced houses with sooty

58

brick facades, cluttered corner shops that sold everything from a yard of elastic to sweet Cyprus sherry from the barrel, and towering mills with massive iron and brass mill gates and names like Bee and King emblazoned in white on the sweating red brick of their chimneys. It was an easy, familiar journey for me. As a small boy and later as a student I had often taken the yellow and orange double-decker bus that ran to the city and then rattled out by tram to the zoo, which stood behind high walls in a wilderness of mean streets, coal mines and railway sidings. This was the unloveliest part of the city, where sparrows sported uniformly sooty black plumage, where the vagrant and ubiquitous pigeons limped along dripping gutters with swollen, arthritic joints and gouty feet, and where the sulphurous fogs of autumn condensed on the clouded-glass windows of the tap rooms of the Engineers Arms and the Lancashire Fusiliers. Today the mills, the dreary dwellings and the churches standing shuttered and forgotten in yards of weeds and broken glass went by unnoticed. I was going to the zoo as its official vet.

Within the high walls of Belle Vue the jungle began. In the grey desert of Manchester there existed this oasis where wild creatures from every part of the globe were to be found. Just beyond the box office on the busy main road, a stone's throw from the mighty pit-shaft wheel of the Bradford colliery and within spitting distance of the London Midland and Scottish railway yard, were Africa and Asia, the impenetrable green of the Mato Grosso and the endless horizon of the steppes. There was no more than an acre of meagre, consumptive-looking grass in the whole park, and that was planted on a bare one-inch layer of soil overlying ashes. In spring the air reeked of engine smoke and in November it stung the eyes. Yet here lurked leopard and lion, eland and elephant. Here as a boy I had scaled the walls, despite the broken glass on top, to gaze down gratis on the tigon, that curious and long-lived hybrid donated a quarter of a century ago by some maharajah, and to make faces at the bears until pursued by irate keepers. It was a magic place for me, and it seemed unbelievable that at long last I was going 'on safari' professionally (at the princely fee of eight shillings and sixpence per visit) among the enchanted beasts behind the high walls.

The zoo was built when the reign of Queen Victoria was at its zenith, when Britain ruled the waves and the flower of the Indian Empire was still in full bloom. It was thought appropriate to design the buildings in the style of Mogul India which the England of the Raj had found so much to its taste, so the animal houses were built with windows, roofs and doorways in which the sensuous curves of Islamic art were wedded firmly to the heavy, worthy Victorian ways of working wood and iron. To the crowds who came from the cotton towns by train on a line that ran right into the zoo grounds, the sea-lion house in its heyday must have seemed like a delicate pavilion transported from the palace lawns of Mysore, the sort of place where, but for the drizzle and the smog and the clank of trams from the road, one might take tiffin among the jacaranda blossom with the Colonel's lady. Gardens and long rose walks were laid out between the animal houses, artificial lakes were dug, trees and bushes were planted, and among the bushes nestled the onion domes and minarets of ornamental mosques and palaces done in stucco.

In these pleasant surroundings the Victorians could promenade and admire the wild animals held behind massive bars or beyond deep pits. When they tired of the animals they could listen to brass bands in one of the several concert halls, eat in cafés, drink in pubs or amuse themselves on carousels and coconut shies in a fairground – all within the same high-walled park. The park had its own brewery and bakery inside the grounds and the facilities for great banquets, balls and fireworks displays. As I drove through the grounds on my way to see the sick baby camel, the light growing dim with the approach of evening, I could imagine what Belle Vue had been like a century before. Even today the crumbling remains of the ornamental mosques peep out of rhododendron bushes, defying the damp and the attrition of small boys' feet who clamber over the 'Keep Off' notices to reach the muezzin's turret. Despite dry rot, peeling pale blue paint, a hundred years of sea lions' splashing and the dank smell of herring impregnating the wooden Mogul arches, the pavilion still stands and there is a tiny bit of one of the rose walks, too. The thick bars are gone, new animal houses have been built of concrete and fine steel, the railway stops far short of the park now and the brewery is derelict, but here and there among the modern things like the speedway and the children's playground, an arch, a dome, a pierced screen or a fragment of curled iron winks out, conjuring up a lost age of stylish self-assurance.

The young camel to which I had been called turned out to be a friendly two-humped (Bactrian) female. As I arrived Mr Legge and Matt Kelly were feeding her from a bottle. I introduced myself to the new director while Kelly stood silently by, frowning in surprise at my appearance. Ray Legge was a slim, pale, military-looking man in his mid-forties, with dark hair and moustache, an aquiline nose and a warm and generous smile. He was neatly dressed and moved easily, with the precision of the rock climber that he was. When he spoke, it was in the crisp, public-school accents of the army officer that he had been. Quite a dramatic change from his predecessors in the post.

He pumped my hand energetically, threatening to pulverize my knuckles. 'Jolly pleased to meet you. As you know, I was at Chester Zoo but I've concentrated on aquaria over the past few years, especially Blackpool Tower aquarium. I'm a fish man really, but my mammals and birds will be brought up to scratch in the next few months. Now, let's show you this camel.'

Kelly the head keeper held the animal with an expression of weary scepticism at this young vet who was all book-learning and had no idea of zoo animal management. As I inquired what seemed to be the trouble, he quietly gritted his teeth and did an impersonation of St Ignatius Loyola staring heavenwards in a baroque painting. He had a ruddy, puckish yet handsome face and a close-cropped head that appeared dice-shaped, cubic with slightly rounded corners, the whole set on a short, stocky body. Matt had put the fear of God into me when I was a student with his apparent omniscience, a sleeveful of zoological tricks and the autocratic bearing of a sergeant-major. Now his powerful hands held open the camel's jaws.

'She isn't suckling strongly,' said Legge, 'and there's this white coating developed in the mouth.'

I looked inside. Sure enough, the entire internal surface of the mouth was covered with a milky white membrane. 'That's thrush infection,' I pronounced immediately, 'the fungus you see so often in human babies. You have been sterilizing your feeding bottles properly, haven't you?'

Matt Kelly cleared his throat, went redder, but said nothing.

'Yes, Matt boils the bottles before each feed,' replied the director. 'Can it be serious?'

'No, not usually. We'll soon have that right. Hold on a minute.'

I went to my car and brought back a bottle of gentian violet solution. While Matt held the camel's mouth open again, I used a small brush to paint the bitter purple liquid over her gums, teeth and lips. The animal screwed up her face at the taste and bubbled out a foam of purple saliva, staining Matt's hands. Gentian violet does not wash off easily. Matt's face was now plum-coloured and I feared his teeth-gritting might shatter every tooth in his head.

'Right,' I said, 'that'll do the trick.' Confidently I said my farewells and set off home with the conviction that I had made the best possible start.

Two days later the zoo telephoned again. It was Matt Kelly. 'This here camel, Dr Taylor,' he said in his light Dublin brogue, 'oi don't think your purple paint's done one bit of good. She's worse.' And then, as if he had already decided the patient was in such a critical state that anything more I might do could not make things any worse, he added, 'Ye can come down if ye like.' Damn, I thought, he talks as if I'm invited to pay my last respects.

The camel was indeed worse. The white membrane was still coating much of her mouth and the animal's general condition and vitality were deteriorating alarmingly. More of the white fungus was coating the bowels and the vagina. I had never seen thrush, a usually mild, yeasty fungus, on the rampage like this, but my training at

62

university had paid scant attention to the germ. It was regarded as an opportunist, secondary bug of little menace under normal circumstances. Yet this camel was very definitely ill. Could the thrush alone be doing that? Much later I would learn that thrush can be rather a tough and sometimes fatal infection for birds and dolphins, but at the time I felt sure the camel case was more complicated than I had first suspected.

Matt raised his eyebrows when I began to mutter my doubts about the case. 'Sure, oi thought all along she wouldn't make it,' he said. 'Bottle-reared animals haven't the resistance.' He adopted an expression of tired patience.

Suddenly something came back to me. Fungi. Yeast fungi. Yeasts, the kind of things that are used in making bread and beer. The yeasts thrive in the bread dough and, during the brewing, on sugar. Sugar, that was it. Somewhere I had read that people with excess sugar in their urine, in other words diabetics, are more susceptible to yeast fungus infections.

'I'm going to take a urine sample, Mr Kelly,' I announced. Matt stared. He had never heard of such a thing being done to a camel. Still, I could imagine him ruminating, young vets do strange things like that when they don't know where the devil they are.

With much difficulty I passed a catheter into the camel's bladder, drew off a few teaspoons of urine and dipped one of my glucose test strips into the sample. It turned deep blue – the camel was diabetic. 'Sugar diabetes, Mr Kelly,' I proclaimed excitedly. Matt scowled. 'Now I want some blood.'

The blood test's abnormally high sugar level confirmed beyond doubt the cause of the camel's disease. The thrush was secondary and could probably be eradicated by anti-fungal drugs, but the question of how to handle the diabetes was a tricky one. I talked it over with Ray Legge.

'It looks as if she'll need a daily injection of insulin,' I warned. 'We'll start off with the fairly long-acting protamine zinc kind and fiddle about with the dose until she's just free of sugar.'

It was not a very encouraging prospect, possibly having

to give shots to a camel for life. I knew a number of dog owners who were used to jabbing their diabetic pets each day with insulin; the animals tended to develop small knobbles all over them and felt like pineapples.

'Couldn't we give anti-diabetic drugs in her food?' asked Ray.

There were at least two kinds of oral drug which were proving effective in some human cases at that time, but they had failed to reduce the sugar level and control the progress of the disease in almost all animal cases. I explained this to the zoo director and we decided to embark on the course of insulin shots. Matt Kelly was armed with a bunch of syringes and needles, and I showed him how to adjust the dose according to the colour of the test strip after it had been in contact with the urine.

'And where do oi get the urine from?' Matt inquired. 'Oi can't stand waitin' behind the craytchure all day long hopin' it'll pee!'

'Of course not,' I replied. 'All you need do is spot a damp patch on the concrete where she's passed water and dab your test strip in that.'

Matt looked at his collection of medical paraphernalia with the enthusiasm of a bilious leprechaun. Crawling about over the floor blotting up camel-juice indeed! Just what he had known would happen if novices like young Taylor started interfering.

The young camel began to put on weight and condition over the next few days as Matt gave the insulin and the anti-fungal treatment annihilated the layers of yeast fungus. Things were progressing admirably. Then, on the ninth day, the youngster refused to feed and took on a drawn and depressed look. The sugar content in the urine rocketed upwards. When Ray Legge went into the hospital on the morning of the tenth day he found the little camel lying dead. Miserable, I drove over to perform the necropsy. The pancreas, the organ which produces natural insulin normally and also serves a number of other vital functions concerning digestion of food, I found to be a shrivelled, almost non-existent piece of tissue. What there was of it was inflamed, red and yellow. Matt Kelly silently returned to me the unused syringes, test strips and injections. So much for vetinerary science.

Despite this early setback, Ray Legge set off to a cracking start at Belle Vue. He supervised the building of one of the finest aquaria and reptile houses in the country and then designed a modern great ape complex complete with isolation rooms, a self-contained kitchen and food store for Len, the senior ape keeper, and underground tunnels leading from centrally heated, glass-fronted indoor quarters to circular open-air pits again protected from the germ-bearing visitors by armour-plated glass. In these new buildings I was going to spend much of my time in the next few years, for it became a mutual, unspoken arrangement that I would visit the zoo regularly at least once a week and not just when I was called. Exciting new inhabitants for both completed residences had been purchased by the zoo, giant tortoises and alligators for the one and a pair of young gorillas for the other. These would join the existing reptiles and apes from the old reptile and great ape houses.

Ray was a stimulating and sympathetic person to work with: a talented artist and sculptor in wood and stone, he had a sensitive and humane approach to zoo animals wonderfully combined with the never-ending curiosity of the born naturalist. To hear him talk, his time with the British Army in India during the war had been one glorious natural history ramble, finding new fish, rare insects or strange plants wherever he was posted. During the Cyprus crisis, when he instructed troops hunting Eoka terrorists in the arts of mountain climbing, he found the greatest excitement in pursuing the nimble lizards of the Troodos Mountains under the concealed rifles of General Griva's guerrilla snipers.

But it was with Matt Kelly that I had to build some sort of bridge if I was to carry out my resolve to learn something of his zoocraft. This most renowned of British head keepers had worked for many years at Belle Vue and before that at Dublin, which at the time had an unrivalled reputation for the quality of its lions. Matt was no naturalist, no lizard chaser, no smooth utterer of Latin names, no scientist; he was simply the perfect head keeper of his time. An out-and-out practical zooman, he was born with that 'feel' for his animals which is to be found in good shepherds and in farmers who rear plump beef cattle efficiently and with apparent ease, not by any high-falutin knowledge of food analyses, digestibility factors or other scientist's jargon, but by observation, experience, personal attention to individual feeding and plain, inborn talent. Also, in the same indefinable way that natural seamen sense impending changes in the weather, Matt had a nose for trouble. Long before it was obvious to others, he would start to fret about the rhinoceros or the ostrich or any other of the numerous creatures that he knew so intimately.

'Matt,' I said one day, shortly after the death of the baby camel, 'you know I learned a lot at Belle Vue as a student. Now, doing the veterinary work myself, I'm going to need your help in showing me a whole lot more of the things a vet doesn't know.'

Matt seemed pleased with my approach. A wide grin, showing broad white teeth like a chimp's, split his face. 'Sure and we'll see what we can make of ye, Dr Taylor,' he replied.

Things, little things, immediately began to go wrong. If there was a wrong way to do something, some particularly obtuse, disastrous or all-fingers-and-thumbs way to do it, I did it. There was the cardinal sin of zoo keeping which I quickly committed – leaving a gate unlocked. Matt and I had been looking at the Barbary sheep as they sprang from rock to rock round the artificial mountain in their pen. Bald, scurfy areas on their coat suggested mange. I would arrange to have them trapped, take skin scrapings for examination and dip them like farm flocks. Ping, ping, ping. Surefootedly on their tiny hooves they leaped from one minute ledge to another with infinite grace. Then, just as surefootedly, one of them went ping, ping, ping out through the gate into the zoo grounds. The last in, I had not bolted the gate behind me. Red-faced, I chased after a fuming Matt Kelly as we pursued the agile creature like two decrepit satyrs on the trail of a wood nymph. Out of the zoo grounds we went and onto the main road that leads to the

city centre. The Barbary sheep was gaining ground; the way it was galloping along one might have thought it was making for the docks and hoping to dash aboard a freighter due any moment to sail for its native North Africa. Eventually, with the aid of Ray Legge, keepers and sundry other citizens who had been informed of or had actually witnessed our puffing, cursing dash towards the town, the creature was cornered in a coal merchant's yard. Master of rocky pinnacles and sandstone cliff faces, the Barbary sheep found that the scree-sloped black pyramids of coal did not provide firm footing. Scrabbling vainly to reach the sooty peak of one mound it slipped relentlessly backwards and was caught.

Covered in coal dust that stuck firmly to our clothes and sweating skin, Matt and I returned to the zoo. 'Jeez, ye made me purple a few weeks ago, Doctor,' he lamented, clicking his teeth, 'and now ye've made me black!'

Our next joint foray concerned a monkey that had been fed the most potentially deadly titbits. Every zoo attracts a tiny proportion of nuts, dangerous eccentrics and vandals among the crowds of paying public. I can understand the impulses that make folk ignore the 'No Feeding' signs and pass potato chips or boiled sweets to elephants or monkeys; I detest it, but see the motivation involved, when drunken louts climb over the walls on a Saturday night after the pubs close and, in the fuddled spirit of bravado which this most primitive of mammalian species exhibits at such times, knock hell out of defenceless creatures like penguins or wallabies or peacocks. But I do not understand, cannot in my wildest dreams explain, the workings of the mind of the human who passed a bunch of thin, new, stainless-steel razor blades through the bars to a monkey. The monkey liked the look of the shining metal wafers and, so that his fellows could not purloin them, put them safely away – in his mouth. Like anyone who has received a present of which he is rather proud, the monkey just had to keep taking them out from time to time to admire and shuffle through them, and it was while he was inspecting his treasure in this way that his keeper spotted the blades and raised the alarm. Quick as a flash, the monkey put his fascinating little collection back into his cheek pouch.

When Matt and I arrived the monkey stared innocently at us. No blood ran from his mouth. His fingers appeared uninjured. Razor blades? What razor blades? his eyes seemed to say. Like some Indian fakir, he had so far avoided doing himself harm by manipulating the blades delicately with his soft tongue and velvety cheek lining. But how were we to retrieve them? I still had no speedy, safe monkey anaesthetics. If we netted him, might he not slice up the inside of his mouth in the fracas?

'What do you think, Matt?' I asked my mentor. 'How do we get the bloody things out without carving him up?'

Matt thought for a moment; then, with an air of relaxed confidence, he said, 'Get me a sweepin' brush.'

I found a brush for Matt, who slipped into the cage through the trapdoor at the back. The monkey darted to a far corner well away from him and prepared to do battle. It was obvious the head keeper was going to try to pin him in the corner with the brush. OK, the monkey was clearly thinking, we would see about that, and he tensed his powerful leg muscles, ready to leap out of the way of the imminent onslaught. With all the space available, the monkey must have reckoned that by jumping rapidly round from bars to branch to ledge to bars again he could wear out this lumbering human with his unwieldy brush in a war of attrition that might, as far as he was concerned, last all day. My forecast of the outcome, inexperienced as I was, agreed with that of my little simian friend; if I had been a betting man, I would have laid my money on the monkey.

Both of us were barking up the wrong tree. Matt's battle plan was quite, quite different. Without warning the stocky Irishman began to shout and swear at the top of his voice. Every oath invented in the isle of saints and sinners came blasting out. His face contorted with rage and he waved the brush vigorously about, clouting it with re-sounding bangs on the walls of the cage. It was an unholy din, but he did not make one move towards the monkey, nor did he bring his weapon within feet of the startled animal's crouching body. To the monkey it must have seemed as though the head keeper had gone mad. Any second this Fury would bring the flailing brush smashing down on his puny frame. With wrath like this he would not be just pinned and caught, he would be smashed to smithereens! This was going to be no game, but a matter of life or death somehow to keep out of range of the murderous maniac. He was going to have to run and run and run.

When running for your life you discard all inessential baggage so, watching for the first thunderbolt, the monkey picked the razor blades out of his mouth and dropped them on the floor. Matt stopped shouting, put down his brush, replaced the expression of mock rage with one of twinkling satisfaction and gathered up the slivers of steel. 'That's the way ye do it, Dr Taylor,' he said. 'Now we can bag him and ye can check him over if ye like.'

I was very impressed. Catching the monkey in a sort of butterfly net did not take long, then the captive was transferred without ceremony to a sack for carrying across to the hospital. When we arrived there the bagful of monkey was put on the table and I prepared to do my bit. I would sedate the monkey with a small shot of barbiturate so that I could examine him. I had the choice of injecting through the sack – an unhygienic procedure – or fishing the animal out, putting a full nelson on him and doing it elegantly in arm or thigh. I decided to extract him, but which end of him was where? There were three or four moving lumps in the wriggling sack, but were they arms, head or buttocks? I reckoned that one spherical lump must be the head and seized it firmly through the sacking. It was not the head – it was the other end. A second later the dagger-like fang teeth of the genuine head end lanced through the sack and sliced my left index finger almost in half. As I tried to stem the bleeding and prepared to go down to the city hospital for suturing and tetanus injections, Matt gave me the word. 'Never try grabbin' a monkey in a bag like that again, Doctor. Remember his eyes are pressed close to the coarse sackin' stuff. Ye can't see where he is, but sure as hell he can see ye.'

Painfully I acknowledged my dumb stupidity and went off to the Manchester hospital, where the house surgeon declined to use one drop of local anaesthetic as he cobbled together my sliced extremity. (My colleagues in human surgery do not realize how easy their primate species are to handle; try doing the same on a young chimp, for example.) He also cauterized the wound deeply and painfully with silver nitrate, neglected to give me any antibiotics and consequently produced a throbbing infection.

It was when the finger was at last settling down and my hand was once more available to do surgery on my own behalf that Ray Legge informed me that one of the zoo's golden pheasants had a lump on its eyelid. When I examined the bird there was no doubt that the hard, yellowish swelling was a tumour, but not very difficult to cut out. I decided to take the bird back to my surgery in Rochdale and do the small operation under gas anaesthesia. Matt Kelly came along with me.

With its striking art-nouveau plumage of scarlet, green, gold and black, the golden pheasant is one of the handsomest birds in the world and definitely among my favourites. Like many other species of pheasant, the male sports a particularly gorgeous flourish of tail feathers, and it was on one such exquisite avian dandy that I was operating. All went well as I cut out the growth with scalpel and forceps and Edith puffed air and a minute quantity of halothane gas into the syrup tin containing the head of the slumbering bird. Matt watched and seemed moderately impressed. After stitching the wound with fine nylon thread, I told Edith to stop the anaesthetic and stood back to admire my work. The bird drowsed peacefully on the operating table. Then, as is the way with birds coming out of anaesthesia, it suddenly blinked its eyes open, flipped itself up onto its feet and fluttered off the table before any of us could move. Rapidly gaining strength, and finding itself in surroundings quite different from its native Tibetan forests or its range at Belle Vue, it dashed merrily round the room, knocking over light pieces of equipment and provoking the cats who sat in wire-mesh boxes waiting their turn for surgical attention. Edith and I gathered our wits and set about retrieving the energetic post-op patient.

'Careful!' shouted Kelly, crouching down in the posture of a rugby full-back about to tackle his man. 'Leave him to me! I'll get him as he comes round!'

But we took no notice and scuttled in hot pursuit, while Matt waited to bag the pheasant as it dashed towards him on its next lap of the room. Anxious to impress the head keeper with my animal handling expertise, I ungallantly elbowed Edith out of the way, put on a spurt and made a determined grab.

'Leave him to me!' Matt yelled again, but I had caught the bird – or so I thought. With a firm grasp of the careering pheasant's proud tail feathers, I applied the brakes and the long plumes came to a halt. The pheasant, to my horror, dashed on, straight into Matt's arms. Now bereft of its full complement of the tiger-barred plumes which in the complete bird make up an arching tail of just the right artistic length, the pheasant was exposing a stubby,

71

yellow-pink butt end reminiscent of a Christmas turkey on Boxing Day.

'Dammit, look!' groaned Matt, his teeth grinding as he struggled to contain more picturesque Irish turns of phrase while Edith was present. 'Look at the bird's ar ... posterior!'

Although unhurt, the bird looked most undignified as it squatted in Matt's folded arms. Both of them, I thought, looked at me with a red and reproachful eye. There was no way of making up for my mistake, no glue nor subterfuge could save my face. It would be many months before nature restored the pheasant's fine cockade and covered the evidence of my ineptitude.

Matt's sour expression confirmed that I had done it again. 'Never catch hold of a bird loike that again,' he instructed as he made for the door and I stood glumly, still clutching my wretched bunch of feathers like a schoolboy caught in the act of picking the neighbour's strawberries.

'And give me those feathers,' he added, holding out a hand. 'Dozens of schoolchildren ask me for such things.' I could imagine him handing this lot out and saying in his fruity brogue, 'And these were pulled out of a golden pheasant by a clumsy young vet. Can ye imagine that?' I was not building much yet in the way of bridges with Mr Matt Kelly, that was certain.

At least Ray Legge was encouraging and tolerant as I stumbled my way painfully through the minefield of practice among creatures too dangerous or too difficult to handle safely, who presented symptoms that bore no resemblance to anything I had seen in cat or pig or cart-horse. I also had to contend with techniques of animal self-defence which I had not met before, from the torpid sloth who is anything but slothful when slashing rapidly and accurately with its front claws, to the coatimundi who, if you pick it up by its tail and hold it safely at arm's length, will athletically climb up its own tail and summarily deal with you. It shares this contortionist ability with the opossum, Matt instructed me. It came as a relief sometimes, though one which I would have vehemently denied at the time, to return at the end of a day of 'guess-agnosis' at the zoo and get stuck into a surgery full of common or garden domestic pets with complaints that seemed like old and trusted friends, where drugs acted predictably and surgery was a romp round anatomy as familiar as one's own back yard.

Matt Kelly continued to supervise my enthusiastic meddling with a melancholy reserve. My wrong diagnoses were shown up when I performed post-mortems. The square-faced Irishman would click his teeth as I prodded around inside the cadaver of an antelope that I had considered to be afflicted with liver infection but whose diseased lungs were manifestly the cause of its death. 'Knew it hadn't much chance,' he would opine as I began to mutter the Latin name of the condition and hopelessly try to baffle him with science. 'Seen it before, oi have, Dr Whittle and oi both. Knew the powders ye gave him would do no good.' Matt would shake his head and reflect aloud on the good old days when yoghurt, cider vinegar, honey and molasses had been the elixirs of life in the zoo and everything from axolotl to zebra had apparently expired only from advanced old age.

It seemed that the only common fact about exotic species was their unwillingness to exhibit symptoms that had much logical connection with the diseased portion of their bodies. In the evenings I would complain to Shelagh as I ate my supper about how a hippopotamus with chronic pneumonia of both lungs had breathed apparently evenly and without difficulty right up to the point of death and had not been heard to cough one single, soft cough. And about how monkeys that I found to be riddled with tuberculosis had played, fought, eaten, mated and harassed their keeper until struck down within the space of five minutes as if smitten by thunderbolts. 'It's as if the zoo animals have some tacit conspiracy to give me a hard time,' I would ruminate as I tackled my steak pudding and peas. 'Maybe Norman Whittle was right. It doesn't make much difference whether I do anything or nothing, the outcome is inevitable.'

'Nonsense!' Shelagh would reply. 'You've got to learn to walk before you can run. And after all, it was your idea to go in for zoo animals.'

With more homilies on the general theme of having to break eggs to make omelettes, she would brew me a mug of coffee and I would go into the lounge to spend an hour or two reading books or journals on exotica. Although there were as yet no books available on zoo medicine, occasional papers were being published here and there by scientists working in Africa, in laboratories and in places such as the mighty San Diego Zoo. For a few minutes in the evenings I could escape from my problems with Belle Vue and Matt Kelly and learn what veterinarians were doing in sunnier climates. Even San Diego, it appeared, did not have it too easy, and the Prosector's Annual Report from London Zoo, a detailed record of the toll of creatures dying from disease and accidental injury, grimly reflected my experience in Manchester. The crying need was still for a range of powerful but safe sedatives and anaesthetics which would enable all of us to examine and treat living exotic creatures more thoroughly. On top of that, we needed a sure way of delivering the drugs to wild and dangerous critters over distances ranging from a few feet to tens of yards. Until we had such weapons in our armoury I would have to go on collecting hair, droppings, urine and other possibly useful stray material from sick animals in the hope of getting enlightenment from the Test (rather like a soothsayer pondering the entrails of a sacrificial chicken), while Matt Kelly stood stolidly by with an expression on his face which said quite clearly that scientific mumbo-jumbo could never take the place of good old-fashioned zooman's know-how.

Chapter Six

I WAS beginning to consider seriously what had always been just a dream: setting up a practice to treat nothing but exotic species. It would be some time yet, though, before my zoo experience and contacts would be wide enough to take such a big step into the unknown, and until then it was back to cows and sheep on moorland farms and cats and dogs in the Rochdale surgery. For exotic animal work I would continue to rely mainly on surgery cases and on Belle Vue Zoo.

It was from there that Ray Legge telephoned me one autumn evening. 'I've got a bear on fire! Get here sharp as you can!' I hardly had time to pick up the phone and put the receiver to my ear before Ray's unusually strident voice rapped out the message. Before I could ask any details, there was a click. He had rung off.

When Ray's abrupt call came in I was just putting the final touches to my favourite dish of hare, Lièvre à la Royale, an exquisite casserole containing cream, cognac and pine kernels. From the dressing of the shot wild hare after it had hung a week, something Shelagh insisted I do alone in the farthest corner of the garden, through the marinading in wine and herbs and the blending of the chopped liver and heart with the brandy, a relaxing and enjoyable culinary exercise with which I insisted Shelagh should not interfere, the whole process took twenty-four hours. Now at last, with its accompanying wafers of glazed carrots and rosemary-sprinkled potatoes, it was almost ready for the table. But the burning bear banished all thoughts of dinner.

'Don't worry, love,' said Shelagh, as I whipped off my blue-and-white-striped cooking apron and picked up my emergency bag, 'it'll warm up tomorrow.' She pushed a couple of apples into my duffle coat pocket.

As I wound my way laboriously through the evening traffic towards the zoo I puzzled over Ray's call. He had sounded worried all right, but more than that I had the impression that he was mightily angry. I had never seen Ray, the epitome of the well-mannered English gentleman, blazing with rage the way he had sounded on the phone. A burning bear? It sounded like vandals. We have more than our fair share of those in a city zoo. Yes, vandals must have done something particularly obnoxious to raise his wrath. A burning bear sounded just that.

When I arrived in the zoo grounds my headlights illuminated a cluster of men standing near the bear pit. One of the group was in a state of great agitation, almost literally jumping up and down and stamping round in small circles. It was Ray Legge. The other figures I recognized as members of the Board of Directors. I stopped the car and walked over to join them.

'And if it happens once more, just once more, I'll walk out of this place and, by God, I'll . . .' Ray was white with anger. The Board members were listening silently; some looked crestfallen, others embarrassed. 'Just look at that animal, will you?' Ray was in full spate. 'You can't have it both ways, you won't have it both ways! It's my animals or your Battle of Waterloo. Your damned Battle of Waterloo will have to go!'

In the bear pit a brown bear sat on a rock licking at a frizzled black patch as big as a saucer on its side. On the ground nearby lay a large burnt-out rocket, a firework with a stick at least four feet long. From its charred casing a plume of grey smoke curled lazily upwards. I understood. Damned Battle of Waterloo! Every autumn Belle Vue presented for two or three weeks a lavish evening firework display. Combined with son et lumière and several dozen men in period costume, historic battles would be re-enacted in a deafening, dazzling pyrotechnic spectacular. Last year it had been General Wolfe storming the heights of Quebec. This year it was Waterloo. The problem was that the hour-long barrage of star shells, firecrackers and smoke bombs was all staged in an arena backing directly onto the bear pits where the collection of Himalayan, brown, sun, polar and sloth bears ate, slept, went about their quiet daily business and, most importantly, mated. They were literally only inches away from the crackling rockets and roaring catherine wheels.

Both Ray and I had been complaining bitterly about the effects on the animals of being compulsorily in the orchestra pit during every performance of the ear-splitting extravaganza. We were particuarly concerned for the polar bears and their efforts to produce young: we were certain that each year our lovely adult female conceived and, if things had progressed as nature intended, she would have delivered one or maybe two little cubs in November or December. It never happened. On came the fireworks at the end of September, and within a few days the keeper cleaning out the dens would find a smear of blood or perhaps remains which proved conclusively that the bear had once again miscarried and devoured the half-grown embryo. It was heart-breaking, but now this!

Ray broke off his tirade and came over to me. 'That bear felt like sleeping outside on the rocks tonight. The keeper couldn't get him into the sleeping quarters.' If a bear feels like napping al fresco on a mild night, there is no easy way of changing his mind. 'Then that bloody pantomime started up, a rocket went off course and landed in the pits.' He was quivering with fury. 'Do you know, when the keeper called me the bear was actually alight! Fur in flames!' He spat out the words with slow, precise venom. 'I've told them. That's the last straw. The fireworks must go because we can't move the bears.'

I darted the bear with a tranquillizing syringe and climbed down a ladder into the pit. The burnt area of the skin had been largely insulated by the dense, sizzling hair

78

but it was still a serious and painful injury. I plastered it liberally with a paste containing local anaesthetic, antibiotic and cortisone. It would heal all right. Climbing back out of the pit, I found Ray still expostulating and gesticulating with the directors.

To our amazement, his war dance did produce all that we could have hoped for. The stray rocket turned out in the end to be a twenty-four-carat blessing in disguise, for it was decided that the annual fireworks displays at Belle Vue should end. Ray and I were delighted. Now maybe we would get our first baby polar bear.

The key to successful breeding of this species in captivity appears to be ultra-quiet privacy for the female. We decided that from October onwards next year, Crystal, Belle Vue's female polar bear, would be placed in strict isolation in a secluded, dark den, with food placed silently from time to time in an adjoining compartment which she could reach through a small door. No mucking out, no regular inspections by flashlight – just leave her alone. Then, if all went well, we might hear the soft squeaks of the hidden cubs some time before Christmas and get our first glimpse of them in the following January when she decided to show them to us.

The next breeding season came round, and true to form the female polar bear conceived. We went ahead with our plan and treated her like a hermit. Just after Christmas the keeper heard faint mewing noises in her den. They continued for a day and then ceased. Some days later the bear moved into the feeding compartment and insisted on staying there, clawing at the door that led to the outside pits. We let her out and searched her den. Inside was the shrivelled body of a full-term cub, but without a drop of mother's milk in its tummy.

The following year the same thing happened, but this time she half ate the baby. Ray and I were despondent. 'Well,' I said, 'next season we'll hand-rear the cub right from birth.'

'How do you reckon to get the cub away before she eats it or at least does it some harm?'

'As soon as the keeper hears any squeaking or gets any

79

hint at all that she's given birth, you (I'm bound to be at least half an hour away, maybe more, and that could be too long) you will knock her out with phencyclidine and grab the cub. Beginning in mid-October we'll have a dart already loaded with the right dose of phencyclidine standing permanently in a jar outside her den. And we'll start the little 'uns off on Carnation milk.'

Ray nodded. All we had to do now was to wait an interminable ten or eleven months to see if our plan would work.

Ironically, in view of my hard-won connection with the zoo and the amount of time I spent there, Belle Vue could not help very much with my increasing interest in learning about marine mammals. The only ones in the zoo were three big old Californian sea lions that lived in the wooden Victorian pavilion, jealously guarded by their trainer, an elderly German lady called Mrs Schmidt. Mrs Schmidt had a lifetime's experience in working with sea lions. She worried and doted and fussed over the honking, snorting, four-hundred-pound monsters, rarely taking a day off and meticulously selecting and preparing all their food herself. No one, but no one, be he head keeper or zoo director, and certainly not that meddlesome harbinger of death, the veterinarian, got within spitting distance of her beloved Adolf, Heinz and Dieter. Mrs Schmidt took no chances; she even took her baths in the sea-lion house, sitting in an old tub and bellowing shrill Teutonic oaths if anyone made to approach the door. It was tacitly accepted by everyone that the sea-lion house was Mrs Schmidt's private preserve. Left alone in her sanctum sanctorum she caused nobody any trouble and asked for nothing but the regular delivery of fish. Even Matt Kelly was a little in awe of her.

There was no salt water in the sea-lion pool, no filtration or chlorination equipment. The sweet water was changed when it became foul. The fish for the animals was fresh from the Lancashire docks and thus did not undergo the deep-freezing that would kill any parasites it contained. As a result of all this, Adolf, Heinz and Dieter were constantly taking in worm eggs by mouth and from time to time would excrete the long, wriggly, clay-coloured adult parasites. This would send Mrs Schmidt hurrying to the nearby chemist's for extract of santonin, the stuff that she had always used on sea lions, as had her father before her. Santonin extract generally resulted in a pleasing expulsion of a biggish bundle of worms, but in the process the animals would suffer a few hours of griping pain in the guts and would grind their teeth with a most despondent air.

Mrs Schmidt was used to that. 'Those verdammte worms!' she would explain. 'They fight to their last gasp to keep a hold. See how they make my three lieblings unhappy while they thrash about and struggle to resist my santonin. Still, all will be well shortly. I always get those verdammte Würmer!' And she would nod contentedly.

Sure enough, the three sea lions would soon recover from the worming and would be rewarded with choice whole whiting – whiting which contained invisible worm eggs and sometimes even invisible baby worm larvae.

If Adolf had a cold, Mrs Schmidt gave him Fenning's fever powders, cloves of garlic and spoonfuls of honey secreted inside the fish. When Dieter got a boil and would not eat, she smeared the throbbing lump with Germolene and kept him locked in his pen away from the pool in the hope that he would drink from a bowl of water into which she had mixed some mysterious 'blood-purifying' salts. In all the years and years that she had been at Belle Vue she had never once taken veterinary advice. I rarely ventured inside her domain and then only to catch the sea lions' show with the paying public. It struck me that the big animals were slow and lethargic considering their high degree of training, but my knowledge of marine mammals was still limited and perhaps it was just their great weight.

There were times when Ray Legge knew that one or another of the sea lions was not up to the mark and he would diplomatically suggest that perhaps Dr Taylor might be able to help – after all, he was being paid for his veterinary advice – but Mrs Schmidt would simply retreat within her pavilion, bolt the door and prepare to withstand a siege. If Ray took a firmer line she would just as adamantly but politely refuse the offer, send her assistant to the chemist so that her lines could not be infiltrated while she herself was away, and even sleep at nights by the side of her charges just in case we tried a secret nocturnal examination of the beasts. 'You can't be too careful' seemed to be her motto.

The worms in the sea lions came and went and new ones took their place. One day Mrs Schmidt noticed an unusually large number of live worms lying on the pool bottom. Mein Gott! The three boys had picked up a bigger load of parasites than ever. She decided to take stern measures with the disgusting invaders. It looked as if a particularly numerous band of the pests was involved; ach so! A double dose of the santonin extract would deal with them. Adolf, Heinz and Dieter duly swallowed their medicine hidden inside a whole fish. Half an hour later it appeared to Mrs Schmidt that the worms were fighting far more ferociously than normal. The sea lions were getting the expected gripes and colly-wobbles, but something she had never seen before was also happening. The animals were beginning to vomit violently, tremble uncontrollably and shake their heads in a bizarre, glassy-eyed fashion. Sudden powerful spasms shook their sleek, chubby bodies. They were in trouble. The worms were winning!

As the minutes passed and the sea lions showed no signs of recovering, Mrs Schmidt made a momentous decision; she would ask Mr Legge's advice. Ray went down to the sea-lion house as soon as she appeared white-faced in his office to tell him with much agitation what had happened. It was plain when he saw the distressed trio that something had gone horribly wrong with the worming, and he called me right away.

Adolf and Co. were in fact showing all the symptoms one could expect from an overdose of santonin. Santonin is a poison derived from the dried buds of a plant named wormwood by ancient apothecaries after they had observed its properties. The use of it in the old days relied on the poison bumping off the parasitic worms at a dose which was low enough not to do the same to the worms' host. It is a chemical that attacks the central nervous

82

system, and the signs that the worms were putting up a heroic resistance, as Mrs Schmidt interpreted them, were in fact the effects of the toxic substance on the sea lions themselves.

Now at last I was presented with my first marine mammal case at Belle Vue. It was a breakthrough, but I could hardly have chosen a more inauspicious debut than three unrestrainable sea-lion bulls with the signs of nerve poisoning produced by a chemical to which there was no antidote.

Although the vomiting and diarrhoea should evacuate any of the santonin that remained unabsorbed by the intestine, the dramatic convulsions continued. I decided to try a tranquillizer, but it would have to be injected, and sea lions are one of the species on which it is risky to use the dart-gun because of the danger of dirt from the skin being carried into the animal's system by the dart.

Kelly had arrived on the scene and was shaking his broad head pessimistically as he looked at the agonized animals. 'Can you and Matt hold them somehow while I give them a shot?' I asked Ray. The sea lions were in a small pen containing a pool from which the water had been drained. They were conscious and obviously aware of our presence. It would be impossible to pin down such heavy creatures and like most sea mammals, the sea lion is designed without any convenient grab handles.

'I'll get a chair,'' said Ray. 'If you can get a needle into the back flipper muscle somehow, I'll try to distract the head end.'

Mrs Schmidt produced a chair, and the zoo director took up the classical lion tamer's pose with the four wooden legs pointing towards the jerking head of the agonized Heinz. We both knew how dirty sea-lion teeth are and what severe bites they can inflict on one another and on man; Mrs Schmidt bore gnarled scars on her hands and arms. Protected, I hoped, by Ray and his chair, I splashed some disinfectant onto Heinz's skin and jabbed a new needle into his rump. He was too wracked with the convulsions to do anything more than turn his head slightly in my direction. The tranquillizer slipped into the muscle. Adolf and Dieter were treated in the same way, then we stood and waited while Mrs Schmidt continued to marvel at the powerful rearguard action by the worms. Slowly the sea lions relaxed, the convulsions diminished and the vomiting ceased. After three quarters of an hour it looked as if the three sea lions were going to be all right. They were drowsy but undoubtedly out of danger.

'Now, Mrs Schmidt,' I said, feeling able to take advantage of the situation, 'that's the last time that you will use santonin on *our* sea lions.' She blinked and did not say a word. Matt stood by, looking like a sergeant-major quietly enjoying the dressing-down of one of his privates by the CO. 'From now on,' I continued, 'we will use something new. It's very effective and not at all poisonous. I'll send you a bottle of piperazine tablets tomorrow.'

Adolf, Heinz and Dieter did fully recover but in a few weeks began to show evidence of worm infestation again. Obediently, Mrs Schmidt gave them the piperazine tablets. Delightedly she watched the worms expelled a few hours later, and much to her amazement not one single worm put up a struggle. The sea lions had no gripes, no diarrhoea, no grinding of teeth.

Mrs Schmidt continued to feel, I think, that although I might be Lord of the Worms, the rest of my medical art was still suspect. At least I had penetrated the sea-lion house and was allowed to look at the animals whenever I wanted – unless their keeper was bathing. It was a major advance, but I still had the impression that the sea lions were slow and sluggish in their movements. They seemed to tire easily and they lay around idly; there was none of the zest I had seen in sea lions at other zoos. At the time little of importance had been published about sea-lion medicine, so the special nutritional problems that pinnipeds (seals, sea lions and walruses) and other marine mammals can develop in captivity had not yet been realized.

One day, as I watched Mrs Schmidt prepare fish pieces for Adolf and his partners, it struck me that for every bucket of fish she filled with choice cuts for her 'boys', she was filling another bucket with waste pieces to throw away. She was neatly filleting the fish, removing bones, heads, tails and all the internal organs. The sea lions got only one hundred per cent meat, first-quality steaks. In the wild, sea lions naturally eat the whole fish, bones, guts and all, as well as huge quantities of squid and cuttlefish. I discovered that for years the Belle Vue sea lions had received only the boneless middle cuts of herring, whiting and mackerel.

'What about supplements?' I asked. 'Do you give minerals or vitamins?'

'No. Nor have I in all the years I been keeping sea lions, Doctor,' came the reply.

'Right, I'm going to give you some multivitamin syrup,' I said. 'Put a tablespoonful in their fish each day.' She agreed. 'And what's more,' I added, 'I want you to stop filleting the fish. You can remove the guts if you like, but I don't see how these animals can get enough calcium without the bones in their diet.'

Mrs. Schmidt looked horrified but she promised to do what I asked. I sent down to her the first multivitamin syrup I laid my hands on in the dispensary, a lemon-flavoured concoction made up for human geriatric patients. Apart from the flavouring it contained nothing but a mixture of the vitamins A, B, C and D.

A few days later I was driving through the zoo grounds when I saw Mrs Schmidt running towards my car waving her arms to attract my attention. Oh-oh, here's trouble, I said to myself as I wound down the window.

'Dr Taylor, Dr Taylor, you must come and see my boys,' she said, puffing with the exertion. Apart from her flushed face I was surprised to see that she did not appear alarmed or angry. If anything she was in rather a pleasant mood. Good Lord, Mrs Schmidt had actually smiled at me!

I went into the sea-lion house. There were Adolf, Heinz and Dieter playing in the pool and gambolling around on the stage. But how they were playing! The three ponderous fellows were no longer torpid or slow-moving. They were sliding, rolling, diving and leaping in the water like young otters.

'It's the vitamins, Doctor,' crowed Mrs Schmidt, 'it's the vitamins. I've never seen them so alert and active. I thought they were in peak condition but look how wrong I was.'

She was right; it was the vitamins, probably the vitamin B_1 in particular. It is a wonder that those animals survived at all when they were deprived of minerals and the all-important vitamin B_1. Years later we were to discover how essential these substances are to marine mammals fed on dead fish like herring and mackerel, which contain a potent enzyme that utterly destroys vitamin B; and how dangerous the lack of salt could be to specimens kept in fresh water.

The conquest of Mrs Schmidt and her sea-lion house was complete, but I became increasingly nervous about driving near the pale blue wooden pavilion. She seemed to sense that I was in the grounds and would come flying out with a thousand questions about every minute thing that might or she imagined might be wrong with her boys. As for the lemon-flavoured liquid, she refused ever to change from it. When more suitable, more concentrated tablets with the same constituents were given to her, she swore that they did not work as well as the lemon syrup. And when the drug company making the product changed the flavouring from lemon to orange for some reason, she kicked up a mighty fuss in Ray Legge's office. 'Dr Taylor said I should use the lemon syrup and look what wonders it performed,' she thundered. I must have the *lemon* one!' When it was made absolutely clear that no more lemon was ever going to be produced and that Dr Taylor had personally checked the credentials of the orange substitute, she gave in. I do not think Mrs Schmidt ever treated another ailment in her sea lions again, and she made it her business to see that no one, but no one, except myself went anywhere near her precious boys.

Driving back to the surgery one day after I had been to the sea-lion house at Mrs Schmidt's excited request to see the effect of my vitamins on her threesome, I stopped at some traffic lights. Casually looking at the other vehicles around me, I thought I recognized an individual sitting next to the driver of the car on my immediate right. Bigger and shaggier than when I had first encountered him when he was a baby, he was dressed in corduroy dungarees, purple chunky-knit woollen sweater and Sinatra hat. He was holding one side of an unfolded road map while his human chauffeur held the other and studied their where-abouts. If I was not mistaken it was Billy, a chimpanzee I had once treated for pinworms. He had been owned at the time by rather overwhelming woman named Mrs Lomax. I tapped on my window. Billy glanced superciliously in my direction and then, apparently unable to place my face as belonging to anyone important, and bored stiff by yet another of those oddballs who would insist on gesticulat-ing, waving, winking and generally making asses of themselves every time he did nothing more remarkable than go out for a drive, he yawned histrionically and looked down at the map. I could not quite see Billy's companion at the wheel, and wondered whether it was Mr Lomax and he was trying to make his way to see me.

I had not been in the surgery for five minutes before Billy and his friend were ushered in. It was indeed Mr Lomax, a portly, pink-faced man with a high-pitched voice, an ever perspiring brow that required frequent mopping with a large blue-spotted handkerchief, and a tight grey suit the pockets of which bristled with pencils and ballpoints and the seat of which was so polished that I might have expected to see Billy's impish reflection glinting in it. Mr Lomax wore socks that did not match.

'Dr Taylor,' he piped, 'my wife sends her apologies. She couldn't come because she has a speaking engagement in Bradford. I've been sent – I mean, I've brought Billy with his problem.'

'Problem? The worms again, you mean?'

Mr Lomax shook his head vigorously. 'Oh no. We, well, he's absolutely OK in that respect these days. What's worrying her, us, is the way his tummy's swelling.'

I looked at the now mature ape sitting placidly on the floor holding the neatly folded road map in both hands. He was big, hairy, muscular and very much the macho male chimpanzee. True enough, he did look eight months pregnant. His purple piece of home knit was stretched over a distinct pot belly.

'Can you handle Billy?' I asked, noting the chimp's now well developed fang teeth, which he displayed from time to time as he gave me the apprehensive chimp grin.

'Not really, to be honest. Billy's a mummy's boy. But if you wouldn't mind looking at him on the floor, and if I keep giving him these Smarties' – hesitantly he produced a large bag of iced chocolate drops from a pocket – 'you can probably examine him down there.'

I certainly did not mind. Not for the first time I would sit on the floor with a patient to avoid starting a potentially disastrous rough-house by trying to get the beast onto the examination table. I am one Mahomet who, for the sake of a peaceful and productive examination, is prepared to go to any mountain anywhere.

'Apart from the swelling has Billy shown any sign of illness?' I inquired.

'He's a bit more peeky than usual, we think. He threw a milk bottle at the next-door neighbour's dog last week – knocked a tooth out and we had to pay the vet's bill – and he's not eating quite as well as usual. Gone off his fried liver and onions and his bedtime Ovaltine. He's still fairly lively though. He got into the bathroom when my sister-in-law was washing her hair, pinched her electric drier and dropped it down the loo. Blew all the fuses. Sister-in-law had to go to a Masonic dinner with a wig on. He's taking his fruit and vegetables fine, though. Droppings? Well, she – my wife – changes his nappies, you know. He did take his clothes off the other night when we were asleep. Nappies and all. Did his business on the piano. No, no sign of diarrhoea or anything. Very normal, I'd say – I know because I cleaned the piano myself.'

I sat on the surgery floor near Billy, and Mr Lomax bent down and started to feed Smarties into the mobile black lips with the frenzy of a slot-machine addict. Cautiously I stroked Billy's head and slyly let my hand caress downwards over one cheek. Billy seemed to like it. He stuck one index finger into my ear. I let it stay there; it was only marginally uncomfortable and seemed a reasonable quid pro quo. As my fingers lay on Billy's cheek I gently pulled down the lower eyelid. He seemed paler than normal. Pretending to flip idly at his lips, I pulled them out a little so that I could inspect the gums; they were not as freshly pink as I would have liked either. Billy kept his finger in my ear and with the other hand tried to push the corner of the road map into my mouth. I pursed my lips and quietly raised my hand to ease away his arm and to indicate that while I might tolerate an earful of finger, a mouthful of paper was out of the question. I also used the opportunity to take his pulse as I held his wrist. It was normal. So far so good. The examination was proceeding well and Billy was still unperturbed. Next I slipped my hand under his sweater. The chimp hooted a warning at me and pulled the finger from my ear, making ready to clout me if I showed any sign of trying to take his clothes off. I cooed at him and tickled his navel as I explored his abdomen beneath the sweater. Billy relaxed, but took a grip of the hem of his sweater just in case.

The swelling of the stomach was undoubtedly more than just obesity or slack abdominal muscles, conditions often seen in young, imperfectly fed great apes, particularly gorillas. A tense, round mass the size of a large grapefruit lay in the body cavity. It did not seem to be painful, and it was possible to move it slightly from place to place within the abdomen.

For ten minutes I carefully explored the contours of the mass and went through the possibilities in my mind. Abscess, cyst, tumour? Amoeba cavity, common in chimps? Tapeworm hydatids? Which organ was involved: liver, spleen, intestines? Or no organ – just an independent mass attached to the peritoneum? I debated whether to take a biopsy sample, but decided that it would only delay the major operation which I felt sure would be necessary. Better perhaps to operate and remove the mass and then confirm its true nature. That would avoid both the need for anaesthetizing twice and the possibility of the biopsy producing side effects like peritonitis; it would also save time if the lump was in any way malignant. On balance I thought that the mass was most likely a non-malignant cyst, lying fairly free in the abdomen or possibly embracing most of the spleen and containing pus produced by the same amoeba parasite that causes dysentery in man. Whatever it was, Billy was going to undergo major surgery.

Mr Lomax had to have a chair to sit on when I stood up

and told him what I had found. 'It's not the thought of the operation that upsets me, Dr Taylor,' he squeaked, sponging his pink jowls with his handkerchief. 'It's, well, it's the thought of telling her – my wife. She'll have a fit! She'll want to know how he got this trouble – she's sure there's no healthier chimp than Billy.'

'I understand,' I replied truthfully – I remembered her as a formidable, excitable woman – 'but it would be unwise to pretend that there is anything else to be done in the circumstances. No operation and there may well be no Billy before long.'

I saw them to the door and watched as they crossed the outer office, Billy carrying the road map in one hand and belabouring Mr Lomax's backside with the Sinatra hat held in the other.

I had arranged for Billy to be brought to the surgery in four days' time, with an empty stomach and a spoonful of tranquillizing syrup administered in a cup of fruit juice just before setting out. Operation day arrived and promptly at ten o'clock Billy, accompanied now by Mrs Lomax herself, was brought into my office. She was a stringy, pale, middle-aged lady, with a querulous voice and fidgety manner. To my dismay the chimp showed no signs of having taken any tranquillizer, and I did not fancy jabbing needles into him while he was fully conscious.

'He just would not drink the fruit juice with the drug in it,' his owner confessed. 'He seemed to know there was something added.'

At my request, the normally modish chimp was undressed. He looked mean and hungry. Spotting a small packet of Nescafé powder and a sugar cube lying on my desk ready for my mid-morning brew of coffee, he swept both items into his mouth with one fast 'lodger's reach', as Lancastrians call such swift light-fingeredness. After swallowing the goodies, he spat out the indigestible paper. Still mean and still hungry, he looked round the room for something else to eat. Ominously he began cracking his knuckles. Everything else was ready for the operation, but first I somehow had to get some injectable anaesthetic into Billy. He was obviously in no mood to be trifled with and there is no way to restrain a full-grown chimp who does not feel like letting folk prick him with needles. I would have to use the dart-gun and, for the first and only time in my career to date, I prepared to shoot a knock-out syringe at a free-ranging chimpanzee on the prowl in my own surgery waiting room. Loading the gas-pistol with a small syringe charged with a dose of phencyclidine, I explained what I planned to do. 'Billy will have to be left on his own in the waiting room.'

'No, never!' wailed Mrs Lomax.

'Yes, definitely. There's no other way and I can't risk having humans about when I start firing darts in a confined space. No one can stay in with Billy. I'll open the door a crack, shoot at him, close the door and then, when he goes to sleep, we'll carry on in the normal way. By the way, Mrs Lomax, I suggest that you go shopping for a couple of hours after he's knocked out.' I did not want her hanging round the premises while I operated.

Vulnerable items like photo frames, potted plants and an electric fire were removed from the waiting room and Billy was slipped in there. Behind the closed door we listened. I had to be certain he was at the other side of the room before I did my bit of sniping. There was a bumping as Billy moved among some of the chairs; then I heard a shuffling noise. He was rifling through the magazines on the table by the far wall. This was my chance.

I opened the door a few inches, put my foot against the bottom of it and held firmly onto the door handle, ready to close it should Billy try joining us. With one eye at the crack I glimpsed a crouching Billy looking at me from a distance of three yards. I took aim with my gun hand and squeezed the trigger. Plop! From the angry screeching I knew that the dart had struck chimp flesh. Before I could close the door, Billy had snatched the missile out of his buttocks, where it had lodged and discharged its contents in a fraction of a second, and flung it accurately back at me. Not for the first time I nearly took a returned dart full in the face. Great apes often return my ammunition in this way, which is helpful of them I suppose, but I shudder to think what would happen if I was hit by one which had not fired its drug load.

There is no antidote to a big dose of phencyclidine, and I can just see the headline in the *Rochdale Observer*: 'Veterinarian put to sleep by chimpanzee.' A different way to go.

The dart whipped through the still partly opened door and embedded itself firmly in the corridor wall. With a crash I shut the door just before Billy hurled himself at the other side. Hollering with annoyance, he pounded the door and threatened to split the panelling. Then he wreaked his fury on our chairs. There were tearing and shredding noises, too, as copies of *The Field* and *Illustrated London News* were turned into ticker tape. Gradually the echoes of bedlam subsided and all was still. Six minutes had passed since the darting. Billy should now be chasing lady chimpanzees in a sunlit happy valley, for we know that small doses of phencyclidine in humans tend to produce fanciful erotic dreams. I opened the door. Sure enough, Billy lay sprawled and sleeping on a heap of chairs and pieces of chair.

With Mrs Lomax sent fretfully packing, the chimpanzee was carried into the operating room and I deepened his anaesthesia with oxygen and halothane gas. Scrubbed and gowned, and with the patient shaved and painted a startling antiseptic red over his bulging belly, I took a scalpel and unzipped his abdomen from top to bottom. Spreading the operation wound open with a set of ratcheted retractors, I felt inside for the round lump. Bit by bit I pulled it close to the opening where I could see it. It was not part of any organ, but an independent, tense sphere containing some sort of thickish fluid and stuck at dozens of points to the loops of intestine. It was going to take a long time to free all those attachments. Beneath it might lie large blood vessels that I could not see; there might be weaknesses in the wall of the thing which would rupture as I separated it. I began cautiously and laboriously to break the adhesions with the handle of my scalpel, as using the sharp blade might pierce the sphere and release the contents, with appalling consequences. After half an hour I had still freed only a small part of the mass. On I went, stopping from time to time to check Billy's pulse, colour and breathing. He slept deeply. Two hours later I had freed all of the mass that I could see. Now for the underneath bit.

As I tried swinging the sphere over so that I could approach the lower adhesions less blindly, I noticed something that made my stomach turn. A pink-brown creamy liquid was beginning to seep up between my fingers. I swabbed it away hurriedly and looked closely. More of the stuff welled up. I gently pressed the spherical mass. It was less tense than before. Somehow, somewhere below it had begun to leak. The unpleasant pink-brown cream was running over Billy's intestines.

Cursing silently, I pressed on rapidly with the complete removal of the lump, now a collapsed and flabby bladder. With that gone, I surveyed the terrible sight before me: an abdominal cavity which was awash with pus full of amoebae and nasty bacteria. No matter what, Billy was going to have quite a case of peritonitis. How could I remove most of the foul stuff? If I put a drain into his tummy, as is done in humans, he would only pluck out the rubber tube when he came to. But would the wound hold if I stitched it with much of that rubbish inside?

Then I recalled watching as part of my surgery course at university an operation on a human patient whose gastric ulcer had burst just after being bombarded with a meal of steak pie, chips and peas, covering his liver, spleen, stomach and all the other bits and pieces of organs inside him with gravy, peas and chewed-up bits of food. The surgeon had not made a big fuss about this dinner that had gone so sadly astray but had dealt with it in a thoroughly down-to-earth, commonsense sort of way: he had ordered up two or three sterilized stainless-steel buckets full of warm saline solution and simply swilled out his patient's innards by pouring in a couple of gallons and letting it wash out. Then he had done it again, just as if he was washing down his garden path after a spot of untidy gardening. The peas and all the rest of the meal were washed away and what small quantities of foreign matter and bacteria remained in the abdominal cavity following this practical bit of laundry were easily controlled by antibiotics. I decided to use the same method. Sending Edith for some bottles of sterile saline solution, I sucked out

94

as much of the pus as I could with a special tube and vacuum pump. When the saline was ready I used it to wash the intestines and surrounding organs, rinsed them again and again, popped everything back into place and sprinkled antibiotic powder in nooks and crevices. The rest was simple: stitching up the various layers of peritoneum, muscle, fat and skin.

Billy gradually began to come round when he was taken off the gas, but because of the phencyclidine still active in his body he would not be fully back to normal until the following day. Mrs Lomax did not object when I insisted that Billy would have to go naked and unadorned until his operation wound healed; chimps' tissues heal rapidly when left dry and open to the oxygen in the air.

By the time Billy came to have his stitches out, he was his old fighting self once more. I did the job only when they had finally succeeded in slipping him some tranquillizer in a sweet plum, seven days after the date originally planned for the appointment. Billy had recovered excellently. There was no sign of peritonitis and he looked the picture of health. My examination of the pus from his lump had shown the presence of both amoebae and bacteria, as I had suspected, but these were dealt with by a course of fruit-flavoured drugs originally designed for children.

'By the way, Dr Taylor,' said Mrs Lomax, when she brought Billy for his final check-up with her perspiring, pink-faced husband standing by, 'this amoeba. Is there any chance that George here brought it home from the office?'

George mopped his forehead and looked appealingly at me, saying nothing.

'No chance, Mrs Lomax,' I replied firmly, 'absolutely no chance.'

George Lomax let out a sigh of happy relief. 'Now, how much do we owe you, Dr Taylor?' he asked.

Chapter Seven

AUTUMN IN Manchester meant chill, clammy air and sulphurous mists that stung the eyes and clutched at the throat. It was the time for smog, the yellow blend of water vapour and industrial smoke, and smog time was always busy for the veterinarian of a city zoo. Each year as October came round, cases of disease and death among the animals at Belle Vue began to soar. Peacocks hacked away like chain-smokers, tigers heaved their chests with the desperate concentration of asthmatics, and chimpanzees wiped running eyes and nostrils with the backs of hairy hands. And animals died. Some, experiencing all this for the first time, died quickly from pneumonia. Others, the time-servers, finally gave up the struggle against fibrous lungs and chronically enlarged hearts and wheezed their last. Most animals do not live long enough to develop the chronic degenerative changes seen in humans, but at Manchester, in the bodies of big cats, rhinoceroses, apes and the like, I saw all the post-mortem signs associated with old human city-dwellers.

That year, not only was the smog particularly bad, but winter must have been snapping at autumn's heels. The leaves browned, fell and were whisked away by the moist wind, and within a few days precocious atoms of ice silvered the bare trees in Belle Vue's Victorian gardens. What was more, as if Matt Kelly, the zoo's Irish head keeper, was not busy enough breaking the ice on moated paddocks to prevent inmates walking their way to freedom, the small boys who daily invade the zoo grounds free by scaling unscalable walls, outrunning corpulent gate keepers and various other means, became unusually active: perhaps it was the early frost that kept them on the move.

Worse still, there was a positive epidemic of animals going 'over the wall' in the other direction. The keepers had neglected to re-clip the flight feathers of the flamingoes at six-monthly intervals, and on a suitably windy day a gang of the gorgeous birds took off and cleared the zoo walls, never to be seen again. With even less chance of survival unless they could reach some centrally heated building, complete with a supply of mice for food, a posse of young rattlesnakes set forth from the reptile house one day after sneaking through a broken pane of glass. When he found seven of the venomous reptiles absent without leave, the keeper in charge decided to keep quiet about it in the hope that either they would turn up or the low temperatures outside would finish the little wanderers and so remove any threat to the local population. If it were known that such creatures were on the loose, he could foresee a drastic reduction in the numbers of visitors coming to the zoo to walk round the exhibits with their children on a Sunday morning. This in turn would undoubtedly lead to the zoo director giving him the boot.

The keeper tried to conceal his loss by stuffing rocks, logs and vegetation of all sorts into the rattlesnake vivarium, so that what had been a fair simulation of the dry, sun-baked environment of a Californian rattler, with coiled serpents easily seen against a sandstone background, was transformed into a dripping, dense and inappropriate jungle, in which the rattlesnakes could rarely be glimpsed, let alone counted. This trick worked until two little girls, coming through the main gates on their way to the fairground, came across a pretty, if rather sluggish, little snake wearily making in the general direction of the bus stop. They picked it up, were quick to spot that it was not a worm, were relieved to see that it had not got a V-mark behind its head – the little girls had been learning about Britain's only poisonous snake, the adder at natural history lessons – and popped it into one of their purses. Their brother would just love to have a grass snake as a pet.

Later that day, back at home, Dad wound the little snake round his fingers, remarking how the warmth was making the little fellow much more agile and alert. Then he noticed the curious rings of loosely jointed dried skin at the tail. For some reason, although he was a builder's mate and this was the middle of Manchester, something worried him about those rings and he reached for a copy of *Pears Cyclopaedia*. Two minutes later he broke into a sweat and dashed to phone the police.

Matt Kelly, the head keeper, was the one who had to clear the mess up, calm down the builder's mate and his family, defuse the concern of the constabulary and divert the Press with blarney. He then fired the reptile keeper.

To add still more to our troubles that autumn, the numbers of animals being bodily purloined rose dramatically. All zoos have stock stolen from time to time: a guinea-pig or two from the Pets' Corner, tortoises from the reptile house, birds particularly parrots and cockatoos, and a variety of small mammals. Although it appeared that 'fences' did not want to touch gorillas, tigers or ostriches, that autumn saw some sizeable creatures disappear. One almost had to admire the thieves who got clean away with a five-foot alligator of irascible temperament in broad daylight, while the two little urchins who were collared half a mile from the zoo, breathlessly lugging home a trio of outraged coatimundi bundled inside a sack, must otherwise have led sainted lives not to have been severely injured by the hard-biting beasts.

Matt Kelly had hardly finished giving the crestfallen young culprits a lecture which, despite his soft Irish brogue, set their ears burning, when he was summoned to the scene of more animals gone a-missing. Two valuable De Brazza monkeys had vanished from the monkey house and the monkey keeper was certain that they had been stolen. A party had been round just before they had gone, a boisterous bunch of noisy schoolchildren. Matt quickly inspected the De Brazza cage; just possibly someone could have forced apart the vertical wires that formed the front. But how could they have grabbed hold of a big, tough species that could bite harder than a dog? Still, Matt had known it happen in the past – a jacket thrown over the animal, or even bare hands and bravado and never mind the bites and the blood when showing off in front of your pals. Before now the head keeper had stopped a coach laden with children before it left the park and had retrieved from under a seat a penguin with its powerful beak safely immobilised by rubber bands, and a wallaby hog-tied by a blushing schoolgirl's black lisle stockings. Anything could happen.

Matt rushed off to the car park with the monkey keeper. They were too late; the school party's coach had gone. The school was traced and its headmaster contacted, but the pair of monkeys, to my mind the most attractive of all primate species with their olive coat, brown and white face and goatee beard, were not forthcoming. Matt cursed and worried. Both of us could imagine the two monkeys stuffed into a dark, cramped rabbit hutch somewhere in Greater Manchester and pressed to take a diet of sweetmeats and peanuts.

The next crisis of that eventful autumn for Belle Vue was not long in coming. Someone was pinching food. Fruit, vegetables and other things were being stolen, particularly from the great ape house, the modern, self-contained unit which housed the chimpanzees, orang-utans and gorillas. Len, the senior great ape keeper, was up in arms about it. Food pilfering by keepers is an unpleasant but not uncommon problem facing all zoos, but a particularly severe outbreak at Belle Vue a few years earlier had led to the most rigid controls being imposed there. Ration sheets were printed for each species, and a cook dispensed all the food to the keepers. The system recommended by Jimmy Chipperfield at his safari parks of chopping all fruit before sending it from the stores was adopted – nobody wants to take home a pocketful of sliced apple or pear – and I personally presented the zoo with a fruit and vegetable chopper of the sort used by farmers for mashing turnips.

I discussed this latest problem with Len and Matt Kelly. 'Whoever's doing it, they're damned sharp at it,' said Len, as he told us how some 'hands' of bananas had vanished during the tea break. 'Funny thing is, I didn't pass any keepers on my way back from the cafeteria.'

The great ape house stood apart from the other units, so anyone entering or leaving the house would have had to cross an area of open ground. The nearest unit was the Pets' Corner.

'Mebbe it's that new feller in there, the one that's lookin' after the goats and the donkeys,' growled Matt. 'Oi'll wander over and root around.'

But Matt found nothing to incriminate anybody in the Pets' Corner in any way – no banana skins in the dustbin, nothing secreted in the staff rest room. Two weeks passed. Each day one section or another reported losses of food. Apples here, tomatoes there, but always Len's great ape house was hardest hit.

Then came the nastiness. First it was a fountain pen that went, then a cigarette lighter. Finally, when a packet of cheroots disappeared while Len nipped over to the men's room, the great ape keeper had had enough. He stormed into the director's office, white-faced behind his spectacles.

'Get the police in,' he demanded. 'This light-fingered sneak-thief's gone too far.'

A report was made to the police and a detective-constable made a perfunctory visit, but there was nothing to show him and even less to be done, except to keep a sharp eye open.

'Oi'll have him. Oi'll catch him with the stuff on him one of these foine days,' proclaimed Matt after Len's lunch, a packet of sandwiches, vanished into thin air. 'Oi think the bloighter's havin' us on, teasin' us.'

It made sense. Pinching juicy peaches or even a lighter was one thing, but having designs on Len's meat paste sandwiches suggested more mischief than criminal dishonesty.

Despite a high level of vigilance, Matt and his men made

no progress in identifying the miscreant and the crime wave grew. Night attacks became more frequent than ones during the day, and the fact that there was no forcing of locks or windows anywhere confirmed our suspicions that a keeper with a key was behind it all. When the real malevolence began, it all seemed to be aimed at the unfortunate Len.

'This – this imbecile, this kleptomaniac has a grudge against me,' he moaned bitterly to me one day, as we wrestled with a baby chimp that needed his polio jab. 'Vindictiveness, that's all it is. It can only be a keeper who thinks I've done wrong by him.'

'Why, what's he done now?' I asked.

Len drew in a great breath and then spat out the words with ripe indignation. 'Crapped in my tea!'

'I'm sorry, I don't understand.'

'Crapped – defecated – in my tea!'

Trying to keep a straight face, I asked 'What, how, when?'

'This morning, at eleven o'clock. I brewed up in the ape house instead of going to the cafeteria, poured a cup for me and one for Harold.' Harold was the patriarch of the orang-utans at Belle Vue, a red-haired potentate with a figure like a Sumo wrestler, who relished a mug of sweet, milky tea. 'I took Harold his, came back to my room, picked up my cup and there it was, floating on the surface.'

I cleared my throat. 'Could it not have been, say, chimpanzee or orang excrement?' The great apes generally are enthusiastic and skilled throwers of faecal matter. Some, such as an orang at Rhenen Zoo in Holland or a male chimp at Dudley, are so adept at inswingers and so accurate, even when bowling backwards, that it beats me why they have not been snapped up by the MCC cricket team or transferred for a fat fee to the New York Yankees.

Len sniffed. 'It could not,' he said. 'No apes were loose. The cup and the table it was on are twenty feet or more away from the nearest animals, which are separated from the passageway leading to my room by a brick wall anyway, and the stainless steel drawers that are set in the wall for passing food through were closed. The only animal that could have had access to my tea was a human!'

'I suppose it could have been a chimp stool that he picked up and dropped in,' I ventured.

'Still a dirty, filthy, perverted sense of humour,' Len scowled.

The next day the invisible thief and defiler of teacups, if they were one and the same person, struck again. This time it was another batch of Len's sandwiches, not stolen but left crowned with a noisome offering. To add insult to injury his daily newspaper had been removed. '*Daily Mirror* gone and crap on my lunch,' Len roared at Matt and me as we tried not to laugh.

As usual there had been no sign of the villain, but interestingly the deed had been done while Len was feeding his animals elsewhere in the house with the outside door to the passageway leading to his room securely locked. Len was also quite certain that the catch had been dropped on the Yale lock when he closed it. Even if the culprit had a key to the house, it would have been useless with the catch down. The only logical answer, if Len was right, was that the villain had been in the house all the time.

I decided to look again at the scene of the crime. Len's room was a bare, smooth-walled place with an empty isolation cage against one wall and a single door. High on the wall facing the door was a window that flapped back on runners, leaving an opening too small for a human to climb through. The only furniture was a small sink with a gas ring, and the table. I looked around. Just possibly someone could throw objects from the outside up and over the window when it was open, but aiming would be impossible. I looked up at the ceiling and at the large, galvanised central heating duct which ran across the width of the room. Then I noticed something. The vent for warm air was a slotted grille in the duct, and it was situated directly over the table.

The great ape house's revolutionary system of channelling warm air to all the exhibits through the galvanised ducting had proved very successful until it was found that

102

thick growths of mould had begun to sprout on the inside of the metal tube, encouraged by the warm, moist air. I had been consulted with an eye to possible health hazards from fungus spores being inhaled by the animals, and had managed to solve the problem by getting Len to spray a non-toxic fungicide into the airstream once a week. I recalled climbing up on a chair and looking into the mould-caked ducting through a manhole. Sure enough, every few yards there was a manhole covered by a disc of metal that was secured by two wing-nuts. The manhole in Len's room was firmly sealed. I walked back down the passageway and looked up at the ducting. Another man-hole, sealed. Then another, its covering plate slightly askew and leaving a gap at one edge. Halfway down the passage was one manhole where the cover was completely off. I looked up at a round black hole from which a draught of warm air blew gently down.

'Get a torch, Len,' I said. 'I'm going to have a look up there.'

When at last a torch was found, Matt produced a step-ladder and I climbed up to the hole. There was just enough room for me to get my head and one arm in. I switched on the torch and shone it down to my left. An empty black tunnel, dusty but no longer choked with mould, stretched down to the end of the house. Wriggling round, I pointed the torch down the length of ducting extending over Len's room.

The torch beam ran along more sheets of grimy black metal, then suddenly it was shining on a colourful, twinkling tableau at the far end, a cross between Fagin's den and Aladdin's cave. There, blinking in the beam of light, caught red-handed with surprise and apprehension written all over their faces, skulked the two missing De Brazza monkeys. They crouched on a bed of paper, shredded cheroots, dried vegetable peel and nutshells, surrounded by fruit of every kind, some fresh, some half-eaten. Bags of nuts, dog biscuits, potato chips and bars of stolen chocolate were near at hand. Amid the debris the polished metal of a lighter and a fountain pen glinted.

'Gotcha!' I said quietly, and climbing grinning down the step-ladder.

'Who's up there? Let me get at 'em,' shouted Len, rushing forward to take my place. There was a silence, then his wrath turned to chuckles as he came face to face with his persecutors at last.

The episode drew to a swift close. The De Brazzas were injected by dart-pistol with phencyclidine, a quick-acting anaesthetic, and when they were unconscious I raked them back to the manhole using a shepherd's crook lashed to the end of a long pole. Matt hauled the two dreaming felons back to their quarters in the monkey house, while Len cleared out the den in the ducting. The total weight of the cache of food and other items was seventy-eight pounds.

I was surprised that Len, while sitting in his room, had not heard any noises in the duct above him; heavily-built specimens like De Brazzas would surely have made a racket moving around on the thin metal floor of their hideaway. But the senior keeper had noticed nothing apart from the gentle scurry of mice, a sound to which he had long been accustomed. We could only assume that the monkeys, like prisoners of war on the run, had lain motionless amid their booty as long as the 'enemy' was present below. It was surely accidental that they had fouled Len's tea and sandwiches in obeying calls of nature close to the air vent. But what had happened when there were no humans about, particularly at night? They must have dropped from the manhole, moved up the passageway to Len's room and left the house through the gap in his permanently flapped-back window. From there it would be easy to enter almost any other building in the zoo through holes, skylights or broken windows. De Brazzas have a distinguished, aristocratic countenance and, loping over the flower beds with armfuls of edible swag, they would have been the nearest thing in the monkey world to Raffles and Bunny.

☆☆☆☆☆☆☆☆☆☆☆☆☆☆

Chapter Eight

☆☆☆☆☆☆☆☆☆☆☆☆☆☆

THE VETERINARY practice I had now started was suffering from a thumping big bad debt, and Norman Whittle, my partner, was not amused. After chasing about for several weeks treating a touring circus's arthritic elephant with injections of gold salts, I found the circus had done the dirty on me. Its owner claimed that the animal rightfully belonged to such and such a clown, who in turn maintained that I had originally been called in by one of a family of acrobats while the circus was in Rochdale. The company was a small one, everyone seemed to be interrelated and the clowns doubled or even trebled as ice-cream sellers, bareback riders or jugglers. Trying to get my fee out of anyone was futile and embarrassing. If I called during a performance everyone was dashing round concealed under greasepaint and tomato-sized rubber noses, and at other times the trailers were silent as the grave when I knocked miserably on the doors for my cash. Strange, when the elephant had been creaking painfully about on puffy, tense joints, I had been able to find the staff in a trice in order to make my examinations. But gradually the circus moved farther and farther away from Rochdale and debt-collecting forays became impossible.

The bad debt led to a bitter exchange with Norman of the sort that made me long to make the great leap and to throw in my lot with wild-animal medicine lock, stock and barrel.

'Apart from the time you've spent gallivanting all over England away from the practice,' Norman said in his undemonstrative, clipped manner as we stood over the unconscious body of a tortoiseshell cat on which we were doing a hysterectomy, 'we're over a hundred quid out of pocket. This circus farce can't go on. Anyway you can't trust travelling folk, fly-by-nights, gipsies. I warned you time and again. And even if they had paid, look at all the time and effort and driving. Compare that to work like this.' He waved a needle holder at the supine she-cat. 'Thirty shillings, nearly all profit and done in five minutes!'

Looked at from a purely financial point of view, it was true; one vet we both knew frequently said that his ideal practice would consist of doing nothing but sterilizing she-cats, six in the morning and six in the afternoon. But that was not my view of veterinary work. Could they not see that taking the pulse of an elephant, feeling the thick artery deep under the dry, crinkly skin, was a reward in itself? Cash cannot be equated with seeing a cub in its foetal membranes emerge like a vacuum-packed pigeon, especially if you have helped it out. Even more especially if, as you peel the membranes from it, it writhes and natters the first feeble protest of its independent life. No, I felt as strongly then as I do now that it was a rare privilege to be allowed to try to heal wild living organisms. Can a stockbroker or banker know anything of the happiness which I have had when seeing a leg walk that I, somehow, have helped tack together?

I had talked before in this vein to Norman, but decided it would be pointless to start again this time. I think he thought I would grow out of it, so he was exasperated by my enthusiastic acceptance of our next circus call. It was from an outfit completely unknown to us at Great Yarmouth, two hundred miles or more away across country on the coast of the wind-washed fens of Norfolk. Again the problem was an elephant, an elephant suspected of foot-and-mouth disease.

'You can't go off down there,' said my partner angrily. 'This zoo and circus work is getting too much. No, we just can't have it.'

An elephant with suspected foot-and-mouth? Nothing could stop me. 'I'm off,' I said, and slipped out of the door before he could say another word.

It was a long drive that took nearly six hours. By now I was receiving calls to exotic animals from all over Britain as the knowledge that I had a special interest in such creatures spread by word of mouth from one owner to another. My mileage was increasing rapidly, and on long journeys I was troubled by being out of contact with my surgery and the rest of the world for most of the day. Anything could be happening while I was doing nothing but acting as taxi driver to myself. To remedy this I had recently done something which was to prove the key to roving zoo practice: I had installed in the car a radio telephone operating on a private network that extended virtually all over the country. My call sign was the zippy 'Jet eight-seven' and I got a great kick from receiving messages on the road like the first one that came over the air from Belle Vue: 'Calling Jet eight-seven, Jet eight-seven. Mr Kelly reports pigmy hippo born. All well. Repeat, all well. Over.'

I had plenty to ponder as I crossed the flat marshes of East Anglia. There were the problems with Norman and my role in the practice: I owed Norman a lot for introducing me to zoo work, and I could understand his frustration at being left to cope on his own so much, but I knew that my first duty was to the animals I was trying to help. Then foot-and-mouth disease. I had never seen a real live case. As for such a thing in elephants, I had heard of a few suspect cases where large ulcers had formed at the back of the mouth, but that was all I knew apart from the fact that no foot-and-mouth disease was being reported in Britain at that time. There must be some likelier explanation.

At last I rolled into Great Yarmouth, a place exactly like dozens of other holiday towns dotted round the English coast, redolent with the faded fashion of Victorian and Regency days when Majorca and the Costa Brava were as far away as the moon. The circus was inside the Hippo-drome Theatre, and I soon found the elephant lines. Near three adult female Indian elephants an old lugubrious-faced German, who turned out to be the elephant trainer, a midget in a Charlie Chaplin outfit, a policeman and another man in a black rubber coat and gumboots were arguing. The midget seemed particularly agitated.

I went over. 'I'm Dr Taylor to see the elephant.'

The man in the rubber coat put out a hand. 'Tompkins,' he said, 'Ministry of Agriculture vet. Came out to see what this report of F-and-M was all about.'

'And they won't pay me my half-crown,' squeaked the midget, tapping me on the knee. 'I want my half-crown.'

'I am Herr Hopfer,' said the German. 'Please, Doktor, come zis way. Gerda iss very ill.' He looked as if he was about to burst into tears.

'My half-crown! It's the rule! My half-crown!' The midget was fairly hopping about by this time and was waving his miniature bent walking-stick at the policeman.

The latter cleared his throat and sighed. He had obviously been saying something similar for the past half-hour. 'I 'ave told you once, Mr Lemon, and I 'ave told you twice. I know nothin' about no 'alf-crown. You'll 'ave to go down to the station and see my sergeant about that.'

'What's this all about?' I asked Tompkins.

'Oh, it's all because he, Mr Lemon, reported the suspect case of F-and-M. Apparently there's something in the law that says if any private citizen suspects a notifiable disease in anybody's animal, whether he knows what he's looking at or not, he can claim two-and-sixpence from the police.'

'Is that right?' I queried.

'Can't say I know anything about it, but the little fellow's mad as hell on getting his cash. Claims to know all about it.'

'Done my duty, done my duty! Where's my half-crown?' The midget started buzzing again.

'Now look 'ere, Mr Lemon,' said the policeman.

'Just give me the money,' yelled Mr Lemon.

Tompkins and I looked silently at one another and simultaneously put our hands in our pockets. We produced one-and-threepence each and pushed the coins at the midget. 'Now can we please have some hush while we look at the bloody elephant!' I said tetchily.

Mr Lemon waddled off, and later I learned that he was

quite right; he was indeed entitled to the reward whatever the diagnosis turned out to be.

Gerda the elephant was standing miserably in a pool of water which streamed slowly from her lower lip to the cobbled floor. The water was her own saliva. I must look inside her mouth at once, but Matt Kelly had warned me of the danger of sticking one's hand blindly into an elephant's mouth: 'If the craytchure moves her lower jaw, ye've a pulverized hand.'

'Get her to open up, Herr Hopfer,' I said. It is one thing all elephant trainers can do with their animals.

'Gerda, auf, auf!' he shouted.

Gerda slowly raised her trunk and opened her soft pink mouth. Tompkins shone his torch in and we both peered into the narrow space between the teeth. Not a blister or an ulcer in sight.

'I don't think elephants can get F-and-M,' said Tompkins. 'Better check her feet, though, just in case.'

He walked cautiously round the elephant, looking at her neatly filed and oiled toenails. Nothing that looked like ulcers there. Tompkins was shining his light on the left rear foot when Gerda felt the urge to pass water. Unwisely, the ministry vet was not wearing the Government-issue black sou'wester that is supposed to be part of the uniform for investigations into notifiable disease. He took the cataract square on top of his head. It went down the inside of his coat and ran out below.

'I 'ave 'eard that yoorine is very good for the complexion,' observed the policeman, as deadpan as if he were making an arrest.

'I'm off,' spluttered Tompkins. 'Negative F-and-M here. End of the affair as far as the Ministry's concerned. Get on with it, Taylor.' Spitting, he squelched away.

'Now, Herr Hopfer,' I said, 'tell me the full story.'

'Zis morning I find her streaming from ze mouss like zis. She vill not eat, not even drink. Maybe she hass a bad tooss.'

Toothache was indeed a possibility. One of the commonest ailments in elephants is an infected or badly positioned molar. I got Hopfer to make Gerda open her

110

mouth again and shone my torch carefully on each tooth with one hand while pressing down the slippery ball of her tongue with the other. One slip and I could lose a finger or three. All the teeth seemed normal. I felt Gerda's glands, ran my hands down over the outside of her throat, took her temperature and drew a blood sample. Everything was OK. But Gerda was miserable and would not eat or drink, and her saliva ran and ran. There was no evidence that her throat was inflamed, her swallowing muscles were not paralysed, there was no logical reason why she should be producing excessive quantities of saliva. I was left with one ominous probability.

'Bring me some bananas and a bucket of water,' I said to Hopfer. I wanted to watch her reaction to food very carefully for myself. Treating elephants was not much different from treating cattle, I was finding, as long as you knew how to handle them and how to love them.

When the elephant trainer returned, I presented Gerda with a peeled banana. She took it with her trunk tip, popped it in her mouth and swallowed readily. Then slowly, slowly, the pulped banana came back and dripped in sticky blobs from the corners of her lips. I put the bucket of water in front of her. Immediately she sucked up a trunkful and squirted it into her mouth. She swallowed. For a moment nothing happened and then the water gushed back out onto the floor.

'What did you feed the elephants last thing yesterday, Herr Hopfer?'

'Chopped carrots and apples.'

'Chopped?'

'Ja, chopped.'

I was certain now that one of the apples had evaded the chopper's cleaver and was jammed somewhere in the gullet. And I could predict that it would be in one of three places: where the gullet enters the chest, where it passes over the heart or where it pierces the diaphragm. Wherever it was, Gerda was in big trouble.

In cattle, similar jammed objects often pass naturally if the animal is left alone for twenty-four hours. That was my first feeble line of attack. I booked in at a nearby hotel and

111

made sure that the hungry and thirsty elephant at least had plenty of water to suck up. Maybe a trickle would get past the apple, I thought optimistically as I added nourishing glucose to the water. The next day, Gerda was much worse. She was sunken-eyed, weak and obviously dehydrated. How to move the apple? If I pushed it somehow, I could rupture the oesophagus. Operating was out of the question; no machine could keep the six-ton monster's lungs inflated with oxygen when the chest cavity was opened. Drugs designed to relax the muscles of the gullet had no effect.

By the third day the poor elephant was so weak that she could almost be pushed off balance by one man. Her eyes were red and her breath was foul. The apple was still firmly lodged and the river of saliva flowed on. Gerda was now desperately thirsty. Stripped down to my underpants, I started a series of hourly enemas, trying to pump water and glucose as far as possible into her lower bowel with a plastic tube and an old stirrup pump borrowed from the Hippodrome's fire-fighting equipment. It was slow, dirty work.

'Ooh!' said the waitress in my hotel when she learnt that I was working at the circus. 'What a super job. Lovely animals and able to have a holiday by the seaside at the same time!'

She should have been there all night, pumping ten gallons of sugary water up an elephant's backside and getting nine gallons sprayed back over her, I thought, as the waitress flounced off for my pot of tea and kippered herrings. Still, it had been worth it. A gallon had stayed up, a gallon that might just keep Gerda going till something turned up.

On the fifth day I had to make a crucial decision. The elephant was deteriorating rapidly. The only thing left was to push a probe down her throat. This meant anaesthesia. By now Gerda was unwilling to lie down for fear of being unable to rise. Left much longer, she would not tolerate doping, for lack of sleep had now been added to starvation and thirst and debility.

I walked along the shingly beach and thought long and

hard. I considered phoning Norman but, remembering the coolness between us, decided against it. The seagulls chivvied me in the cold, grey sky with incomprehensible advice. For a moment I envied the fishermen sitting muffled on the end of the pier, sucking contented pipes and off home soon to baked beans and TV. Then I decided. I would dope Gerda lightly, pass a probang, a long leather tube with a bulbous brass end, down her gullet and take her life in my inexperienced hands.

Later that day I gave the elephant a massive dose of acetylpromazine, a strong sedative rather than a true anaesthetic. After half an hour she slowly sank to the ground and lay, still drooling, on her side. Herr Hopfer pulled the upper jaw and the diminutive Mr Lemon, who like most midgets was immensely strong for his size, tugged on the lower. Greasing the probang with cod-liver oil, I pushed it carefully to the back of Gerda's throat. When a couple of feet of tube had disappeared, I stopped and went to the end of the probang outside the elephant and put it to my ear. I could feel no puff of air as Gerda breathed, so at least I was not going the wrong way, down the windpipe. I pushed the probang on slowly. Suddenly it stopped; it would go no farther. I marked the tube and withdrew it so that by measuring it over the outside of the elephant's body I could tell exactly how far down the obstruction lay. The mark on the tube told me that the apple was jammed at the point where the oesophagus passes the great heart. I must push it on. I re-introduced the probang and arrived once more at the obstruction. The moment had arrived. The next strong shove could stop the heart. It could burst the gullet and send the apple into the chest cavity. Or it could succeed. I gritted my teeth and steadily increased pressure on the probang. All at once it began to move freely once more. Something had given. I was sweating and my lip was bleeding where I had bitten it. Had the apple moved on or was it now bobbing around on the lungs with a ragged, gaping hole in the gullet beside it? Through my stethoscope I could hear no ugly noises from the lungs. Hardly daring to breathe, I slowly withdrew the probang. After what seemed an hour, its gleaming brass end flopped out of Gerda's mouth. It was coated in clear slime and shreds of banana pulp but not one drop of blood. I had done it!

Gerda was drowsy for many hours as the sedative wore off. The waiting was intolerable. I went to the cinema but came out after five minutes. I did not feel like eating or drinking. I ran along the beach. I played the one-armed bandits on the pier. Every half-hour I was back at the Hippodrome. At last, at nine o'clock that night, Gerda regained enough energy to rise groggily to her feet.

'Don't do a thing, Herr Hopfer!' I shouted. 'I'll do this.'

I took a bucket of hay tea, an infusion of hot water and new meadow hay, and placed it in front of Gerda. Her trunk flapped weakly. I grabbed it and stuck it into the golden liquid. The bucket half emptied. Gerda's slow and unsteady trunk curled towards her mouth and injected its contents. I saw the gullet muscles contract. A wave passed down her throat. She had swallowed. We waited, frozen like statues. The hay tea did not come back. Gerda's trunk was already back in the bucket, draining it dry.

'A banana, a banana!' I shouted excitedly.

The German ran for a bunch of fruit and handed it to me. I stuffed one straight into the elephant's jaws without peeling it. Squelch! It was gone. Nothing drooled back. The ropes of saliva no longer hung from Gerda's bottom lip. Her sunken red eye was on the remainder of the bunch of bananas. A perfect lady, and anyway still appallingly weak, she reached delicately for them. We were on our way.

That night I stayed up with Gerda again, making sure that she was not overloaded too suddenly with food or water, but gradually building up her much-needed intake. By day-break she was visibly much stronger and the signs of dehydration were disappearing fast. I went back to my hotel when Herr Hopfer woke and relieved me.

'Ooh!' said the waitress as I slumped into my chair at the breakfast table. 'Been out on the town, eh? Naughty boy! Told you you'd have a smashin' time at Great Yarmouth. Must be all play, your job.'

'Yes,' I said wearily. 'Bring me an extra pair of kippers, will you? I'm celebrating.'

On my return from Great Yarmouth Norman tackled me again about my travels round the country in pursuit of exotic patients. 'Anyway,' he said, 'can you really square your conscience with being involved in zoo and circus animal work? Aren't you just part of the shady business of exploiting wild creatures?'

It is a question people often ask me and from time to time, as I lie in bed, I ask it myself, just to make sure that the answer I give is still the same one, the one I believe in.

I believe in zoos, marinelands, safari parks. To come into close contact with the creatures of the earth – to see, to smell and, if you are lucky enough, to touch the beasts – is a vital part of human experience. Just as cinema cannot catch the atmosphere of the live stage, films of elephants or lions or buffaloes cannot give that spark of magic which flesh-and-blood presence provides. To be snuffled over by the damp tip of an elephant's trunk, to have one's hair lifted by the curling rasp of a giraffe's tongue – out of such experiences spring real feeling and love for fellow animals. There is nothing more rewarding than escorting a group of blind people round a zoo. They truly appreciate, in every sense of the word, camels, puma cubs, snakes, ostriches and the rest of the species to which I feel it is safe to introduce them.

It is pie in the sky to talk of us all going to see the wild animals in their natural habitats. The habitats are shrinking fast, not least because of tourism. The cruel impact of man on animals' natural homes will inevitably lead to more and more birds, mammals, fish and insects becoming extinct in the wild. Wilful greed and careless pollution are taking a terrible toll, and zoos and marinelands have a real part to play in helping at least some creatures to avoid the fate of the dodo, the Steller's sea cow and the quagga. No, zoos are essential for all the kids in New York, London, Rome and a thousand other cities who will never in a million years get the chance to go on a jet-set safari to the Serengeti.

As for me, my job is to represent the animals' interests, to see their point of view. There are disgraceful black spots, disgusting examples of cruelty, neglect and naked exploitation, in animal trapping, zoos, circuses and laboratories in

115

all parts of the world. But by working from the inside, by encouraging breeding here and improving diets there, by trying to heal the sick animals, educating their ignorant owners and proving to them that cruelty and neglect are counter-productive purely in terms of cash, I know things are slowly but steadily getting better. I am proud to be a part of it.

When I explained how I felt to Norman, he grunted and said that was all very well, but how was he expected to run a two-man practice when one of the partners was never there? I wondered what he would say if he knew that I had just received my first call abroad, to go over to Holland the following weekend to inspect and then accompany six young African elephants to England. Since it was Norman's weekend duty anyway, I thought it would be more prudent just to go, and to tell him about it when I got back.

I made the tedious journey by truck and ferry. After the truck had burnt its brakes out and hours had been wasted finding a replacement, I eventually got my charges onto the Rotterdam–Hull overnight boat. I sat alone during the crossing, guarding the elephants and feeding them from time to time with hay, bananas and apples. It was further invaluable experience in animal handling and transportation.

One of my jobs was to keep curious passengers and crew from interfering with the elephants. All went well until the middle of the night when, tired out by the day's exertions, I was unable to keep my eyelids open any longer. Fighting against it, I finally fell asleep propped up in a sitting position against one of the elephant crates.

Three hours later I woke to find that some misguided animal lover had fed my entire stock of apples and bananas to the ever-willing beasts. So much fruit in so short a time could cause six elephantine cases of colic before we docked, and I prepared for the worst. Luckily colic did not develop, but the surfeit of fruit certainly made its presence felt. After half a day spent ministering to a handful of elephants with acute diarrhoea, I knew a little of what it must have been like to be a bell-carrying leper in the Middle Ages, and

116

when I got home Shelagh made me strip down to my underclothes outside the back door.

A few weeks later I was back in Holland, to capture Mr van den Baars's onagers, and soon after that I took a much longer trip. Its purpose was not to treat any one case but to learn more about one great group of wild mammals of which I still had no experience. These creatures, taking their name from the Greek word for sea monster, second in intelligence only to man himself and descended from insignificant pig-like foragers that rooted around marshy land millions of years ago, were the cetaceans: whales, dolphins and porpoises. In the mid-sixties dolphins became the most fashionable and popular of zoo animals in America. Then Flipper and his relatives came to Europe, and I decided that it was time for me to start learning something about the care and medicine of these beautiful but mysterious beasts. I suspected that marinelands and dolphinaria were going to mushroom in Britain and on the Continent, and that dolphin doctoring was going to become an established branch of the veterinary art.

Today we know more about the dolphin than about any other animal except man and the dog, yet little more than a dozen years ago virtually nothing was known and still less published about cetacean disease. It was uniquely challenging, for this was not a case of trying out horse techniques in zebras or cattle medicine in buffaloes. Cetaceans do not abide by the rules. They have reconquered the watery places of the earth by adapting to a marine existence all the benefits of being a mammal, and combining that with ingenuity in doing things that mammals out at sea would not be expected to do. For that they have to be different: different in body structure, function and behaviour. The Atlantic bottle-nosed dolphin is an air-breathing, warm-blooded animal with three stomachs like a cow's, kidneys like a camel's, a brain as big as a man's, the swimming skills of a shark and the sonar equipment of a bat. It can dive deep and ascend fast without fear of decompression illnesses, endure long periods without oxygen but ignore levels of carbon dioxide that would

117

black out other beasts, and drink nothing but sea water, the brine which drives thirsty castaways mad, and it has a bundle of other feats of mystery and imagination at its command.

Only the handful of veterinarians working full time with marine mammals in the United States had the knowledge I would need if I was to treat cetaceans effectively. Leaving the long-suffering Norman in sole charge of the practice once again, and digging deep into my personal savings, I went first to Point Mugu in California, where the US Navy Undersea Warfare Division had a small but high-powered veterinary team led by Dr Sam Ridgway. Among their research pools and complex of laboratories set on the shore of the Pacific, I embarked on a crash course of sea-going veterinary medicine. Apart from the very different surroundings, it was rather like my first months at Belle Vue under the thumb of Matt Kelly. I learned that dolphins can contract influenza, mumps, polio and gastric ulcers, that their anatomical and physiological adaptations make them the safest creatures in the world to pass a stomach tube on but the most tricky to anaesthetize, and that they require each day three hundred times more Vitamin B_1 than a human of the same weight. An apparently simple thing but most vital of all, I was given my first opportunity to take blood samples from the animals. The smooth, shining skin of a dolphin betrays almost no evidence of where blood vessels might run. You can fish the beast out of the water and apply tourniquets to the flippers or the tail, but still the unco-operative veins and arteries refuse to reveal themselves. They lie beneath a tight, inflexible layer of blubber, each artery completely surrounded by a cluster of veins. Find the areas where the blubber is thinned and you find a cluster of blood vessels, the vets at Point Mugu told me. Easier said than done. Slight skin discoloration, a depression here and there, the glint of a shallow groove if the moistened tail is held to reflect the light; by such things I would be guided. Then a short needle could be placed in a vessel and a sample of venous, arterial or frequently a mixture of the two bloods taken.

My first essay in blood sampling was right on target. I

struck oil. 'It don't matter much,' said Dr Sam in his relaxed Texan drawl, 'if your needle takes blood from vein or artery or a bit of both if you're doin' routine analysis and such, 'cept of course oxygen levels, but don't forget the layout in these critters if you ever want to do an intravenous injection. It's easy as hell to git some of the drug into an artery, it lyin' so close to the veins an' all. So watch out, buddy.'

I saw the point. A drug inadvertently injected into an artery instead of a vein will damage the delicate arterial lining, stopping the circulation to tissues supplied by the artery beyond the injection site and causing them to die. At least in land mammals the tough-walled, pulsating arteries are usually easily located and are rarely close to the veins in places where the veterinarian roams in search of injection sites. Already these mermen were leading me, as they were said to lead ancient Greek seafarers, into a new life.

☆☆☆☆☆☆☆☆☆☆☆☆☆☆☆

Chapter Nine

☆☆☆☆☆☆☆☆☆☆☆☆☆☆☆

FOR A long time after the incident of Chloe's thumb, Norman Whittle's Wednesday afternoons, vacations and odd days in bed with influenza came and went with the same monotonous absence of disease at Belle Vue. Freezing snaps accompanied by choking yellow fog on November Wednesdays never seemed to provoke the acute lung emergencies in giraffe or antelope that sent Norman dashing out in like weather on every other day of the week, and in summer the milling crowds of visitors who fed the elephants with mouldy sausage rolls, umbrellas or cigarettes, or threw contraceptives, pins or bits of glass into the monkeys' cages, seemed to be on their most civilized behaviour whenever Norman was away and unavailable to deal personally with the resulting cases of colic and acute enteritis.

There was one source of practical experience: the trickle of wild and exotic animals that ran fitfully through my daily work with farm animals and domestic pets. Even in darkest Lancashire there were folk who preferred keeping slow lorises to Siamese cats or who had a penchant for pythons. If their pets needed medical attention, more often than not they telephoned Belle Vue Zoo who referred them to us. It was not much compared to the experience with real zoo animals that I longed for, but it taught a callow young vet a thing or two the hard way – and sometimes more about humans than about animals.

Most numerous among my exotic patients at this time were parrots, the choleric, beady-eyed individuals that perch behind the bars of numerous pubs in Greater Manchester, sweetly and ever so gently take peanuts placed on the capacious bosoms of the landladies whom they adore and, cursing raucously, try to take the fingers off all other members of the human race who come within reach. Without exception, these birds of glorious plumage and lengthy life-span dislike me and, as I count a fine collection of old scars on my hands, I am not sure that I am very partial to them. Parrots were small beer, I thought, but the beer soon turned distinctly sour.

Thus it was after I had been working with Norman Whittle for about a year that I met Charlie, a fine blue and gold macaw with claws overgrown as a result of twenty years without exercise behind the bar of a Manchester pub and a surfeit of fattening sweet sherry, his favourite tipple. Would I kindly trim his toenails? Certainly. The macaw glowered darkly in his carrying cage, which had been set in the middle of my surgery table. His owner, the pub's landlady, stood smiling proudly at her 'cheeky little Charlie'. She was a large lady with a bosom like the prow of a galleon and with peroxide-blond hair rolled tightly in curlers.

'Er, can you hold him for me?' I asked. Cheeky little Charlie turned his head to one side and fixed me with a malevolent, red-rimmed eye. A low, sinister, grating noise came from his scraggy throat and he thoughtfully honed one half of his beak against the other.

'Oh goodness, no, my dear,' exclaimed the landlady. 'Charlie's a darling little boy but he won't let me handle him. He'd tear me to bits. And he hates men.' I reflected that I had known more promising cases. I had yet to learn the art of mastering parrots by using a piece of stick and a kung-fu-like flick that renders them harmless and unhurt in the twinkling of an eye.

Charlie rocked slowly on his perch from one foot to the other, like a boxer limbering up for a fight.

121

'Well, can you at least entice him out of his cage?' I asked. I was not going in to fight, so how about him coming out and settling this thing man to man?

'Well, he might come out for his favourites, after-dinner mints. He adores those. He sits on my shoulder and takes one that I hold between my lips. He's ever so gentle!'

It turned out that we had no after-dinner mints between us and I sent Edith, my receptionist, across the road to buy some; I would learn in time that a zoo vet carries a variety of delicacies in his medical bag along with the drugs and instruments; one's essential first-aid kit must include after-dinner mints for a wide variety of monkeys, parrots and small mammals, clear mints for wallabies, sugar lumps for elephants and small cheroots for aoudads and other members of the goat tribe.

'Now,' said the landlady when we had the mints, 'I'll put a mint between my lips, Charlie will come out, and while he's nibbling it perhaps you can clip his toes.'

The macaw acted absolutely according to phase one of the plan. As soon as he spied the sweet he waddled along his perch and out of the door of the cage, and sat squarely on his owner's shoulder hard by her ear. With one golden eye he watched her place the mint between her lips and with the other he kept me under unblinking observation. Like a ventriloquist's dummy, he reached round the woman's cheek and began to nibble the mint. Slowly I sidled up and, feigning nonchalance, began to raise the clippers towards the parrot's long toenails, which were perfectly displayed against her dress just below her left shoulder. Six inches, three inches, one inch; I was getting closer to the curved talons. They certainly needed chiropody, with some grown almost to full circles. Somewhere inside them was a core of flesh with nerves and blood. I must avoid cutting into that area and simply trim back the dead overgrown portion. But how could I tell exactly where the core of each shiny, black, opaque nail was? I would have to compromise to begin with and snip off just a little bit, see how that looked and then maybe take a sliver more.

As I reached the first claw and gingerly touched it with the tip of my clippers, Charlie kept his eye fixed firmly on me but continued to crunch at the mint without budging. Very gently I slipped the toenail clippers over the end of the first claw. Suddenly Charlie decided he had had enough. Something dastardly was afoot, and he was not going to stand by and let it happen. In order to lean forward and launch a pre-emptive attack on me and my clippers he would have to have a more secure base to perch on, so with the black claws of his left foot, Charlie dug through the landlady's dress and deeply into the flesh of her shoulder. The poor woman spat out the mint and uttered a piercing shriek that set the waiting dogs in the reception room barking and howling. A nimble tactician, Charlie was determined to bring his steely bill into close combat with the foe, but to stop himself from pressing the attack too far and too fast, with the result that he might fall off his defensive position, he needed another good secure hold for his right foot. The object he sought was right there – his owner's ear. Charlie grabbed it tightly and dug in his curly nails. The lady let out a second, more raucous shriek and clutched the parrot with both hands, whereupon he bit a plump finger and drew blood. More shrieks.

All this flurry of action had taken only a few seconds, during which time I had seemed to be transfixed, incapable of action, but now I moved forward. Impotently waving my clippers, I tried to separate the struggling mass of feathers, hair, claws and fingers on the landlady's shoulder. Scrunch, scrunch – I was painfully bitten on two fingers. Wild-eyed, ruffled and squawking, Charlie launched a new attack on my clippers. Clang! His gaping black beak punched sharply forward and knocked them from my grasp. They slipped neatly down the inside of the landlady's dress.

With the enemy now in complete disarray, Charlie was still in command of his redoubt. The ear, bright red and resembling a crushed strawberry, remained under requisition for essential military purposes, and he had given up not one inch of ground on the left shoulder. He had sacrificed a few green feathers and in the excitement of battle had elected not to desert his post to go to the latrine but to obey the call of nature just where he stood. It improved neither the lady's appearance nor her morale.

'For God's sake, can't you do something?' she yelled. 'Get the little beggar off me!'

Charlie bit the back of one of her scrabbling hands. When I tried again to grab him he reinforced his hold on ear and shoulder, whisked his beak to and fro and deftly removed a piece of nail from my left index finger.

I looked desperately round for something to help me. A towel hung by the sink; perhaps I could use it to keep his deadly beak occupied long enough for me to unpick him from his owner and get him back into his cage. The nails would have to wait. I grabbed the towel, tossed it over the bird and stood back. Somewhere underneath, Charlie wriggled, screamed, chewed and blustered furiously.

'Don't worry,' I gasped with some relief, 'I think we've got him now.'

'He's still got my ear, though!' the landlady wailed as the towelled mass on her shoulder threw itself about.

Before picking up the entrapped parrot it would be prudent to ascertain where the beak-bearing head end was.

124

I took a pencil and gently prodded the stuffed towel. With a crisp crack the pencil was split into two and fell apart; I had found the head end. Without losing more time I grabbed hold of the part that was probably the plump little belly and tugged hard. The parrot tugged hard at the lady's ear. Her shrieking resumed. Feeling in need of reinforcement, I took off my white surgery coat and threw that on top of the towel, completely covering the woman's head. As best I could I felt for the parrot's head, held it and set about releasing the grip on the mutilated ear. The landlady put both her hands on the hidden bird and allowed me to try to detach the claw dug into her shoulder. When I got beneath the towelling I found that the other claw was now also firmly attached to her shoulder. Charlie was no pushover.

Suddenly I realized that I was touching the very things that had been the cause of all the bother: the overgrown nails. I carefully lifted a corner of the towel and looked at them. There they all were, side by side. A perfect opportunity! With the vicious end of Charlie still gurgling and spitting somewhere higher up in the folds of material I might well be able to do my stuff – if I had my clippers. Then I remembered that they were still lying somewhere in the décolletage of the buxom lady who stood before me, my white coat draped over her head and both hands clasped to a jumble of protesting towelling on her shoulder.

'Er, I can do his nails very well now,' I began. 'I've got his claws out perfectly. Can you hold on like that for a few moments more?'

'Yes, but get on with it. My ear's hurting like hell. Little beggar. Get on with it!'

'Er, well, my clippers . . . you've got my clippers in your . . .'

'I know. Get them out. I can't hold him much longer!'

'I'll have to put my hand down your dress, madam . . .'

'Of course you will. GET ON WITH IT!'

Squeezing my fingers together rather as if I were preparing to lamb a ewe, I entered the talcumed valley and probed downwards in search of my instrument. When my unwilling hand was completely within her dress and I was beginning to worry about just how far down I was going to have to go, I mercifully felt metal lodged behind some item of twangy underwear.

'I'm awfully sorry about all this,' I was saying in embarrassed confusion as I pinned the clippers between two fingers and began to extract them. Then the surgery door opened and Edith, the receptionist, came in. My hand was still down the front of the landlady's dress.

'Just cutting the parrot's toenails, Edith,' I explained brightly.

Edith was a non-conformist lay preacher, and I often wondered whether she treated her Maker with the same brisk and relentless efficiency which could be a source of terror to both slow-paying farmers and ham-fisted young veterinarians. She glared icily through her spectacles and backed briskly out again. Meanwhile I had re-armed myself with the clippers and started to trim the bird's claws. Following my plan to cut back a little at a time, I pruned them bit by bit to what seemed a more reasonable length. When I had finished I noticed that the end of each nail was showing a little blood. It was only the merest drop but I had obviously cut back just a fraction too far. I dabbed each nail with a styptic liquid to seal it up neatly.

At last Charlie, almost apoplectic with rage, was securely back in his cage. The landlady adjusted her dress, I put some antiseptic on her abused ear, bandaged her wounded fingers, sponged her down and talked soothingly about what lovable if naughty little fellows these parrots were. She seemed reassured and even grateful, and if anyone's dignity had suffered wounds from our experience, it apparently was not hers.

To my dismay, Charlie's owner and his vet did not bear the only physical wounds from our encounter that morning, for Charlie had not been gone from my surgery for more than ten minutes before his toenails began to bleed again. It was only after ten days and considerable care that the intermittent bleeding completely stopped. On subsequent visits I learned to handle him more deftly, and the experience also taught me something about cutting the sensitive nails of other Charlies to come.

These were plenty of them, for Manchester parrots

seemed particularly prone to overgrown toenails, to di-arrhoeas that resisted treatment because the unco-operative birds steadfastly refused to take their medicines, to coughs and sneezes that resisted treatment because the unco-operative microbes causing these complaints just as steadfastly ignored the medicaments, and to baldness. The baldness was self-inflicted – the parrots persistently plucked out all their feathers (except the ones on the top of their heads, of course) until they became pink-nude, pot-bellied and scrawny-necked. They reminded me of bellicose miniature Colonel Blimps emerging from the Turkish baths. I could find no itchy skin parasites or nutritional deficiency to cause this craze for full frontal exhibitionism.

My failure to counter what seemed sheer cussedness on the part of my malevolent parrot patients was underlined by the raucous cursing that they heaped upon me week after week as I surveyed the results of my impotent efforts to grow even one single plume on their old men's bodies. What irritated me about the nudists was their sheer cheek; having extracted almost all its plumage, one of these infuriating creatures would sit on its perch, tilt a choleric, red-rimmed eye in my direction – and then shiver. Of course you'll shiver, you dum-dum! I wanted to shout in my frustration. If I had had the temerity to write a considered dissertation on the Diseases of the Parrot, it would have consisted of but two sentences, written in blood on the finest parchment: 'Parrots are incontinent, wheezing asthmatics in need of chiropody and tungsten-wire whole-body toupees. They get well if they feel like it, or they don't.'

Nevertheless, I had to carry on. Dump the parrots and there might never be any condors or cassowaries or King penguins. And I had to do something to reassure the doting owners that Rochdale was the Mecca for infirm and irascible parrots. Although my treatment of their pets' ailments seemed to be meeting with a singular lack of obvious success, I decided that at the very least I could thwart the parrot nudist brigade in its efforts to commit suicide by self-refrigeration, I was damned if I would let these birds have the last laugh by developing hypothermia or pneumonia or frostbite.

First I gave instructions for all such patients to be confined day and night for one or two weeks at least to rooms where the temperature never dropped below 80 degrees Fahrenheit. Then it struck me that parrots really did appear to be old-fashioned sort of fellows; the analogy to Colonel Blimp really did stick. Where more genteel birds such as doves might get tipsy now and then when feasting on fermenting berries in the fall, parrots have the leery, rheumy eye of the hard-liquor drinker who prefers the grain to the grape all the year round. If the incontinent wheezers spurned my antibiotics and sulpha drugs, let's see how they fared on a drop of the hard stuff. As soon as I began to prescribe minute tots of rum or brandy for all my sick parrots I began to have successes. My knowledge of disease in exotic birds had not advanced very much, but a combination of the Turkish bath and hard-liquor regime for nearly all my cases resulted in more and more incontinent birds passing normal stools, the wheezers beginning to breathe more easily and some of the Kojak types even growing a soft covering of grey down and later the colourful plumage that was their rightful attire. As time went on the booze-'em-and-bake-'em therapy persuaded quite a few parrot owners that Dr Whittle's partner had a knack with their favourite bird.

I also earned the rather more demonstrative gratitude of a lady almost as exotic as her pet. It all began when the surgery telephone rang as I was showing out yet another parrot owner who was looking forward to giving his wife the perfect excuse for taking out the brandy bottle as soon as he got home.

'Hello,' said a sultry voice as I picked up the receiver. 'Is that Dr Taylor?'

'It is,' I replied. 'Who's this speaking?'

'It's Miss Seksi. I expect you've heard of me. I'm the speciality danseuse at the Garden of Eden.'

This surprising statement did not perplex me as it might have done, for I knew of the Garden of Eden, a sleazy

128

Manchester night-club from whose doors there wafted a permanent smell of stale beer, yesterday's cigars and cheap perfume.

'What can I do for you, Miss, er, Seksi?' I asked. Edith looked up sharply from her book-keeping.

'Well, it's very confidential. Private, if you know what I mean.'

'I see, but how can I help? Do you wish me to visit or will you come to the surgery?'

'Well, if you can be sure it's all confidential I'll come with him to the surgery if you'll give me an appointment.'

'Er . . . come with who, Miss, er, Miss Seksi?'

'My Oscar, of course.'

Who or what was her Oscar? I doubted if she had won a Hollywood Academy Award and decided Oscar must be a friend or husband. Well, I thought, she must realize I'm not a people doctor. We had had cases of Pakistanis and displaced persons from Eastern Europe queuing patiently for hours among the dogs, cats and budgerigars in the waiting room, only to find when it was their turn that we did not extract human teeth or issue National Health Service sick notes. This lady sounded one hundred per cent English, but she still wanted me to treat this chap Oscar. Then again, I thought, I had had a few human patients. There was the window cleaner who regularly had our fiery horse linament for his arthritic knee, many a farmer swore our medicaments were the most likely to cure the ringworm he had contracted from his calves, and I had dealt with all sorts of problems from impetigo to impotence among the hill-farming folk of the Pennines, who found it easier to talk to the vet, sitting over a cup of tea in the farmhouse after calving a cow, than to the doctor in his surgery in town.

'But, er, are you and Oscar bringing the animal?' I asked Miss Seksi.

'I work with Oscar. Oscar is my python.'

'Oh,' I said, grateful that at any rate part of the mystery had been solved.

A confidential consultation, with no nurse and no assistant present, was arranged for the ailing Oscar for three o'clock, and I waited in intrigued anticipation. Punctually at three, a taxi pulled up outside the waiting-room door and Edith ushered in a startlingly painted lady of Junoesque proportions dressed in an imitation tiger-skin coat that seemed to be afflicted here and there with remarkably accurate imitations of sarcoptic mange. She teetered on six-inch stiletto heels, lugging awkwardly in one hand a large canvas bag. As she sat down she dabbed the perspiration from her face and touched up the paint-work expertly. Then she switched on the multi-volt smile that had been designed to cut its way through cigar smoke, wolf whistles, rude remarks and embarrassing silence with the ease of a disposable scalpel. Her first words to me were 'Bloody heavy, he is, poor little darlin'.'

Undoing some cord tied tightly around the neck of the canvas bag, Miss Seksi switched off the head-splitting smile and plunged an arm inside. Slowly she withdrew a glistening, plump snake, an anaconda that must have been every bit of twelve feet long.

'There he is,' said my client. 'Poor, poor Oscar; I'm really worried about him.'

'What seems to be the problem?' I faltered, looking down the undulating length of Miss Seksi's partner as he gently wound himself round her shoulders and waist. His weight seemed normal and there was a healthy fluorescent glint as the light caught his rippling scales. Oscar was trying to disappear inside Miss Seksi's fur coat. Already the first six feet of him were making her torso bulge and warp beneath her coat as if she were made of rubber; in a moment my patient would have gone completely to ground. Remembering Charlie the parrot and the fate of my toenail clippers, I firmly resolved that I was not going in there after him. Instead I grasped twelve inches of Oscar's tail end, flexed my biceps and stood firmly with my legs apart. Oscar, like all such non-venomous constrictor snakes, was ninety per cent muscle. He continued to contract his powerful twelve-foot body as I held staunchly onto his tail and refused to be pulled inside the perfumed recesses of Miss Seksi's tiger-skin coat. The result was predictable. If I was not going to release the tail and if Oscar continued doggedly to go places, there was only one thing left that had to give way: Miss Seksi. The contracting snake pulled her right into me. 'Dear God, keep Edith out of here at this moment!' I prayed, as I stood nose to nose and thigh to thigh with the lady from the Garden of Eden. Oscar wedded us like Scotch tape; as he threw a loop or two around my wrist, I wondered who was holding whom.

'The, er, the problem,' said Miss Seksi from two inches away, 'the problem is personal. It's his eyes.' She breathed a cloud of Chanel No. 5 and onions into my face. 'If you can reach my handbag, Doctor, you'll find the card; you'll see what I mean.'

Still clutching my bit of Oscar with one hand, I clicked open her handbag with the other, fished vaguely about inside it and pulled out an oblong card.

'That's it,' she said. 'That's the card from the clinic.'

I had no idea what she was talking about. 'What clinic?' I asked.

'The venereal disease clinic.' She lowered her voice confidentially and looked at the door to make sure it was firmly closed. 'I think Oscar's got it.'

'Got what, venereal disease?'

'Yes. You see, Oscar and I are in the burlesque business. We've appeared in Paris and Beirut, haven't we, Oscar?' Oscar's head had emerged from below Miss Seksi's coat and, with flicking tongue, he had begun to investigate my shoes. 'Yes, we've been very well received, Oscar and I. Very exotic, very good money.'

'But how do you and Oscar work together?'

'I'm a speciality danseuse . . . exotique . . . you know.'

'A stripper?' I hazarded.

Miss Seksi gave me a five-second, full-power burst of the smile. 'Yes, but not low-class, my dear,' she said. 'Seksi's my stage name; actually it's Schofield.'

'Please go on, Miss Schofield.'

'Well, during our act I do a very exotique speciality dance as Cleopatra. See what I mean? That's where Oscar fits in.'

An embryonic glimmer of light began to spark in my brain. We bumped foreheads.

'During the act – it went down *awfully* well in Beirut – I

disrobe to exotique music' (Miss Schofield emphasized the *tique* each time she uttered her favourite word) 'and the climax, when I'm in the buff – you know what I mean, Doctor – is when I commit suicide.'

'So Oscar is Cleopatra's asp?'

'Exactly. Oscar is the asp. Rather exotique, don't you think?'

If Cleopatra really did shuffle off this mortal coil with the aid of a reptile it must have been one of the small venomous Egyptian snakes, possibly a cobra, but certainly not a 65-pound South American constrictor.

'Yes, Doctor,' went on Miss Seksi. 'My agent thinks it's a really dramatic finale, with Oscar twining all round my body.'

'I see, I see,' I interposed quickly.

'Now. The thing is, Doctor, I've had a touch of, er, VD. The clinic gave me cards to hand out to anybody I might have had what they call contact with. I've dished out the cards, of course, though I couldn't care a fig for my boy friends – they're all pigs. But Oscar, he's my partner, my little darling. He's everything to me.'

'Why do you think Oscar might have picked up an infection from you?'

'His eyes, Doctor, look at his eyes. I'm worried sick by them. It's his work, Doctor. He's got it from me, I'm sure.' Miss Seksi was becoming tearful. We were still so closely entangled that any sobbing on her part was likely to soak my tie.

'Trouble is,' she continued, 'the clinic wouldn't see him, even though I told them all about him, how he worked with me. That's the National Health Service for you! So that's why I came to you.'

'Let's get ourselves sorted out and have a look at his head,' I said. My own head was spinning. Whatever it was that did not look right with his eyes, it certainly could not be VD. That disease of humans does not affect other mammals, and in reptiles like Oscar it is out of the question. Although, I reflected, I could not be positive that no scientific paper had ever been published stating categorically that anacondas and their like were immune to the gonorrhoea microbe.

Eventually Miss Seksi/Schofield unravelled the snake and I took a relieved step backwards. For the first time I had a good view of his head. 'Look at his eyes, Doctor!' his owner wailed. 'They've gone like that in less than a week!'

Both the anaconda's eyes were indeed abnormal. Instead of being limpid dark jewels they were blind, milk-white blobs. Looking at them carefully through the magnifying lens of an ophthalmoscope with its intense beam of light, I was able to make out the eye lying beneath the milky film.

'When did Oscar last shed his skin?' I asked. I had not seen this eye condition in snakes before, but an idea was forming in my mind.

'About a week or ten days ago. Came off as clean as a whistle.'

'And round about then you first noticed his eyes?'

'Yes.'

Snakes' eyes are completely covered by a non-moving transparent third eyelid. As the rest of the skin is shed from time to time as the animal grows, the old outer layers of the third eyelid are sloughed too. Or rather they should be. I was convinced that the 'VD' infection of Oscar's eyes was the old third eyelid which had not fallen off with the rest of his skin. It was a sheet of tough, dead tissue covering an otherwise healthy eye.

While I prepared to try and restore the sight of the uncomplaining trouper there and then, his owner became tearful again. 'If he's blind, I won't be able to work with him anymore,' she moaned. I did not quite see how vision was essential for Oscar's act. 'How can I replace him? I just couldn't get another like him. It would mean back to my Florence Nightingale routine – and at half the salary.' The wailing increased as I dropped a little paraffin oil into each of the white eyes.

'Hold tightly onto his head, please,' I instructed. Oscar began once again to intertwine us both, and I felt his rear end drag me into another bout of intimate contact with his mistress. The latter was now red-faced and sweating as well as weepy. Even her mask of make-up was beginning to erode.

With a pair of fine-toothed forceps I gently began to tease up the edge of the white film covering one of the snake's eyes. Bit by bit, and using more drops of oil as I progressed, I slowly freed the crust. A dark gold glint showed that Oscar's eye lay uninjured underneath. At last the entire piece of dead tissue came away. Oscar eyed me, unblinking and inscrutable. I set to work on the other side of the head and soon the second eye was clear as well. The 'VD' had gone. Putting down my instruments, I struggled out of Oscar's coils and stood back to survey my handiwork.

Miss Seksi was open-mouthed in astonishment and delight, gurgling and smiling real, unprofessional smiles. Releasing Oscar's head and letting him roam where he would, she came over and hugged me. 'Doctor, how can I ever thank you?' she purred. Then she imprisoned me in a python-like embrace and planted a big, soggy, bright red kiss on my forehead, just as Edith came back into the surgery.

134

'Ah, you're just in time, Edith . . .' I said.

'So I see,' she interrupted drily.

'. . . to help get Oscar back into his bag.'

Between us we untangled the now clear-eyed anaconda, and Edith saw Miss Seksi out.

'We can do without that sort,' she said, coming back into the room where I was sterilizing the forceps.

For all her stagey manner, Miss Seksi had enlivened my afternoon, and there was nothing artificial or overblown about Oscar: he had provided my first experience of what I later found to be a common problem in snakes.

'Oh no, we can't, Edith,' I replied.

☆☆☆☆☆☆☆☆☆☆☆☆☆☆

Chapter Ten

☆☆☆☆☆☆☆☆☆☆☆☆☆☆

CHRISTIANITY, UNLIKE some of the world's other great religions, has no particular theology of animals. After establishing that the Deity constructed whales and other marine creatures on the fifth day and turned his attention to terrestrial fauna on the sixth, it has fussed and feuded pretty exclusively over one often rather unattractive and unreliable species of naked ape. True, Thomas Aquinas split scholarly hairs over the nature of the brutish soul, and Francis would have been on the Assisi branch committee of the RSPCA if there had been such a thing in the twelfth century; but Protestant bishops can be run to earth in the huntin', shootin', fishin' fraternity, devout Orthodox peasants of the Mediterranean trap small songbirds by the million, Latin Catholics leave Mass to attend the ritual torture of black bulls on a Sunday afternoon. I find it odd. The more I have studied, looked at and handled animals, seen their intrinsic beauty, the perfection with which they spin their strands in the web of life, the more I have tilted towards a unified theology of all living creatures, the scorpion and the maggot just as much as the tiger or the whale. Dead, beneath my autopsy knife, they reveal not just themselves but also what I am: part of the all-purposeful, all-beautiful, endless wheel of growth and change, of death and regeneration. Nothing is chaos.

Look close, with seeing eyes, and even a blob of pus is a wondrous, active, ordered microcosm.

The Church of England often exhibits a rather dotty concern for animals, however, which I experienced when a vicar friend of mine in a country parish across the Pennines in Yorkshire invited me to read the lesson at a special church service for pets. The occasion was graced by the presence of a bishop, who preached a sermon full of round plummy aphorisms about sparrows and their welfare-state existence, Daniel's way with big cats and how much happier we all would be if we lived like armadilloes, although for the life of me I could not make out what it was about these nocturnal miniature tanks that so impressed the gaitered cleric as epitomizing the Christian ideal. To illustrate his point he produced a small, curled-up representative of the species from beneath his purple cassock. It had been borrowed from a nearby zoo, and its dramatic appearance had an electrifying effect on the chancel full of nodding choirboys.

Unfortunately His Lordship mishandled the armour-plated ball and dropped it, whereupon it rolled down the pulpit steps, galvanizing the choirboys still more. A full complement leapt unceremoniously from their seats in both front rows and scrabbled to retrieve the creature, which made off towards the organ. The armadillo won by a short head, nipped behind the forest of pipes and was not seen again until halfway through Evensong a week later.

The young congregation would never have guessed from the bishop's admonition, 'In being kind to beasts we are honouring the work of God's hands,' that the reverend gentleman hunted two days a week and was the proud possessor of a well-used pair of Purdey shotguns. There were children with dogs and cats, budgies and rabbits. Some clustered outside the porch with their ponies. Doting parents, sly-eyed schoolboys with grass snakes in jars and toads in their pockets, girls clutching goldfish bowls, all sat side by side in the pews of the seventeenth-century stone church. There was one lad with a monkey, a chunky, muscle-bound pig-tailed macaque. It continually raised its eyebrows towards the preacher in the typical mildly challenging grimace of macaques, which made it seem like a sceptical, possibly agnostic listener. Its owner kept a firm grip on the leash with which it was restrained.

Blessing animals is, I suppose, a cut above doing the same thing to motor bikes or lawn mowers. Services for pets at least provide the small boys who attend such gatherings with the hope that something might turn up. On this occasion it already had, and the absconding armadillo brought back memories of forfeiting my place on the annual choir outing to Blackpool: a white mouse released under the long blue cassock of a middle-aged lady chorister at St Edmund's Church had resulted in the unusual spectacle of the lady vaulting clean over the choir stall in the middle of the reading of the banns and streaking off into the vestry.

'. . . and so I leave you with these words. Kindness, patience, goodwill to all creatures, not least the wonderful creatures that bring us so much joy. In the name of the Father' etc, etc. The bishop came to the end of his address. A final hymn was sung and everyone trooped outside. The bishop was going to move among the crowd assembled in the churchyard and bless the beasts – human and otherwise.

In the churchyard it was warm and sunny. My part in the proceedings was over. I stood watching the milling crowd and saying good-bye to the vicar before making my way back over the hills to Rochdale. The bishop was in a jolly, expansive mood as he wandered through the chattering throng, his right hand raised in benediction. He cooed to the budgies thrust up towards his face, tugged the ears of some of the dogs and had his picture taken as he sat perilously on a donkey. All at once the boy who had brought the macaque barged through the crowd waving a leather leash, at the end of which there was no sign of a monkey. The press of jostling humans and animals parted like the Red Sea before Moses as a squat brown figure bounded between them. The pig-tailed macaque shot down the church path, through the ancient lych-gate and straight through the partly open window of a sparkling new Bentley parked directly outside. He was pursued by his owner, closely followed by all the small boys present, and behind came the rest of us.

Inside the car the monkey was having a fine time. He quickly pulled open the door of the glove compartment and spilled out all the contents. A tin of pipe tobacco lying on the front seat was thrown out of the window, and the plastic cover of the interior light was prized off and bitten in two.

'Harry!' shouted the monkey's owner. 'Stop that and come here!' He opened the car door a fraction.

Harry bared his wicked-looking canine teeth, grimaced as histrionically as any villain of Japanese theatre, and savagely bit the right hand of his owner as it moved towards him. Bleeding profusely and in obvious pain, the gallant lad advanced his other hand. Harry grabbed it, pulled it up to his jaws and lacerated the palm with a slash of his fangs. The poor boy fell back and the door was slammed to. The vicar led the casualty away.

By now the bishop had pushed through the crowd. 'I say,' he said, his genial expression fading fast, 'that's my car, you know.' He looked through the window at the macaque, which by now was flying round the interior like an angry bluebottle in a jam jar. 'We really ought to get the chappie out of there.' No one volunteered.

Then Harry spotted the dashboard, a surface bristling with interesting knobs and levers, glinting bits of chrome, plastic and glass. Just beneath the dashboard was an inviting twist of coloured wire which the inquiring mind of the would-be engineer could not ignore. As he reached down and pulled it there was a satisfying click, and the panel covering the tangle of assorted gadgetry behind the dashboard fell away.

'We must get that monkey out of my car,' said the bishop, pale but calm.

The jungle of gleaming electronics now exposed fascinated Harry. With one powerful leathery hand he grasped a bunch of wires and plugs and pulled. They came away and bits of metal and plastic tinkled onto the floor. The electric clock stopped.

Harry looked at the bishop, raised his eyebrows sceptically and pressed the horn button. As its wires had just been disconnected it did not work. Harry pulled and the horn button broke off. He threw it out of the window.

'Please, sir, you haven't blessed Chirpy yet,' said a little girl, worming her way through to the bishop's side and straining upwards with a fistful of budgerigar.

'Hrumph,' said His Lordship.

Meanwhile I was marvelling at the speed with which a small monkey was dismantling a solidly built vehicle. If a gang of Harrys could be trained to work as fast assembling the various pieces of metalwork that now lay around the inside of the car, the labour problems of the automobile industry would be a thing of the past.

'Somebody do something! This bloody monkey is tearing my car apart!'

'Please, sir, you haven't done Chirpy,' persisted the little girl, her budgerigar by now almost suffocated in her grip.

'Next year, next year!' shouted the bishop, purple-faced now as well as purple-robed. He patted the child so hard on the head that I expected to see her reel away cross-eyed.

I must confess I had thoroughly enjoyed the unique experience. The inside of the car was now in utter ruin. Harry was sitting in the back seat, looking round for anything he might have missed. Stirring myself, I decided I must do something. Pig-tailed macaques are one of the toughest and most dangerous species of monkey, and to tackle one single-handed in the close confines of a car would be foolhardy. I had no dart-gun with me, but I did have some anaesthetic in my car and plenty of syringes. I sent the vicar's wife to fetch a banana while I inspected the partly opened car window. The gap had been big enough for Harry to get in, so he could get out as well if he wished, and I could not wind the window up without opening the door. I sent a choirboy into the church for one of the thick hassocks, or kneeling pads. 'Now,' I said when he returned, 'get up on the roof of the car just above the window, and when I give you the word jam the hassock hard down over the side.

Enthusiastically the boy scrambled up the gleaming paintwork. The bishop leaned against the lych-gate groaning, a hand across his eyes.

140

I held a piece of banana through the window. Harry sniffed at it, passed it as undoctored and ate it. It tasted good. I proffered another piece, holding it just outside the window gap. Harry slowly put his hand out to take it. 'Jam it down!' I yelled to the boy on the roof as I seized Harry's hand and pulled with all my strength. Harry screamed and struggled vigorously but the boy with the hassock had narrowed the gap enough to stop me pulling an agitated twenty-five pounds of steely muscle and teeth completely out of the car. In half a second I had plunged the hypodermic into Harry's arm and whammed down the plunger. I released my grip and Harry retreated onto the rear window ledge, hollering furiously. In two minutes he began to drool, his eyes became dreamy and he emptied his bowels over the bishop's top hat. In another two minutes it was all over; Harry fell into a drowsing heap on the back seat and I opened the door to pull him out. We had been lucky – he would never be taken in that way again.

There was no hope of getting the bishop's car to start. It had to be towed to the next town for major repairs. I offered to drop His Lordship at the station on my way home.

'Many thanks, Doctor,' he said as I stopped outside the ticket office. 'Wouldn't have your job for the world. Damned brutes!'

If the Right Reverend gentleman's last two words are literally true, Old Nick is going to have a hell of a time dealing with Harry one of these days.

Despite my experience with the bishop and his Bentley, in the normal run of things I do not have to cross swords with the Established Church. With other faiths things can be different. There are many Moslem Pakistani folk living in the north of England, and at certain religious festivals they slaughter lambs. The rules lay down that the sacrifices must on no account be eaten by human beings, but it is perfectly acceptable for the lambs to be fed to wild beasts. At these times vans containing beautifully dressed and wholesome carcasses arrive at zoos and Pakistani gentlemen request that the meat be fed to the big cats. Solemnly the lamb is unloaded into the meat store and the van driver goes away, happy in the knowledge that the tenets of the faith have been upheld. Later, nominally Christian zoo keepers can be seen assembling in the zoo kitchen, armed with meat saws and cleavers and ready to decide who gets what for their family's Sunday joints.

The Moslem calendar was pinned up in the office of one head keeper whose animals I treated, with red lines marking the weeks when the staff could be sure to dine daily on mutton. Even the youngest assistant keeper of the Pets' Corner could tell you when Ramadan ended, although I doubt if he even knew what month Easter was in. Beside the head keeper's calendar were pinned two other pieces of paper. One listed the staff in order of the precedence for the share-out:

Zoo director:	Loin, 2 shoulders, 2 legs, breast
Veterinarian:	2 shoulders, 2 legs, also likes kidneys, breast
Head keeper:	2 shoulders, 1 leg, liver, breast
Asst head keeper:	1 leg, kidneys
Head bird keeper:	4 cutlets
Reptile keeper:	1 cutlet, head

and so on down to:

Trainee keeper:	liver.

The other piece of paper was most important. When the lamb came, it came in abundance, and the head keeper was hard put to it to see that his staff's taste for the meat did not become jaded. It read:

Suggestions for all staff:

Mondays:	Lamb Argenteuil
Tuesdays:	Carré d'agneau Dordonnaise
Wednesdays:	Lamb Kashmir
Thursdays:	Kebabs
Fridays:	Navarin of lamb
Saturdays:	Lamb and vegetable casserole
Sundays:	Epigrammes d'agneau

NB. Recipes for the above can be had from Nellie in the cash office.

Nellie kept a pile of duplicated instructions, for which useful service she received a choice roasting shoulder from the head keeper every Saturday during the sacrificing season.

Came the sad day when one of the Pakistani meat donors forgot his gloves and returned to the zoo stores shortly after making a delivery. Inside he found a dozen amateur butchers merrily dividing the spoils according to the list of precedence under the eagle eye of the head keeper. The scene that ensued, with the Pakistani snatching up a chopper and advancing hysterically on the red-faced sacrilegists, could have been the start of a holy war. Luckily the zoo director made an opportune appearance (coming to collect the ingredients for his favourite crown roast with cranberry stuffing) and the matter was temporarily shelved.

Some days later a polite Pakistani called at my home and introduced himself as the imam of the community whose sacrifice had been profaned by the zoo. Wild beasts were not particularly common in the north of England, at least not ones big enough to devour whole sheep carcasses, so the zoos were an essential means of disposal. Dumping on the municipal rubbish tip or incineration were out of the question. Could I advise him professionally?

Much as I had enjoyed my illicit share of meat, I was ethically bound to give him the best possible advice. 'When you have sacrificed the lambs,' I said, 'splash some non-poisonous green vegetable dye over the carcasses. That will not harm lions and tigers but will render the meat unappetizing to humans.'

The imam thought for a moment. 'Yes, I can recommend that to my people. Such colouring will not defile the sacrifice.'

It was settled. Supplies of sacrificed lambs to the zoo resumed. The big cats enjoyed the new arrangements and the threat of a jehad erupting in the zoo grounds receded. But the head keeper and his staff had the very devil of a job cutting any uncoloured meat out of the carcasses, and I noticed that the precedence list in his office had been altered. Now the very bottom entry on the list read:

Veterinarian: 1 kidney (if any left over).

The zoo which narrowly escaped being decimated by a holy war was one of several in the north of England which I was by now visiting regularly. Belle Vue was still my major zoo client, however, as it had been throughout the five years since I took over the care of its animals from Norman Whittle, and there Matt Kelly had noticed something odd about the way Simba, a four-month-old lion cub, was moving.

Simba led a happy, carefree life with his parents and brothers and sisters until one day, for no obvious reason, his father suddenly bit him on the back. The wound did not look bad, just a pair of small puncture holes in the skin, but the cub started to become wobbly on his hind legs. When Matt called me in I found from an X-ray of Simba's back that he was becoming steadily paralysed; one of the adult lion's teeth had penetrated down to his backbone and a spinal abscess had developed.

I anaesthetized Simba and took him back to Rochdale in my car and there explored the area deep in the lumbar region of his spine, where the dirty tooth had set up a nasty pocket of diseased, pus-filled bone. With a scalpel and a special spoon-shaped gouge I removed the infected bone and put a small rubber drain tube into the wound. Stitched up, Simba looked like an inflatable toy lion with a red rubber valve projecting out of the middle of his back, ready for someone to attach a bicycle pump. Now for a long period of post-operative nursing; Simba was partially paralysed and incontinent, symptoms which would not go overnight. I needed somewhere to hospitalize him where I could keep a personal eye on him, and it was Shelagh who came up with the answer.

Our home in Rochdale, a Jacobean stone farmhouse on the edge of the moor, had one acre of walled market garden attached. Shelagh decided to build a lion hospital there. To the passer-by, and eventually to the tax-man, who considered the lion hospital a poor cover story to use in industrial Lancashire when we were claiming the building expenses, it looks like a wooden garden shed. It is now the home of Henry, my favourite and most intelligent goat, who no doubt considers it a perfect goat shed. It was erected, however, Henry and the tax man notwithstanding, as a bona fide, custom-built lion hospital. There Simba would be nursed back to health and to full use of his limbs and bladder.

This was the sort of thing Shelagh loves. While I attended to the medical side, giving the daily injections and checking the reflexes, Shelagh was Simba's nurse, physiotherapist, cook, companion and latrine attendant all rolled into one. Every two hours she meticulously bathed the protesting cub in baby soap and water so that his hind parts would not become sore because of his incontinence, dried him on one of a specially commandeered bunch of my bath towels and smeared the vulnerable areas with silicone ointment. Nourished on an appetizing steak tartare mixture that had me drooling at the mouth, and encouraged to use his legs outside on the grass when it was fine, Simba gradually mended.

In these days when lion cubs are cheaper than ten a penny, when the boxes they are carried in cost more than themselves and they are worth a hundred times more as a dead skin than they could possibly be alive, it is sad to reflect that the very success of breeding and safely rearing lion cubs in zoos and safari parks over recent years has made some lion owners regard these big cats as characterless and as expendable as sausages out of a machine. I know they are lazy fellows but, like every other animal, the more you know them the more fascinating their ways and workings are seen to be. That was something Shelagh and I quickly learnt from Simba.

After a summer of Shelagh's physiotherapy, and to the relief of the farm cats who could not pursue voles in the market garden without finding themselves the quarry of a gleefully growling creature with sandy hair and enormous paws, it was time for the fully recovered lion to go back to the zoo. First I took him to make his and my debut on television. We were going to be interviewed about the cub's paralysis and subsequent recovery.

It became obvious when I led him into the studios on a

dog lead that Simba, by now grown to an impressive size, was by no means filled with awe at passing the portals of the Temple of the Holy Box. An extra in full costume and make-up as a Roman senator came fussing down a corridor towards us. Busy primping himself in a small hand mirror, he had not noticed the lion ambling along by my side. His sandalled feet came level with us and Simba decided it was time for a bit of provocative rough-housing. As the senator passed, the lion clubbed with sheathed claws at the back of his knees, buckling them and bringing him crashing to the floor in a flurry of toga and velveteen jockey briefs. Apologizing, I helped the unharmed but fluttering actor to his feet. Then he saw Simba sitting blandly on his haunches waiting for me to resume our exploration.

'Ooh, my God, darling, what's that?' he exclaimed, clutching me with both hands like a scrawny vulture. 'Have props brought a real lion in for the *Julius Caesar*?' He scurried off, theatrically casting the loose end of his toga over his shoulder.

We found the studio where the interviewer was waiting for us. Simba did not like the lights nor the way the sound man seemed to tease him with the boom microphone, swinging it to and fro above his head. It was just out of reach; perhaps, Simba thought, it was some sort of game. He decided to find out. With a great leap upwards he managed to get one set of claws on the microphone before the sound man could whisk it away. The wire-gauze casing of the microphone crashed to the floor. Simba looked up with watery eyes; not a bad game, this.

When I eventually settled in my seat with the lion at my side, Simba had a call of nature. Waddling away from me into the middle of the floor, he squatted and relieved his bowels. Within moments the studio reeked with the heavy and unforgettable odour of lion droppings. I retrieved the animal and asked for a shovel and bucket. 'Don't worry yourself,' they told me, 'it will be dealt with.' Minutes went by and it wasn't. The smell got stronger. Two men came into the studio, walked over to the pile of droppings, talked for a couple of minutes over it and then went out. The droppings continued to sit noisomely in the middle of

146

the studio floor. People wandered around with contorted features and handkerchiefs over their noses, regarding the monument to Simba's healthy colonic function from a respectful distance. I asked again for something with which to clear up the mess. No one seemed inclined to listen.

'Now come on,' I said loudly, beginning to lose my patience, 'all I need is a shovel and I'll do the cleaning up in a trice.'

An elegantly dressed girl assistant hurried over to me. 'Please, Dr Taylor, please,' she said earnestly, taking my arm, 'don't get involved. It's the unions.'

'Unions – what unions?' I asked incredulously.

'Well, the question is, which union in the building should be responsible for cleaning up the, er, stuff?'

'But it can be done in less time than it takes to tell. What unions are involved?'

'There's the union that the television centre's normal cleaning staff belong to and there's the quite separate union for the people inside the studio here, the scene shifters and so on.'

'And you mean they can't agree who clears up the, er, stuff?'

'No.'

'Both unions want the privilege of shovelling that lot?'

'Well, not exactly. You see this type of, well, dirt is extraordinary according to the rule book. It's not only who does the cleaning, but how much extra pay will the chosen ones get.'

More folk were now inspecting the mound of excrement which was the centre of the dispute and walking in circles round it, conversing intently. It might have been a suspected bomb. Another girl assistant came in with an air-freshener aerosol and filled the room with the stench of cheap rose perfume. Mixed with the existing odour of lion it made a still more repulsive blend.

'Well, what's going on now?' I growled in disgust.

'They're having a meeting in the corridor outside. Then it will be decided.'

Time went by. The girl drifted off. 'Oh, look here,' I said to the assembled company, without addressing anyone in particular, 'if it will ease matters, couldn't I as a paid-up member of the Lion Shitshifters Brotherhood get you off the hook by removing the stuff with a piece of newspaper?'

''Fraid not, old boy. You're not a member of the right union,' replied a voice.

Another ten minutes went by, with Simba's trouble-making offering lying centre stage, before a man came into the studio and announced that the matter had been settled. In just under ten seconds two fellows with dustpans and brushes had the studio floor clear and sparkling.

'Which union won?' I asked the girl assistant.

'The scene shifters. They argued that the, er, stuff should be regarded as a prop, not as ordinary dirt. Eventually that was accepted. The lion, er, stuff was a prop so they shifted it. As it was a prop extraordinaire and could be classed as dirty work in the rule book, they got a bonus.'

I wished Shelagh had had a union from which to claim a bonus for all the lion, er, stuff that she had removed from

Simba's convalescent home in the market garden at Rochdale.

There is of course a special satisfaction in helping zoo babies such as Simba, so I was delighted when Katja, one of the Belle Vue chimpanzees, presented Robert the thumb-remover with a daughter. Christened Topaz, this sister for Lee had something of her brother's adventurous nature and an apparent interest in race relations! The quarters for the orang-utans and chimpanzees are side by side at Bell Vue, although they are separated by a solid brick wall so the two groups are unable to see one another. At the front of the centrally heated indoor compartments are widely spaced and decorative iron grilles, and outside these there is armoured glass sheeting dividing the animals from the humans and keeping airborne human bugs and viruses at bay. Between the grilles and the glass is a narrow passageway that runs without interruption the length of the house.

Normally baby chimpanzees do not venture far from their mothers, and although we realized that they were small enough to squeeze through the grille at the cage front, we had never known one do so – until Topaz came along. She would run happily in and out of the cage, playing some game such as chasing her shadow and passing between the metal bars with ease. Katja, her mother, did not seem to mind, and the little animal always returned after a few moments' expedition into what for her was the outside world. But one day, as Shelagh and I were standing with Len outside the plate glass watching young Topaz play, she suddenly did something new, something that made us all gasp as we instantly appreciated the possibly serious consequences.

Leaving the chimp cage she moved along the passageway to the left until she found herself for the first time in her life standing outside the living room of the orang-utans. She was fascinated. There through the grille was the great Harold, patriarch and sage of his group, sitting in the middle of the domestic circle with Jane and his other wives tending the orang babies, doing a bit of grooming of their lord and master and sorting through the day's ration of fruit and vegetables which Len had carefully mixed with their wood-wool bedding to set them a sort of treasure hunt to pass the time. The three of us stood in growing apprehension as little Topaz stared goggle-eyed at the covey of chestnut-coloured men of the woods, as their name means in Malay.

Of the three types of great ape, gorilla, chimpanzee and orang-utan, orangs have always been my favourite. They are a peaceable, gentle and tolerant species, and I have become much closer to them than to the saturnine gorillas or mercurial chimps. Nevertheless they can be swiftly vicious and immensely strong if provoked, as when Len had lost a toe and half a shoe to a liverish Harold. It was impossible to predict what might happen to a little foreigner like Topaz who suddenly came upon the scene. Harold and the family had already noticed the visitor waiting without. It was too late for us to do anything like rushing round to the back of the house. We might as well stay where we were, keep our fingers crossed and hope that the young chimp would quickly wander back to Katja before she was set upon as an intruder.

Having gazed at the family group from outside the bars, Topaz apparently found it most inviting, for without more ado she popped through the grille and shuffled up to the mighty Harold with her lips drawn back and her teeth showing in the grin that indicates friendship among chimpanzees. Now for it, I thought. If Harold or one of the females was in a bad mood, little Topaz might be pulled limb from limb before our eyes.

In fact, quite the reverse happened. The baby chimp was accepted into the orang family circle as if she was one of their young daughters who had just come home from school. She took her place at the feet of Harold, who looked down his nose at her and stuck out one index finger, apparently for her to play with. He never moved another muscle. The baby orangs came and sat next to her and solicitously arranged the wood-wool bedding round her bottom to make her more comfortable. Jane half peeled a banana and thrust it into Topaz's face. It was a wonderful spectacle. Here was Uncle Harold playing perfect host and

150

benefactor to his favourite niece from next door; you would not have guessed that he had never before clapped eyes on her. Topaz enjoyed it immensely, and before long was sitting on Uncle Harold's capacious pot belly and gleefully wrapping his long tresses of red hair about her. Harold indulged her like a sultan with one of his numerous offspring.

Shelagh and I stayed watching the touching sight for half an hour. Then we saw Katja come to the grille of the adjoining cage and start chattering anxiously. She could almost have been calling to her infant, 'Come on back home now, Topaz. You really can't presume on too much of Uncle Harold's time. Be a good girl and say thank you politely. There will always be another day.'

Topaz slid off Harold's belly, put a finger to the lips of the female orangs in a gesture of closeness and went back the way she had come. Katja gathered her up in her arms, far less hairy than those of Uncle Harold, and took her back to father Robert, who does not possess Harold's belly either. Were they saying to her, 'Well, tell us all about the folk next door, and did you have a good time?'

So began a delightful association. When Robert and Katja were busy or had had enough of the ever-active chimp, Topaz would slope off and spend a few hours with the neighbours. On at least one occasion she was seen to take Uncle Harold a present of a carrot.

The visiting only stopped when Topaz grew too large to slip between the bars of the grille, but by that time she had other things outside to interest her. Ray Legge liked to take her on his rounds through the zoo and would sometimes let her sit with him in his office when he did his paperwork. She revelled in new places and new faces, and was particularly interested in a group of Arabian camels that had come into quarantine at Belle Vue some months before. They were a sorry sight when they arrived. Every one was thoroughly infested with the microscopic little mite that causes sarcoptic mange, a very common skin disease of camels that is related to human scabies. We began an intensive programme to try to rid the grumpy animals of the troublesome complaint. We sprayed them and dipped

151

them and anointed the bleeding areas each day with soothing creams and ointments, but the mites had burrowed deep into the skin and were protected from chemicals by all the thickening and scaliness they had produced. In the end I decided to bring on the big guns of organophosphorus insecticides, helping them to penetrate the layers over the mites by scrubbing off the scales with specially bought yard brushes and hot water.

Topaz accompanied Ray on his many visits to supervise the keepers brushing and scrubbing the insecticides into the camels, and she became familiar with their routine of filling buckets with hot water, adding the chemicals and then applying them vigorously to the bodies and legs of the diseased dromedaries. One day after this had been going on for several weeks an assistant keeper in the great ape house rang Ray's office in a panic. He admitted his fault right away – he had left the door to Topaz's cage open while cleaning it – and now he had to report that the young chimp had disappeared somewhere into the zoo grounds. It was not that she was in any way a dangerous or unpredictable animal, she posed no threat to any child or little old lady that she might meet on her travels, but what might happen if she naïvely paid a visit to the lion compound or the polar bear pit? She might not be as lucky there as she had been with Uncle Harold.

A full search was started, and keepers combed every section of the zoo from aquarium to elephant house. Eventually Topaz was found. It was the keeper of the camels who sent for Ray to come and collect the fugitive, and quite a sight greeted the zoo director when he went into the camel house. Topaz had obviously been fascinated by all this business of treating the camels, and after escaping from her cage she had gone to their house to help us out with the anti-mange treatment. There she stood, in the middle of a group of camels that towered above her, but which had so far apparently tolerated her presence and had not begun covering her with ejected stomach contents, their normal sign of disapproval. The little ape had decided to give them a good scrubbing down – if the humans were making such heavy weather of it, she would see what a

sharp young chimpanzee with muscles and application could do. She had pulled a fire bucket full of water into the thick of the forest of camels' legs and had armed herself with one of the keepers' sweeping brushes.

As Ray and the camel keeper watched, Topaz dipped the brush into the fire bucket and then, constantly displaying the wry grimace of appeasement and keeping up a fussy chatter, which was presumably her way of exhorting the camels to stand still, she scrubbed away at the limbs and the undersurfaces of the bellies all around her. She continued doing this after the humans arrived, pausing only occasionally to look over her shoulder at them as if to assure herself that her efforts to help were not going unnoticed by her superiors. It is hard, wet, repetitive work dressing camels and other hoofed stock for mange, so perhaps one day such chores might be carried out by trained groups of chimpanzee veterinary auxiliaries!

It was not quite the end of the affair when Topaz was safely restored to the great ape house. One week later she began to show signs of itchiness on her arms and chest, and I found that she had broken out in a very fine rash. At first I thought it was an allergic reaction to something she had eaten; but tests showed that she had contracted the mange parasite from the camels. Topaz had scabies. She was not very pleased when it was her turn to be thoroughly lathered and bathed in the special shampoo every few days but, as I told her, picking up such complaints is the sort of thing that a chimpanzee has got to learn to expect when she embarks on a career as a zoo vet.

Chapter Eleven

FROM THE vast room's high ceiling, tattered strips of red velvet wallpaper hung down in rows like Tibetan prayer flags. In the centre of the floor stood a full-length billiard table lit by hooded lights and with a small Capuchin monkey curled up asleep on the green baize over the spot reserved for the blue ball. The air was heavy with an aroma of mothballs, Cologne water, Capuchin monkey and sheer age. A velvet-covered sofa was drawn up before the deep, broad hearth where a cheap electric fire's single bar glowed dully amid gently waving cobwebs.

On the sofa reclined Mrs Crabbe. A Singer sewing machine and a large pile of Tetley teabags were on a card table nearby. She had been neatly stitching two lines across the middle of each teabag and then separating the halves with a snip of her scissors when we arrived. Renowned in the town for 'having nowt to learn about making brass go a long way', Mrs Crabbe was worth half a million and found it easy to stay that way. Two stools, low and wooden like milking stools, were placed before her and slightly to one side to avoid blocking the feeble heat from the fire. On one sat Dr Aspinall, Doctor of Medicine, humans for the treatment of, and on the other sat I, Doctor of Veterinary Medicine, physician to the countless other living things on this planet that Dr Aspinall was not concerned with. Dr Aspinall and I both held a liqueur glass brimming with a thick yellow liquid. Mrs Crabbe had a firm grasp on a tumbler filled with the same stuff. Dr Aspinall and I sat in silence, glumly sipping the sickly Advocaat from time to time. Mrs Crabbe gulped large mouthfuls at frequent intervals while giving us an imperious dressing-down.

Over eighty, small and wiry, with hennaed hair and a face thickly powdered with what looked like flour, the old lady was not having any nonsense. It was the first time Aspinall or I had met her, but like every Rochdalian we had heard much about the history of this remarkable woman. Widow of the Crabbe who expanded the Crabbe cotton textile mills into the largest family concern west of the Pennines, she had chased over the moors on foot, following the Rochdale Hunt, until well into her seventies; with one swipe of a lacrosse stick she had broken the arm of a canvasser who had imprudently distributed Labour Party leaflets to her gardeners; and she had literally closed down a Methodist chapel of which she was the patroness and main financial support when the new young minister had professed a belief in evolution. Since her spouse had abruptly expired while doing the hokey-kokey at a Masonic function twenty years before, Mrs Crabbe had soldiered on in the great black stone house, served faithfully by a small staff, the youngest of whom, referred to as 't' gardener's lad', could not have been more than ten years younger than his mistress. Time creaked along in the house set on the moor edge above the chimneys of the family mills that filled the narrow valley below with smoke. House and inhabitants were slowly grinding to a halt. Essentials were attended to. Non-essentials were not. The brass knobs and knockers bearing the ornate 'C' were crusty with verdigris, the Victorian wood and ironwork were dull. The kitchen, which six nights a week had handled the victualling of a gaggle of mill owners, Conservative Party notables, parsons and their wives, lay cold and dank, its shelves empty but for Weetabix and Ovaltine. The garden, once trim and spruce, was regaining a wild beauty and making for the moorland. The cellar, though, was full – not, as in years gone by, with crusted port and well-bred clarets but with rack upon rack of Advocaat. Mrs Crabbe doted, depended, survived upon egg-flip. Therein lay the problem, for both Dr Aspinall and myself.

It was actually by pure coincidence that the doctor and I had driven up to the house at precisely the same moment. We had parked our cars on the circle of cobbles through which a forest of vigorous weeds was thrusting six inches high, greeted one another – Aspinall had stitched me up once and I had treated some of his sheep-farmer patients who had picked up orf virus from their flocks – and knocked on the imposing front door.

'D'ye think we've been called to see the same patient?' Aspinall chuckled as we waited.

'Hope not,' I said. 'Apparently the old lady's got a monkey. What are you here for?'

'Mrs Crabbe herself.' He sighed heavily. 'This is my first visit. She's a private patient, just switched to us from Landau's practice. I can't say I'm over-enthusiastic. She's a bit of a tartar by all accounts. She led Dr Landau a hell of a dance and would never take his advice.'

The door opened at last with much groaning of hinges to reveal a bad-tempered crone in high button-boots. She showed us into the room where Mrs Crabbe was treadling furiously away at the suturing of teabags. The whirring of the machine continued until the old lady had bisected several rows of bags to her satisfaction, then she stretched out on the sofa, protectively nestling two bottles of Advocaat in the crook of one arm and surveying us unblinkingly over the tilted brim of her glass. Breaking the ice, I suggested that I wait outside while Dr Aspinall did his stuff. I had already spotted my patient slumbering soundly on the billiard table.

Mrs Crabbe emptied the glass, looked from one to the other of us dolefully, slowly passed a furry tongue across thin lips and then reached for one of her bottles. Without speaking she leaned sideways, felt under the sofa and produced two liqueur glasses. These she filled before replenishing her own glass. Eventually she addressed us in loud and plummy tones.

'Sit down there, both of you. Take a glass. And listen.'

We did as we were told.

'Let me make myself clear,' she continued. 'Ethel, my housekeeper, let you in at the front door. You came to the *front door.*' She uttered the words 'front door' like Edith Evans as Lady Bracknell referring to 'a *handbag*' in *The Importance of Being Earnest.* 'The front door is never opened. I want that clearly understood. In future please remember to use the tradesmen's entrance.'

Dr Aspinall and I cowered on our stools. Mrs Crabbe downed half her tumbler and made a gargling noise.

'Now then.' The old lady's plumminess was sounding distinctly over-ripe. 'I take it you are the two doctors. Are you going to look first at Thoth?' She turned her head briefly towards the sleeping monkey.

'I'm here to see you, Mrs Crabbe,' said Aspinall bravely. 'I'm Dr Aspinall, your new doctor. I've come to give you a check-up and . . .'

'Who's that, then?' interrupted Mrs Crabbe, pointing accusingly towards me and snatching a deep swig that emptied the tumbler.

'Er – I'm the vet. To see the monkey. You rang, I believe.' I smiled reassuringly.

She kept her pointing finger firmly in position and frowned intently. Her dark, deep-sunken eyes bored into me. 'You're Dr Aspinall then. What do you know about monkeys?'

Aspinall groaned and put down his glass. 'Mrs Crabbe, if I might explain, Dr Taylor is here to see your monkey and I'm here to . . .'

Mrs Crabbe's imperious finger swung instantly round, aiming at the unfortunate Aspinall. 'Ah, I see,' she interrupted effortlessly. 'You're his assistant. Quite right. Good. Must have the best for poor Thoth there. Now you may examine him. But don't hurt him, mind. You, Dr Taylor' – she was speaking to my companion – 'hold him gently. Watch what Dr Aspinall does. I've heard he's got quite a way with monkeys.'

I looked at the doctor and he stared helplessly at me. It was perfectly plain that the old battleaxe was suffering from a combination of the passage of time and a surfeit of egg-flip. I raised my eyebrows and bit on the edge of my liqueur glass. With a sharp crack a crescent of glass broke off the rim and dropped from my lips onto the carpet.

'Really, Dr Landau!' barked Mrs Crabbe. 'That's Waterford. Fifteen and sixpence if I'm not mistaken. I shall deduct it from your bill at the end of the quarter.'

Dear God, I thought as I dabbed my bleeding lip with my handkerchief, quarters! What I needed was clients who paid cash or at least promptly after receiving one of Shelagh's monthly accounts.

Aspinall shrugged and rolled his eyes. I tried once more. 'But you sent for the doctor yourself,' I explained. 'Wouldn't it be better if Dr Aspinall – he – your own human doctor examined you elsewhere while I attended to the monkey, to Thoth?'

The old lady grunted indignantly. 'Certainly not. Examined by your assistant, Doctor? What are things coming to? No, sir. You must see to my poor Thoth first, then you can take a look at me and see about my little problem.'

'But, Mrs Crabbe, he is your doctor.'

'Doctor? Doctor? Is he or isn't he a veterinarian, qualified to work with monkeys?'

'No, madam, he isn't, but . . .'

'Quite so.' She squeezed out a stern smile. 'I don't mind him assisting you, Dr Aspinall, while he learns, but I couldn't possibly allow him to treat Thoth alone.'

'I'm the veterinarian, Dr Taylor,' I half-shouted in exasperation.

'Of course you are, Doctor,' she said quietly. 'That's why I called you. And I've every faith in you.'

'Tell you what – why don't you look at the monkey and get that part over with?' Aspinall sounded strangely faint. He stood up and stared intently at the peeling ceiling.

I walked over to the billiard table and looked down at the monkey. 'What's been worrying you about Thoth, Mrs Crabbe?' I asked.

'It's his teeth, Doctor. They seem to be giving him a bit of trouble. He drools and holds his face and is easily offended.'

'Offended?'

'Yes. For example, old Fairbanks, my solicitor, looked at

159

Thoth in a wrong sort of way the other day and Thoth bit his ear.'

'How long have you had him, Mrs Crabbe?'

'Oh, at least forty-five years.'

I gasped. Forty-five years was a sensationally long life-span for a Capuchin monkey.

'Forty-five years for sure?' I asked.

'At least. Possibly longer. He was ever such a smart young fellow when my late husband was in short trousers. I remember his father before him.'

'He was bred round here, you mean?'

Mrs Crabbe slopped a thick stream of Advocaat into the tumbler again. Taking a mouthful, she closed her eyes and seemed to be thinking deeply. 'I think not, Doctor,' she said eventually. 'His family originated in Rhodesia or Nyasaland or somewhere like that.'

'Thoth? He's a South American species, not African, Mrs Crabbe.'

'What are you talking about, Doctor? Old Fairbanks' parents lived in Bulawayo as near as I can recall. Fine stock.'

A muffled choking noise came from the direction of my medical colleague. I dared not look round at him.

'How long have you had Thoth, Mrs Crabbe?' I persevered.

'Nearly ten years now. He's never had a day's illness. You may wake him up if you like.'

I tickled the little creature at the back of his head and, remembering Fairbanks' luck, put on an expression of which the monkey would approve when he opened his eyes. He awoke immediately and glared at me. Then, baring his teeth, he crawled off awkwardly and stuck both legs in a corner pocket. I looked at him carefully. He was an ugly specimen, with a swollen, punch-drunk boxer's face and lips bulging over an upper jaw that seemed too big for his mouth. No, ugly was not a fair word to use. His whole face was deformed. There was no symmetry to it and all the features were askew. Its bones were lumpy and seemed to be trying to press out through the skin.

I approached the Capuchin warily and put out a hand. He pulled himself out of the pocket and shuffled on his knees across the green surface of the table. Now I could see that not only his face but the whole of his puny body was totally deformed. With grotesquely bowed limbs and sunken ribs, this monkey was a hunchback, a miniature Quasimodo. I went after him, grabbed him swiftly behind the neck and with one hand swept his arms behind him into a full nelson. He gibbered infuriatedly but was not able to reach me with his teeth. Gently I put him down onto the floor and released him. The distorted little body dragged itself like a wounded beetle across the dusty carpet. It was not walking. Its feet were redundant. It was crawling, slithering, hauling itself along on elbows and knees.

'Has he always moved like this?' I asked, dismayed.

'Always,' came the reply. 'Why? Capuchin monkeys always walk like that, as you should know, Doctor. Have you ever seen a nicer specimen? It's just those teeth, those naughty peggy-wegs that bother him.'

Quite often I had come across owners, pet-shop dealers, folk who claimed to know a bit about monkeys, who really believed that Capuchins and other New World species such as woolly and spider monkeys naturally haul themselves about in this bizarre and pitiable manner. As a student I had heard zoo men declare that such a way of moving was a classic characteristic of a group of primates who spent their entire lives high in the forest canopy and whose legs as a result were as obsolescent as the human appendix.

I picked the monkey up again, immobilised him in the full nelson and lifted his upper lip. Mrs Crabbe was quite right: Thoth had a mouthful of tooth problems. Looking in, I saw a scene of utter shambles as if a miniature grenade had exploded between the jaws and blasted every tooth out of its foundations. The teeth were there OK but apart from that everything was most definitely not OK. There were teeth growing down from the middle of the roof of the mouth, under the tongue, in clusters one on top of another, three or four abreast struggling to occupy a socket meant for a single one. There were teeth doing their own thing – growing upside down with their roots just visible and their

161

crowns buried deep in the gum, some pointing in towards the tongue, others taking the opposite direction and burrowing into the cheeks.

'Look at this, Doctor,' I said. Aspinall was still studying the ceiling.

'Yes, young man,' said Mrs Crabbe. 'Go and give Dr Taylor a hand and learn something. You'll never be much of a monkey vet if you moon about like that.'

As if in a trance the doctor quietly obeyed.

'SAPD – South American Primate Disease, worst case I've ever seen,' I whispered. 'Malnutrition essentially. Head bones soften while the teeth are developing, letting them drift off into any old place. Ribs cave in. I'm surprised he's not dead long ago with pneumonia. I'll probably find half a dozen pathological fractures in his limbs if I X-ray him.'

The doctor nodded. A more complex and dramatic disease, it nevertheless has some of the features of human rickets.

162

'What does Thoth eat?' I asked, although I had a pretty shrewd idea – sugary junk with minimum protein and hardly a vitamin.

Mrs Crabbe was silent.

Right, I thought. 'Grapes, bananas, chocolates, sweeties, cakes, biscuits, apples, oranges, sugar lumps, tea, fruit drinks – that's the sort of thing he has, isn't it, Mrs Crabbe?' I inquired confidently.

'No, Dr Aspinall. Definitely not.' Mrs Crabbe's voice was distinctly plummier. 'Thoth has what I have. None of that rubbish you mention. He's got a very sweet tooth and I see he gets plenty of nourishment.'

'What exactly, Mrs Crabbe?' There seemed to be a bleat of desperation in my voice.

'Good wholesome food.'

'Yes, but what exactly? In the wild these monkeys get very high levels of protein including animal protein, minerals and a massive daily intake of vitamin D_3. Does he get meat, chicken, vitamins, cereals as well as vegetables?'

'He gets eggs.'

'That's good. What else?'

'Eggs.'

'And?'

'Eggs in the most nourishing form.'

Light dawned. Of course – the Advocaat.

'Does he drink the egg-flip, Mrs Crabbe?' I asked.

'Of course. I do. It's what keeps me as fit as I am. So does Thoth. It has eggs – there's a whole meal in eggs, Doctor – sugar for energy and grape spirit. It's first-rate stuff.'

'What else does he get, Mrs Crabbe?'

'What else? Nothing else. What else would one need, sir? Advocaat's a perfect diet. Tell me any other monkey you know that's so well cared for. Advocaat's not cheap, you know.'

I lifted Thoth back onto the billiard table and returned to my stool. 'Mrs Crabbe,' I said, picking my words carefully, 'you're killing Thoth. Advocaat is an atrocious diet. He's a cripple because of it. He's deformed because of it. His chest is collapsing because of it.'

The old lady stared at me in stunned amazement.

I went on, 'I can't undo all the damage you've done, but with a little luck I can help him. Maybe he'll walk again for the first time in years. But no more Advocaat for him, ever again. From now it's going to be meat, chicken, milk, nuts, cereals, fruit and daily vitamins and calcium. I want you to have a run built for him outside so that he can get direct sunlight with its ultra-violet light. As for medicine, I'm going to give him some stuff called Sterogyl – an ampoule now and another in three weeks. You understand?'

Mrs Crabbe poured herself another tumbler of the yellow cream and glowered at me. Then she muttered acidly, 'Very well, Dr Aspinall, but I hope you know what you're doing. However, I have decided that I do not need you to examine me. I'll do very well, thank you.' She fussed pettishly with the hem of her dress.

'But there's your doctor.' I pointed at Aspinall. It was starting again.

'I will certainly not be handled by your assistant, Doctor.'

Admitting defeat in the battle of words, I took an ampoule of Sterogyl out of my bag, broke it and poured the alcoholic solution of vitamin D down Thoth's mouth. A connoisseur of booze, he seemed to relish the change of liquor.

'That's me done,' I said. 'Now I'll leave you with Dr Aspinall. I can assure you he's an excellent doctor.' I made for the door.

'Come back,' boomed the plummy voice as I put my hand on the knob. 'Very well then, have your way with a poor old lady. Get on with your examination. After all, Thoth seemed to like you. But please ask this animal doctor friend of yours to leave the room while I undress.'

I turned the door-knob and kept going.

Three weeks later I revisited the black stone house. There was no sign of Dr Aspinall this time. Again I banged on the front door. After four or five minutes I heard someone come to the door, the letter box was flapped open and the housekeeper's tetchy voice told me to find the tradesmen's entrance. It was a sunny day and I was in a good mood so I walked round to the back of the house.

In the billiard room something dark brown and chirruping darted about the floor. It was Thoth. Mrs Crabbe, reclining on the sofa, greeted me with a charming smile and asked me to sit next to her. There was no sign of Advocaat bottles anywhere.

'Dr Landau, how nice to see you,' she murmured, taking me by the hand. 'Now do please have a little of this.' She reached under the sofa as before and pulled out a bottle of dark red liquid. Two glasses followed, a sherry size for me and the tumbler for her. She poured out the Buckfast Tonic Wine.

'Not drinking Advocaat, I see,' I said, toasting her.

'Oh dear me no, not since that nice Dr Taylor was here the other week. He gave me a thorough examination and said that I was short of protein, vitamins, roughage and heaven knows what else in my diet. He made me have steak and fish every day. Vitamin pills, too. I feel marvellous. I might even consider getting married again.' She gave me a roguish wink. 'Yes, Dr Taylor said that having the Advocaat and not much else to eat was giving me these dizzy spells and cracked lips. Anyway, I mustn't go on about me. You've come to see Thoth, haven't you, Dr Landau?'

Though still grossly mis-shapen, Thoth was indeed a different monkey. He was using his legs, walking and even running for short distances. He looked happier and more energetic. His pugilist's face had softened, the lumpy bones were not as prominent. The progressive collapse of his skeleton had been halted, though he would be scarred for life. It was a dramatic change that I had seen many times before in such cases. Now, with the jaws firmer and less likely to shatter as I pulled with my tooth forceps, I could begin sorting out the jumble of teeth in his mouth. Thoth was going to need at least three sessions of dental surgery under general anaesthetic.

'Isn't it absolutely wonderful, Doctor?' said Mrs Crabbe. 'A miracle in three weeks. I'd never have believed it. But what about the toothache?'

I explained the next stages of treatment, gave the monkey another ampoule of Sterogyl and inquired how well Thoth had taken to his proper, teetotal diet.

'Have a close look at the billiard table, Dr Aspinall,' commanded Mrs Crabbe.

I looked. The six net pockets had been lined with pieces of newspaper. One had been filled with chopped hard-boiled egg, another with peanuts, a third with dates and raisins and so on. Each pocket contained some item of suitable food. One was even brimming with shiny, writhing mealworms, a fine Capuchin delicacy. A crystal bowl of milk stood on the pink spot and a matching piece containing vitaminised water was on the yellow spot.

'First-rate,' I said.

'Now before you go, Dr Taylor,' beamed Mrs Crabbe, 'just have a little drop more of this most wholesome wine and tell me what you think about this rheumatic joint of mine.'

She began unbuttoning her dress before I could say a word.

The balanced diet and the Sterogyl continued to transform Thoth. Under anaesthetic I extracted all the rogue teeth and left him with a small but adequate set. At last the time came for my final visit. Thoth now had his outside run built onto the billiard room. As far as I could see he was on the wagon, and seemed to relish his mixed diet and his new-found ability to exercise with gusto. He did not drool, showed no sign of pain in his mouth and was altogether more amiable. He had not drawn another drop of human blood and did not seem to care how you looked at him. Apart from his physical improvement, I assumed that his mind was enjoying a certain clarity of thought after ten years of toping; Thoth the easily offended had probably been the equivalent of the bellicose bar-fly.

Mrs Crabbe, on the other hand, had quickly dispensed with Dr Aspinall's diet and was subsisting on voluminous quantities of the tonic wine which, as she said, had the added spiritual dimension to its nutritive qualities of 'having the church behind it'. Naturally her dizzy spells had reappeared.

'Thank you for everything, dear Dr Aspinall,' she said thickly when I told her that Thoth, though hardly a show specimen, should get along fine if she stuck to the diet. 'Now before you go, there's something I want you to have. Follow me.'

I followed her uncertain path through the corridors of the old house, up a wide staircase of orange marble where our steps raised puffs of dust and sent balls of fluff rolling like tumbleweed, and through rooms smelling like mushroom farms. Eventually we came to a small boxroom that was empty save for an enormous, rust-encrusted safe.

Rocking slightly on her heels, Mrs Crabbe brought forth a large key from her décolletage and with much difficulty found the keyhole.

'Now, Dr Landau,' she puffed. 'Please turn the handle for me and pull open the door.'

I twisted the heavy brass lever and heaved against the protesting stiffness of the old hinges. The door gradually yielded and came open.

Mrs Crabbe stepped forward and started sorting through a heap of trays and boxes. It was a stupendous sight: dull gold rings by the score; old-fashioned pendants and earrings heavy with succulent emeralds and rubies as big as damsons; dusty tiaras which burst into diamond flame as the old lady blew winey breath over them; the baubles of Freemasonry, the tie-pins, signet rings, seals, swizzle-sticks, cuff-links, loving cups, heirlooms of the Crabbes; silver presentation salvers from the mills; gold fobs from Victorian Crabbes; sapphire souvenirs from Edwardian cruises long forgotten.

'In here I have something specially for you, my dear Doctor,' she whispered as she rooted about.

It was as exciting as Christmas morning. What was she going to bestow on me? Some nugget, some pea-sized diamond of the first water that had belonged to old Crabbe? I could not see anything that was not worthy a tidy sum. How very unprofessional, a little voice chivvied inside me. How bloody marvellous, breathed another.

At last Mrs Crabbe appeared to have found what she was looking for. She withdrew a lumpy, brown paper bag, about the size of two clenched fists. 'There,' she said, giving me the bag, 'and thank you so much, Dr Landau. Please also thank your assistant, Dr Taylor.'

We retraced our steps with me clutching my present and my mind whirling. The bag weighed about one pound, I guessed, but its lumpy shape mystified me. Precious stones, gold dust, an assortment of jewellery, watches? I could hardly wait to get outside to my car and look inside. Anyway, I thought, as I shook hands at the door (tradesmen's entrance), from what I've seen of the safe's treasures, whatever it is it's bound to be fabulous.

Jumping into the car, I opened the bag and looked inside. Beneath a scrap of paper, on which was scribbled in pencil 'To Doctor Aspinall, the best vet in the world, with grateful thanks from Thoth', lay seven or eight plump, fresh tomatoes, undoubtedly not long picked from the greenhouses behind the big black stone house.

'Where did you get these from?' asked Shelagh, as she sliced the tomatoes that evening and mixed them with slivers of raw mushrooms and onion to make my favourite salad.

'Well, love, in a nutshell,' I explained, 'from treating the monkey of an old lady who thinks I do wonders for her rheumatism and whose doctor is a dab hand at . . . oh, forget it – it's so confusing that I'm not quite sure who I am anyway.'

My wife gave me a curious look and kept on slicing. Stephanie and Lindsey, drawing at the kitchen table, looked at each other then raised their eyes to the heavens at this further evidence of the mysterious behaviour of grown-ups.

Dotty and befuddled Mrs Crabbe may have been, but she justified the townsfolk's opinion of her canny attention to all matters financial. Months later, when my bill was settled, she faithfully deducted exactly fifteen shillings and sixpence.

It was not long after my encounter with Thoth that I found myself sitting on a Derbyshire hillside one freezing winter's afternoon, cradling my dart-rifle.

Whereas America has its Big-foot and the Himalayas

168

their Yeti, not forgetting Scotland's own *Nessiteras rhombop-teryx* as Sir Peter Scott so precipitately named her, the English have to make do with the more mundane monsters which are reported every six months or so in the newspapers and are usually identified as pumas, or, less frequently, lions. Regularly these large felines are spotted by ostensibly sober members of the community in the suburbs of Birmingham or on the village green at Wormwood Magna. 'I was hoeing the radishes one evening when this mountain lion walked out of the privet hedge and jumped over the fence into next door's garden,' affirms a worthy citizen, or 'I glanced out of the loo window of the bingo hall and there was this puma mooching round the dustbins.' Occasionally in mud or snow, Footprints are Found, which the 'local naturalist' pronounces as those of no animal known to science. The constabulary wearily assure the townsfolk that they are checking all zoos and circuses in the vicinity just in case no-one noticed that one of the big cats had not shown up at roll call. The story hangs around in the papers for up to a week and then, no doubt tiring of the humdrum series of brief encounters with postmen, gardeners, schoolboys and late-night strollers, the beast clears off and lies low for a few months, to re-appear as sure as fate miles away.

I often marvel at the certainty with which folk whose knowledge of the jungle is limited to admiring the Town Hall palms will cry wolf (or tiger, or puma) when a twitching brown tail is spied vanishing into a thicket three hundred yards away. Sadly, lions no longer roam wild in England, bears and wolves became extinct more recently and, unlike the Scots, we cannot boast even one wild cat in our forests. The mystery pumas are almost invariably big dogs enhanced by the unreliability of the human eye, a fertile imagination, alcohol or fabrication.

The 'puma' which surfaced that January in Derbyshire, fifty miles south of Rochdale, was bothering the inhabitants of a little town set on a hillside criss-crossed with limestone walls. The beast had been seen by the schoolmaster, several farmers and various other people. It was exactly three feet to eight feet long, a minimum of four feet to six feet high at the shoulder and was variously black, dark brown, gingery and light yellow. It was known to have a long tail or none at all, showed no signs of timidity or shot off at the slightest sound, and ate remarkable quantities of other people's chickens, cats, pet rabbits, dustbin waste and garden-pond goldfish. I was asked to go over with a dart-rifle and join in a concerted hunt by police, RSPCA men, journalists and small boys.

Apart from the cold, the weather was good for puma hunting. I was being paid well for a leisurely stroll over fine countryside, and was confident that I would end up by tea-time, when the exercise was due to end, feeling as fit as a fiddle and without having seen anything more wild than a hare. There are wild wallabies living and breeding successfully in the Derbyshire heather; they are rarely spotted but I reckoned that the 'puma', if it existed at all, was probably one of them.

The local village constable organised the sweep of the countryside very efficiently. He had plotted the most recent sightings on a map and when I arrived was distributing walkie-talkies, maps and thermos flasks of tea. He lined us up and announced the Orders of the Day as if he was sending us in after Bonnie and Clyde. Off we set, and I soon found myself alone on the hillside, pushing through beds of dripping bracken with the wind making my cheeks tingle. When I was almost at the top of the main ridge and could look down at the streets of glistening grey slate roofs, I was told over the walkie-talkie to find a sheltered spot by one of the moorland walls and wait. The constable had deployed his posse in a circle enclosing hundreds of acres. I was the centre point of that circle and the order to beat inwards would now be given.

Squatting on a dry stone out of the wind, I passed the time outstaring the curious sheep that had gathered to inspect me. The object of our game was to see who blinked first. I could not see any of the other searchers although I could hear the constable chivvying his right flank, his left flank and his centre with the authority of Rommel making a dash for Tobruk. There was no doubt, I thought, that before long the complete bunch of hunters would find themselves on top of me, puma-less.

The sheep got bored with me and resumed grazing. Suddenly I heard my name called urgently over the walkie-talkie. I took in the astounding message that came crackling over the air in the excited voice of the village constable: 'Dr Taylor, Dr Taylor, hold your position. Animal sighted coming in your direction.'

I looked hurriedly around and pressed in against the dry-stone wall. My heart began to beat rapidly with excitement. The beast existed and was on its way! I still could not see any of the men and there was no sign of the monster. I carefully checked that the safety catch on the dart-gun was securely in the 'off' position. When the man-eating minotaur or whatever it was breathed fire down my earhole I did not want a repetition of what had happened once when I was called to recapture an escaped axis deer in Sussex. After hours of painstaking stalking, its keepers had driven it so that it stood, a perfect target, only a few feet away from a special camouflaged hide in which I lurked, peering out through a tiny hole. I had aimed, pulled the trigger of the dart-gun and heard that depressing 'clunk' which means that the safety catch is on. Like lightning the deer had leapt off, startled by the 'clunk' and far too rapidly to let me put my mistake right by flicking the dratted catch. No axis deer had been retrieved that embarrassing day.

Now I was certain my gun was in fighting condition. There was a new compressed-air cylinder in the chamber, a syringe loaded with enough phencyclidine to clobber a grizzly bear was up the spout and the safety catch was most definitely off.

The walkie-talkie crackled again. 'Dr Taylor, Dr Taylor, keep down, keep down. Animal seen still coming your way, approximately quarter of a mile from you. Other side of your wall. Running at present time parallel to wall.'

If they had been able to identify the creature, no-one had bothered to tell me. I decided not to talk back in case it was frightened off. At this point, quite honestly, I felt a trifle apprehensive. I had tangled with big cats many times in zoos and in Africa, but under controlled conditions. Still, I

171

thought, the poor whatever-it-was was probably scared to death. Escaped zoo big cats never enjoy life on the run and appear positively relieved once they are back in their own territory, among sights and sounds they know, with warm beds and regular meals.

The difficulty I faced now was knowing when to stand up and look over the wall. Too soon or too late could obviously be disastrous. The wall was too well built to have any chinks in it. The trusty constable solved the problem almost at once. 'Dr Taylor, Dr Taylor, animal now one hundred yards approximately to your left. Still running parallel to wall.'

He said nothing about speed or range from the wall. My mind raced. I would have only a few seconds in which to stand up, aim and fire after taking into account the wind, which might deflect the bulky dart, and the low temperature, which affected the gas pressure and consequently the maximum range of my weapon. Whatever it was, I would aim for the middle of the target. That would give me some latitude for error. I had fitted my shortest barbed needle, so

that no matter what the creature or virtually where I hit it, there was the smallest risk of the needle entering a major body cavity. I would swing the gun round with the movement of the animal, assuming it was still running. I do not like using the dart-gun on moving targets, but that way I might have least risk of a bounce-off.

The nettle must be grasped at once. I stood up and rammed my rifle over the wall. Twenty feet away, slightly to my left and going at a steady pace, loped a tawny creature which at first sight looked dramatically like the Hound of the Baskervilles.

The beast that had been blamed in the locality for every sort of misdeed, with the possible exception of the spate of obscene phone calls that was also occupying the constable's busy life, was a long lanky Great Dane. Looking closer, I saw it was in terrible shape. Scurfy skin was stretched tight over its prominent skeleton, its sides were disfigured with numerous red scars and L-shaped wounds where wire and thorns had left their marks, the eyes were sunk and desperate and ropes of glutinous saliva speckled with soil hung from the slack lips. It was an animal that must have been out on the run for weeks if not months, and it was easy to see from the slight sway of its hindquarters that it was coming to the end of the road.

All the same, my sudden emergence like a jack-in-the-box produced a surge of alarm and determination in the dog. Its eyes bulged with the effort as it strained for more speed and veered away from me. I looked down the gun barrel, made my split-second assessment of wind and likely trajectory and fired. The dart flew strong and straight – straight the back of the Great Dane. It thwacked impotently into a tussock fifteen yards away, the dog vanished over a rise in the ground and I shouted unrepeatable epithets at the regathering sheep. You never get a second chance in such cases.

It was a very subdued marksman who shortly afterwards explained to the constable and his troops what had happened. They took it very politely and we started another, rather half-hearted hunt. By late afternoon there had not even been another sighting of the dog and we were about

173

to call it a day when an amazing piece of good news came up from the town: the Great Dane had dashed into a timber yard and someone had had the good sense to close the yard gates. It was holed up behind a pile of wood and was in a mean mood.

Somewhat cheered by this turn of events, I went down to the yard with the constable and some of his men. Distressed and terrified, the animal crouched behind a pile of wood, obviously prepared to go down fighting. It was snarling and snapping in earnest, and no-one dared go near it. There was no way I could find to get a shot at the dog other than from directly in front, but with the way it was barking and moving its head, and with its emaciated frame presenting no expanses of muscle from that angle, I was afraid that the dart might hit the head. Even hungry animals like this one are not always easy to knock out by drugging meat, but I sent a boy to the nearest butcher's shop for a pound of pork sausages. When he came back with them I threw a couple to the dog, which swallowed them ravenously. Next I took a third sausage and carefully pressed it in the middle. The meat within the sausage skin compacted towards each end, leaving an inch of empty skin in the middle. Now, with a fine hypodermic needle passed through the sausage meat and into the empty space, I slowly injected a quantity of powerful narcotic. The sausage was now fixed and ready, with no smell and no taste. I tossed the Trojan Horse morsel to the wide-eyed dog. One gulp and it was gone. In eight minutes the poor creature was sound asleep and I could approach him to make a thorough examination which confirmed my earlier opinion. He must have been straying for a very long time and was suffering from malnutrition, multiple wounds, a grass awn embedded in the cornea of one eye and a tumour on the breast.

The owner was never traced but the story ended happily. Now no longer equipped with an operating room for domestic animals, I arranged with a colleague to hospitalise the wanderer, operate on his eye, remove the breast growth and generally tack him together. A good home was found for him by the RSPCA, and when I saw him a month

174

later he had become plump, glossy and relaxed on an intensive diet of steak, eggs, fish and milk – but no more sausages. And the would-be 'puma' nearly licked my hand off.

☆☆☆☆☆☆☆☆☆☆☆☆☆☆☆

Chapter Twelve

☆☆☆☆☆☆☆☆☆☆☆☆☆☆☆

O NE WAY Matt Kelly demonstrated his inborn zooman's skill brilliantly was in knowing exactly when it was safe to go into a cage or den with a seriously ill animal, even a dangerous one. He had an eye for picking the earliest moment when, providing I did what I was told, I might get away with injecting an ailing lion, lancing an abscess on the butt of a blood-poisoned and uncaring bear or snatching a quick feel of a tigress's swollen belly without losing a limb or my life in the process.

My first such venture was a David-in-the-leopard's-den episode involving a cat that had picked up the miserable running cold symptoms of feline influenza, no doubt from some mundane domestic puss who had wandered through the big cat house at night in search of stray morsels of meat. Feeling and looking just like a human on the first day of an acute attack of 'flu, the leopard lay in his cage, sneezing miserably, drooling ropes of saliva and blinking blearily through inflamed and watery eyes. I was most impressed when Matt produced his keys and unlocked the cage door.

'Oi think we can go in,' he said. 'Stick close behind me all the time.' I nodded. 'All the time,' Matt repeated as we crept warily through the door and closed it behind us.

The leopard sneezed, snuffled and snorted where he lay in the straw, but appeared not to notice us. 'Oi'm goin' to

176

grab his tail,' Matt whispered. 'Keep behoind me and jab your injection into it.' Tail injections in domestic animals are considered to be utterly beyond the pale, but in zoo animals one sometimes has to give thanks for whatever bit of the patient's anatomy the Good Lord provides. I had my syringe and needle full and ready.

Matt walked quietly over to the leopard, with me shadowing him a full six inches behind. Bending slowly down, he picked up the leopard's tail and pulled. The leopard, miserable as he was, just had to react to such provocation. Growling, he dug his claws through the straw into the wooden floor and glared back over his shoulder at his tormentors. Matt continued pulling. 'While he's like this, if oi keep pullin', he can't get his head round and into me,' he grunted.

Suddenly the grip of the leopard's claws on the floor gave way and the animal skidded back towards us. Angered now, he slewed his front half round and lashed out with his front claws. Matt continued to pull the tail and started to skip backwards. 'Oi've got to keep the tail at full stretch,' he said more loudly as I skipped backwards too, trying to match my footsteps with his to avoid our legs tangling and both of us tumbling over with an increasingly irate, probably headachy leopard on top.

Back we went and back came the cat. The more he struggled, the faster we went. As we came near a corner, we backed off at an angle. Our strange paso doble, or rather paso triple, continued round the cage. We just could not afford to let the leopard catch up with the end of his tail.

'Roight, now,' said Matt eventually, puffing with the exertion of the dance, 'reach round me and stick it in!'

It was not easy, tripping energetically backwards, with Matt's bulk blocking my view of the rear half of the spitting 'flu victim, to reach round and stick the hypodermic needle under the skin of the tail. I looked round Matt as we danced, chose my point and thrust forward my syringe. Matt's shoulder obstructed my line of sight again. I prodded blindly towards the position I had chosen. 'Bejasus,' yelled Matt, 'ye've jabbed me hand!'

Startled, I pulled back my needle. Luckily I had not

begun depressing the plunger, but the back of Matt's neck had gone the colour of smoked salmon.

'Again, again, try again,' he shouted testily, 'but for Gawd's sake look where ye're goin'.'

Still trotting backwards behind the now-sweating head keeper, I steadied myself with one arm round his waist, craned my neck awkwardly to the right, spotted the tail once more and launched a second attempt. This time I struck home and was greeted by the manhandled leopard with a throaty roar of outrage. 'Done,' I declared. 'What do we do now?'

'Keep goin' till we're next by the door,' replied Matt, 'then ye back out. Oi'll throw him forwards and follow ye.' It was our last circumnavigation of the cage. When I was in position I retreated from the dance floor and crashed with relief through the doorway. With a skilful flick of his strong wrists Matt threw the leopard forward and away from him. Before the animal had time to gather himself for a riposte,

Matt had joined me outside the cage and banged the door to.

Puffing, the head keeper wiped his forehead and sucked the red spot on his hand where I had punctured him. 'Not bad, young feller,' he said, 'not bad.' I was delighted. That 'not bad' from Matt was worth a thousand guineas to me. 'But ye'll have to practise your Oswaldtwistle Barn Dance.' He reminded me about it the following Christmas when, at the annual Belle Vue party, he took the floor for this English north country dance where partners go three by three. Not a bad dancer, Matt.

My successful injection of the fully conscious savage beast produced a euphoria which was to last all of twenty minutes. Walking back from the big cat house, Matt and I passed the ape house. In the sunlit open-air cage was a fit-looking three-year-old chimp with eyes as bright as buttons.

'Who's that?' I asked the head keeper.

'That's Lee, son of Katja and Robert, a grand little feller.'

I stood for a moment to admire the chimpanzees. Lee seemed positively entranced by me; his eyes never left me. Could it be, I thought in the afterglow of my feat of derring-do with the leopard, that he senses in me something of Dr Dolittle? Maybe I have got that special way with animals. Lee stared on. True, he did not seem to be quite catching my eye, but there was no doubt that something about me was riveting his attention.

I vaulted the metal barrier designed to stop the public from doing what I was about to do and went closer to the cage. My confidence knew no bounds. Lee continued to gaze adoringly at me but seemed to be fascinated by my chest rather than my face. The reason rapidly became clear as he pushed an arm through the bars of the cage and with a lightning-fast movement snatched at my shirt, an expensive pink one lightly embroidered with glossy whorls in light brown, of which I was rather fond. With one single, precise yank, he pulled the garment clean away from my body. I stood unhurt but dumbfounded, naked from the waist up. In the background the Irishman began to scoff loudly as Lee shuffled off to the back of the cage with his prize and tried it on for size. It was not a very good fit, but that did not seem to bother him at all.

'My shirt,' I exclaimed pointlessly. 'My shirt.'

'Ye've seen the last of that,' chuckled Kelly. 'All the tea in China couldn't get it away from him; oi've told ye before about goin' close to primate cages.' He had. One of the first lessons I had learned when walking along the narrow central corridor that divides the sleeping quarters of Belle Vue's monkey house was to keep dead on the middle line, or grey, brown, black or greenish little arms would snake out and pull my hair, give me a thick ear or steal any detachable object such as fountain pen or stethoscope. Now my shirt was very definitely Lee's. For long after you could still see the remains of it lovingly hoarded in his bed, fragmented and less recognizable, but Lee appeared to treasure it even more than I ever had.

I felt rather exposed setting off home half naked, as Matt grinned and said something to Len, the head ape keeper, about 'young boyos with more larnin' than sense'.

'Hello, Tarzan,' said Shelagh with a giggle as I walked into the kitchen, 'tea's ready.'

It would be wrong to give the impression that everything I attempted in the zoo fulfilled Matt's gloomy predictions by ending in disaster. Cracked toenails on elephants did well on the hoof oil I prescribed, and I had cleared a llama or two of lice – but Matt Kelly had been getting similar results on zoo animals before I was born. Maybe he had used automobile engine oil on the elephants' feet and simple flowers of sulphur to destroy the llamas' parasites, but they had worked almost as well and nearly as quickly as my up-to-date drugs. To break into the business properly and become a zoo vet in Matt's eyes I would have to do better than that. I consoled myself with the thought that the director, Ray Legge, seemed to appreciate my efforts. Perhaps it was because, as an aquarist, he too was learning in this hotch-potch of a captive jungle.

We learnt together on one emergency which happened on Matt Kelly's day off. Some mindless member of the public had thrown a ball of string over the wire into the big cat enclosure, and a puma had decided to play with it. It was fun! When he tapped it, it rolled along the grass. A thwack from a paw and it spun through the air. The puma pounced on it and gnawed it, pretending it was a rabbit that he had cleverly stalked and finally seized in one irresistible attack. The ball of string began to unravel. The big cat licked idly at the imaginary body of his prey and a loose end of string stuck to his tongue. All cats' tongues have harsh, abrasive upper surfaces on which prickly cells point backwards to help the animal lap up liquids efficiently. The puma continued licking when he felt the string in his mouth, and the movement of his tongue inevitably pushed it farther and farther backwards. Like the incurving fangs of a snake, the scales on the tongue provided a one-way ratchet, making it difficult if not impossible for the creature to spit out what had been taken in. The puma felt the string at the back of his throat and pawed vainly in an effort to dislodge the tickly thread. The string stayed put, so the puma started to lick and swallow to try to put an end to the irritation. The end of the string disappeared. The puma licked and swallowed. The unravelling ball of string became smaller as inch by inch it crept down the animal's gullet.

Ray Legge telephone me early in the morning. 'Will you come over and look at one of the young pumas? It's an odd case. There's one piece of string hanging out of the mouth and another from the anus.'

When I arrived at Belle Vue the position had not changed. Sure enough, the animal had about three inches of string dangling from one end and a slightly smaller length trailing from the other. Ray and I agreed that both bits of string looked very much alike and might well be one and the same piece. The puma was not bothering to lick at the fragment hanging from his lips and appeared perfectly healthy. The possibility that we were looking at two ends of a single piece had ominous undertones. Endless opportunities for trouble in the bowel were offered by such a foreign body. I would have to anaesthetize the animal.

Ray had designed a new cat house with special squeeze compartments where I could get to grips safely with my

181

patients, but it was not easy to entice the animal into the restraining device to give it a shot of anaesthetic. I made a mental note to order one of the new darting pistols that I had just heard were being produced in the United States. At last the puma was immobilized and I gave my anaesthetic. In ten minutes he was sleeping peacefully and we pulled him out into the passageway of the cat house so that I could examine him.

Kneeling down and concentrating on the puma, I made the cardinal error of forgetting about my rear when in a confined space flanked by caged animals. As I bent to give a gentle pull to the string hanging from the puma's jaws, a nearby leopard whipped its forepaw through the bars, dug a hooked claw deeply into my right ankle, anchoring itself behind my Achilles tendon, and tried to haul me into its cage. In agony I tumbled round and literally unpicked the tough hook of nail from my bleeding leg. Thank goodness Matt isn't here, was all I could think, I've fumbled it again.

Pausing to stick some of the penicillin cream normally used up cows' udders into my wound and bind it with gauze, I returned my attentions to the puma. Tugging the string at either end did not budge it a millimetre. I decided that it might not be wise to pull really hard; I was not sure why, but I felt that if the string did not slip conveniently out the force might do untold damage to the animal's insides. Besides, I still could not be certain that the two portions were not separate. 'I'll have to open him up,' I told Ray. 'I'll go into the abdomen first to find out how far the string extends and then maybe open the intestines.'

We carried the unconscious big cat on a wheelbarrow over to the dispensary and the operation was soon under way. I inspected the loops of bowel. Sure enough, I could feel the firm thread of string running right through the animal's alimentary canal.

'My hands are sterile – will you try pulling the string at the back end, Ray?' I asked. The zoo director pulled lightly at the puma's rear beyond the draped operation sheets, while I watched the effect on the exposed bowel loops. When Ray pulled, the intestines began to concertina together as if he were drawing the cord on a pair of unoccupied pyjamas. I told him to stop pulling at once. Any more of that and the string would begin to cut in to the delicate folded lining of the bowel tube. Thank God I had not tried brute force in extracting the string – it would have sliced open the intestines at a couple of dozen points. There was only one way. At six places between the duodenum and rectum I had to pierce the intestine wall, fish in for the string, cut it and then sew up the wall with waterproof stitching. At every second incision I pulled out the freed section of string after cutting it.

An hour later it was completed. The puma had six patches in his food canal and I had all the string. With his abdomen sewn up and pumped full of antibiotics to prevent peritonitis, the still-sleeping puma was wheeled back to his night house.

'Marvellous job,' said Ray, patting me on the back, 'really worthwhile.' Pity old Kelly wasn't there, I thought. Telling him tomorrow won't have the impact of the real thing.

Ten days later I took the stiches out of the recovered puma with Matt helping me to give the anaesthetic. 'You ought to have seen it, Matt,' I said proudly. 'String from end to end like a bunch of black puddings. Good thing I operated.'

Matt nodded and spat accurately at a drain. 'Pumas,' he said, 'pumas. Sure, they're a drug on the market. Dime a dozen these days. Makes me wonder if they're worth spendin' money on.'

Despite Matt's scepticism, my experience was beginning to extend beyond split toenails and lousy llamas. If there was the slightest chance of saving an animal's life Ray and I took it, and Matt was roped in to help as I fitted a custom-built wooden leg, complete with ingenious articulated foot, to a flamingo whose limb I had amputated because of gangrene; he held the bowl of water while I took casts of a newborn zebra foal's neck which had been bitten and broken by its father shortly after birth, and for which I designed a glass fibre support to keep the foal's head up while the bones healed. Times were gradually changing, and a major turning-point came the day I received through

183

the post from America my gas-powered dart-gun. What was more the drug company, Parke, Davis, had sent me a supply of a promising new drug, phencyclidine, to try out on zoo animals. Concentrated enough to be used in the dart-gun syringes, and said to be fast-acting, it gave me a new optimism about my future as a zoo vet.

I took my new toys over to Belle Vue to show Ray, but he was not in his office so I drove through the grounds to the animal kitchen. Walking into the room where the diets are made up, I found Matt standing at the sink shaving. The foamy lather from his face was dropping onto a tray of frozen sprats that were being thawed out for the penguins.

'Dear me, Mr Kelly,' I said sternly, 'what are you doing? It's hardly the right thing to do one's ablutions all over the animal food. The practice will have to stop at once.'

The stocky Irishman glared at me like an apoplectic Father Christmas, blew a few soapy bubbles but said nothing. He began rinsing the sprats. I went out, leaving the crestfallen Matt with half his beard still on. I grinned to myself when I was out of sight. A belated comeback, I thought; one point to me.

Now that I had a dart-gun and the new drug, I was all set to break for ever with the old days of impotent guesswork from the other side of the bars or the opposite bank of the moat. The use of tranquillizers in the food of zoo animals had not proved to be very reliable – most of the drugs then available were designed for humans and did not necessarily work on wild beasts. Anyway, the animals could not be guaranteed to take the pills ground up and mixed with their food, and if they did the stuff often got lost among the vast quantities of digesting material churning around in their stomachs and either produced no sign of sleepiness or did so hours later when we were long gone and in bed. The doses of human tranquillizers also had to be multiplied many times when administered to exotic animals, even small ones, and the thousands of pills that would be required for a biggy like an elephant made the whole business farcical. Ray Legge and I had also tried jabbing injections of dope into awkward animals like giraffe with syringes attached to the end of long poles, but it never really worked. We just broke a lot of needles and even more poles.

The first animals on which I tried my gun and phencyclidine were some wolves that Ray wanted to move from one lot of quarters to another within the zoo. Nervously I loaded a dozen darts and then, one after the other, fired them at the prowling animals. Plop, plop, plop. I learned how easy it was to hit shoulder, thigh or neck muscle. Within ten minutes all the wolves were asleep – we had never seen anything like it. The whole transfer was completed within half an hour. I went on to lions and then bears. Never a hitch, never a fatality. The drug was ideal on monkeys, chimps, gorillas. It kept the animals unconscious for about an hour and then wore off gradually over the next day or so. Phencyclidine appeared to be the universal bringer of dreams I had been seeking.

Then I hit the first snags. I lost my first elephant, Mary, after a long operation to remove a tooth with a root abscess; the prolonged period of recovery from phencyclidine in such a large creature resulted in fatal congestion of the lungs. I experimented on zebras needing emergency suturing of wounds. The phencyclidine put the animals down but the nightmares they seemed to experience, and the hours of frantic crashing about as the chemical faded slowly from their systems, were painful to witness. After one awful night spent with Matt Kelly in a straw-smothered loose box, soothing and struggling to hold down a lathered, wild-eyed zebra stallion that was coming round from a phencyclidine anaesthesia, I vowed never to use the drug again on equines. Fortunately, two newer drugs, xylazine and etorphine, would soon appear and prove the answer to doping zebra.

Although phencyclidine was first-class in bears, the polar bear was more sensitive to it than its cousins were and needed a much smaller dose to knock it out. It was my success in anaesthetizing polar bears at Belle Vue which led to my first piece of circus work. Billy Smart's Circus was at Prestwick in Scotland and had a male polar bear with the irritating condition common in these deceptive and highly

185

dangerous creatures, ulceration between the toes. Polar bears have lots of fur on their feet to insulate them against the cold ice and snow, but in captivity it often becomes matted between their toes into hard little balls. The balls act as foreign bodies and rub uncomfortably at the soft flesh on either side of them. Gradually ulcers are formed which attract fungus and other types of infection, and the accumulated hair balls must be cut out. The Smarts and I had met at the circus held every Christmas at Belle Vue, and they asked me to go up to Prestwick to dope the bear and clean up his feet.

I felt wildly elated as I drove back down from Scotland after darting in the phencyclidine and then taking my scissors and soothing ointments to the massive paws of the slumbering white giant. Zoo work is one thing; impressing the hard-bitten animal men of the circus world, who tend to have firm prejudices about veterinary matters, is another thing altogether. The Smarts had seemed very impressed with my fast, no-nonsense anaesthesia.

The gun and the new drugs could be the key to bringing veterinary help to circus animals as well, then, but the next patient on which I used it was back at Belle Vue. One morning Matt Kelly telephoned in a terrible flap; Ray Legge was away on holiday and he was acting zoo director. He sounded desperate yet resigned. 'Get down as soon as ye can, Doctor. It's an oryx cow. She's just calved and all her insoides are hangin' out. It looks very bad.'

Listening to Matt's brief description I could guess what had happened, but I did not waste time telling him about it over the telephone. I told him to keep the animal quiet, to cover the 'insoides' with a clean, moist sheet to keep them from becoming damaged or dirty, and to wait for me. Then I jumped into my car and set off for Manchester.

Matt's face was long and sombre as I walked into the oryx shed. I had never seen him looking so downcast. He did not bother to greet me but just announced bleakly, 'She's had it. No question. Oi've never seen such a mess in all me years as a zoo keeper.'

The Beisa oryx was lying on her side on a pile of straw,

her hind quarters draped in white sheeting stained with large fuzzy shadows of red. Under the sheet a bloody pink balloon of flesh, studded with purple cherry-like objects and as big as the animal's head and neck, lay on the straw. It was attached by a narrow neck to the vulva. As I had guessed, the oryx had calved and discharged the afterbirth; then the whole of the womb, with the ovaries attached, had turned inside out and fallen through the pelvis into the fresh air. The oryx's entire womb and associated structures had prolapsed and were lying on the ground for all to see.

'Just look at her,' continued Matt. 'She's had it, oi can tell ye that. No animal can survoive havin' all its insoides turned out. Fancy drugs and such can't help her!' He clicked his teeth agitatedly.

Uterine prolapse is fairly common in sheep and cattle and occasionally occurs spectacularly in sows. It is rarely seen in wild animals. This was the first time Matt or I had come across it in the zoo, but unlike him I knew what it was and had wrestled with many similar cases in farm animals. I decided to keep that to myself for the moment. 'Get some warm water and plenty of towels,' I instructed. Matt went out sighing.

As I went towards the oryx's head to examine her, she threatened me with her wicked straight horns which I had seen driven with accuracy through two-inch wood planking. I would have to dope her before tackling her hind end, although I could not be sure what the effect of phencyclidine would be on her four-stomach digestion. Matt watched while I also injected 10 cc of locl anaesthetic to paralyse her spinal cord and stop her straining by reflex action when I began to work. Next I thoroughly washed the exposed lining of the womb and its 'cherries', which were the attachment points of the calf's placenta, and picked off bits of straw and grime. 'Now then, Matt,' I said when it was clean, 'I want you to put a towelling sling under the womb and hold it clear of the ground to stop it getting dirty again.'

He took a towel, looped it under the flabby mess of raw flesh and lifted it off the straw. I coated the womb liberally with a sulphonamide antiseptic cream. Now for the tough bit. As the womb had fallen inside out, I had to replace it gently but firmly by rolling it inwards from the centre as if it were a plastic bag or woollen sock that was inside out. Womb walls are thick and spongy but easily punctured by too rough fingers, so I had to be extremely careful to use only the balls of my fingertips. Bit by bit the womb began to fold inwards. I kept lubricating it with obstetric cream. The size of the exposed womb began to decrease as I worked away with both arms groping in the oryx's pelvic canal.

Matt said nothing as he strained to hold the towelling up, and I knelt below him, concentrating, with my tongue stuck between my lips. At last, with a satisfying sucking noise, the last bit of the womb disappeared inside the vulva. I pushed it well forward inside the animal. Luckily I have a long arm with a smallish hand, ideal for this sort of obstetrical problem.

'Get me a milk bottle, Matt,' I said finally.

The head keeper broke his silence. 'A milk bottle? What for?'

'Get it please, and quick!' I replied sternly.

Matt dropped the towel and disappeared again. He came back with a milk bottle which, while he watched curiously, I disinfected with iodine soap. Then to his amazement I plunged my arm back inside the oryx's womb with the bottle held firmly by the neck. Using its blunt bottom as an extension to my arm, I made sure that the part of the womb beyond the reach of my fingers was folded back into its proper position. If I did not do that, the thing would be out again in no time. Withdrawing the milk bottle and still not explaining its function, or what indeed the whole business had been about, I finished off by putting a few clips into the vulva as a precaution. I would remove them after thirty-six hours. Done. The animal's colour, pulse and respiration were good.

I scrubbed my hands and arms and then turned to Matt. 'She'll be right as a clock by tonight,' I said. 'It was just a prolapsed uterus.'

Matt stared at the clean and tidy hind end of the oryx and cleared his throat. 'Incredible,' he said at last. 'Incredible. The foinest bit of work oi've ever seen in all me years. Oi take me hat off, Dr Taylor.'

That was some reward, coming from Matt. Better still, just as I had predicted, by evening the oryx was indeed as good as new, and I tried hard not to gloat as Matt and I stood watching her suckle her lusty calf.

The disease problems of primates, apes and monkeys, had always fascinated me, so I was stung by a remark by Ray Legge that medical doctors were by tradition more equipped to deal with such animals than veterinarians. I decided to embark on a study course in an attempt to prove him wrong and in the process to gain a Fellowship of the Royal College of Veterinary Surgeons. After a year and a half's hard work, sandwiching the studies in where I could between my day-to-day clinical work and attending postgraduate courses at the medical school in Manchester, I got my Fellowship, the first ever given where zoo animals were named as the speciality. Not only did my practice with great apes in particular now have a firm base, but through the study I had had to do at home for the Fellowship Shelagh was becoming increasingly involved with some of my simian patients.

Soon after I gained my Fellowship, Jane, a charming female orang-utan at Belle Vue, was pregnant for the first time. Then, with about two months still to go before her time was due, she suddenly had a miscarriage. A premature scrap of an orang infant was born dead one night.

The effect on Jane was remarkable and profound. All the other female orangs had live, healthy babies. She sat alone in a corner hugging the shrivelled corpse of her baby, trying in vain to make it suckle and whimpering in distress. I am not a sentimentalist prone to seeing the whole range of human emotions in animals, but when I first saw Jane after the miscarriage, I felt tears in my eyes. She was heartbroken. Try as we might we could not get her to give up the baby's body. I began to consider darting her with a sedative in order to remove it before it putrefied further. The distraught female would not touch food and she began to lose weight alarmingly.

I took Shelagh with me to the zoo when I finally decided to knock Jane out and take the infant cadaver. We went into

the isolation room where Jane sat pitifully in a large cage. Shelagh looked at the orang and the orang looked at her. I saw her eyes fill. Matt and I stood silently.

'Before you try darting,' said Shelagh suddenly, 'I want to go in with her.'

My wife was asking to go in with a full-grown orang that was undoubtedly in a disturbed and unpredictable mood.

'I mean it,' she said. 'Open the door please, Mr Kelly.'

Matt started to speak but I interrupted him. 'OK,' I said. 'Open it, Matt.'

Matt undid the lock and cautiously swung open the barred door. Shelagh climbed into the cage and on hands and knees crawled straight over to Jane. When she reached the orang, she at once began talking to the animal in soothing low tones. 'What's the matter, love?' she murmured. 'I know all about it. Come on, put an arm round me.' On and on she talked, with the orang looking straight into her face. Shelagh sat down beside Jane and gave her a cuddle that was full of love and understanding. To our delight and astonishment, Jane snuggled into her and put her broad lips to Shelagh's mouth. Shelagh stroked Jane's

190

hair and kept up the flow of sympathetic talk. Then, just like that, Jane gave Shelagh the dead orang. Shelagh took it, cradled it, talked admiringly about it, then slowly slipped it into one of her pockets. Jane did not make one gesture of protest.

'Pass me some food,' Shelagh said to us. We handed in some bananas and grapes. Shelagh took them, broke them into portions and presented them to the orang's mouth. Jane took them one by one.

'I'd like to give her a stimulant, Shelagh,' I said quietly. 'I'll come in too.'

'No, you won't,' she replied. 'Fill your syringe, tell me where to put it and I'll do it – won't I, Jane dear?'

'But Mrs Taylor,' Matt remonstrated, 'she'll boite. Oi think we'd . . .'

Shelagh was having none of it. Reluctantly I made up a syringe and passed it in to my wife. 'In the thigh muscle,' I instructed. Cooing to her friend, with one arm still hugging her, Shelagh slipped the needle into Jane's leg. She did not budge a millimetre.

After a while, Shelagh left the cage and gave us the little corpse. Jane was no longer whimpering. She looked more tranquil as she watched my wife close the door. 'I'll be in again tomorrow,' said Shelagh briskly to Matt and me. She had taken over.

And that is how it was. Every day Shelagh went in with Jane, feeding her by hand, talking to her just like women do to their girl friends, particularly when they have suffered some misfortune, and giving her lots of loving cuddles. Jane responded. She began to cuddle Shelagh in return and stopped losing weight. Gradually she started to feed herself again. In three weeks she appeared completely normal.

I am certain that the injections that Shelagh gave sitting cheek by jowl with a great ape that could have broken every bone in her body did not play much part in Jane's recovery. As Shelagh said, 'There are some things in zoo work that just can't be left to men.'

☆☆☆☆☆☆☆☆☆☆☆☆☆☆☆

Chapter Thirteen

☆☆☆☆☆☆☆☆☆☆☆☆☆☆☆

PHENCYCLIDINE WAS the first breakthrough in the anaesthesia of most exotic species, and the invention of the dart-gun solved almost completely the problem of getting the anaesthetic to the patient while the vet stayed well out of range of its claws, teeth, hooves or horns. Gradually, pharmaceutical firms began to develop new experimental chemicals. They did the laboratory work; it was up to me to test the drugs in real live wild animals in the field. The bottles of prototype drugs with labels bearing only code numbers arrived regularly on my desk, accompanied by all available data concerning their effects on cats, rabbits, dogs or pigs. I could not risk losing or injuring any animals, but the new drugs were badly needed and very cautiously I began to try them out on my zoo patients. Bit by bit, feeling my way with the dosage levels, varying the strengths of the injected solutions, ringing the changes on 'cocktails' made up of mixtures of drugs, and working with emergency cases in a widening circle of species, I began to find means of sedating almost all zoo animals safely and quickly to any desired level. The process continued until eventually there were only two species which I found particularly difficult to anaesthetise without worry, the sealion and the giraffe.

In other ways, too, there have been dramatic advances in zoo medicine over the past twenty-five years. I doubt, for example, whether I shall ever again see an elephant destroyed because of osteo-arthritis. Powerful X-ray machines can easily penetrate the tree-trunks that are an elephant's legs and pick out the first signs of disease. With ingenious fine fibre-optic tubes carrying lights and lenses I can actually look inside the joint cavities and inspect the diseased surfaces. Although I still use poultices of freshly-brewed infusions of comfrey leaves, the herbal 'knitbone' therapy so popular among the older Lancashire people of the Pennines where I was born, on the legs of elephants, now I can reinforce such time-honoured methods with injection into the joint of modern cortico-steroids, the feeding of tasteless new anti-arthritic drugs in the food, and courses of healing and pain-relieving ultrasonics.

Chota and Mary, the Manchester elephants, both died because the drugs, equipment and techniques available could not cope with the special problems posed by their massive bulk. Because of its sheer size the elephant is the species which illustrates most clearly and dramatically the developments in zoo medicine, and it was through his elephants that I first met Billy Smart junior, when he brought his troupe to Manchester for the Christmas circus. The animals were quartered in stables behind the King's Hall in Belle Vue. One of the elephants had begun to show signs of arthritis identical to those displayed by the ill-fated Chota. The pain had affected her normally placid temperament and on the evening before my visit she had attacked and beaten a circus elephant keeper so badly that he had had to be taken to hospital for emergency removal of a ruptured spleen. The keeper had made things much worse for himself by going into the elephant lines late at night after returning somewhat the worse for an evening's drinking. Elephants, like many other animals, are very sensitive to changes in the manner and mood of those who attend them. Reeking of beer, with perhaps a louder voice and rougher style of speech than normal, and probably moving on his feet less deliberately and calmly than usual, the keeper was not recognised as its friend by the aching elephant which had settled down in its usual place for the night. The man was on his own and could easily have been killed.

It is always risky as a stranger to move among elephants unaccompanied. Elephants look after one another. They have special friends and mates among their companions from whom in sickness or health, they are usually inseparable. As I move between two elephants to prod or feel at something they will tend to press together, making me a filling inside a great living elephant sandwich. It can be difficult to squeeze out, and I usually find myself dropping down and wriggling out between the forest of massive legs. If I inject one elephant its protective neighbour will often reach out and clout me sternly with its trunk or, worse, if it has tusks, lunge out with the ivory points at my body. One has to keep talking gently but firmly, to move steadily and decisively and to bear gifts: Polo mints are very well received.

The Smarts' elephant was indeed in the early stages of arthritis, but after a fortnight's treatment with the new arsenal of anti-arthritic drugs that were just becoming available, the animal was back to normal. When the troupe left Manchester at the end of the Christmas season she was walking normally and showed no sign of joint damage. Billy Smart seemed pleased with the result and said that he would contact me when next he had problems with the elephants, his special love. A few months later I was in Cyprus on holiday with my family when we saw a large photograph on a Cypriot magazine cover displayed in a bookshop in Nicosia. It showed Billy Smart standing in a car-wash with an elephant which was being shampooed in this modern and rather novel way. Prominently visible on the thigh of the animal was a lump the size of a cricket ball. An abscess or a tumour, I remarked to Shelagh, my wife. We had no way of knowing when the photograph had been taken. Perhaps it was something which had been dealt with long ago. I soon forgot about it.

When I returned to England I found myself busy with elephants again, this time a group of baby African elephants which had been brought to Flamingo Park in Yorkshire. They were a wild and riotous bunch, fourteen in number and all about four feet high. They had come straight from the African bush and although youngsters were fearless and aggressive. They had to be examined carefully: some had weak and bent ankle joints, others I suspected of being ruptured at the navels. But as soon as I approached closely to inspect them, they flared their ear flaps and charged at me, squealing angrily. One young male took such a dislike to my attentions that he chased me across the elephant house and beat me against the concrete wall with a blow of his broad bony forehead. I literally saw stars. It was obviously going to be necessary to use anaesthetic on these young tearaways if I was to have any chance of giving them a thorough check-up.

First supplies of a new anaesthetic drug called M99 were just coming in. Good reports about it were being published by vets working with wildlife in Africa and I had already found it first-class for knocking out deer and wildebeest, but this would be my first attempt to anaesthetise an elephant since the sad affair of Mary. M99 is a drug of the morphine family but thousands of times stronger. It is effective in minute doses, particularly in elephants, and most important of all it can be instantly neutralised by an antidote drug. So efficient is the antidote that animals return from anaesthesia to complete normality within seconds and without any grogginess or hangover. For the young African elephants at Flamingo Park I decided to use M99 even though at that time it was costing approximately £480,000 per pound. Very little, just a few milligrammes, would be required for each animal, I was assured.

Each young elephant was injected by a flying dart fired from a special gas-powered rifle. One to two minutes after the dart had struck an elephant's plump buttocks, the animal would sink quietly without any sign of alarm or dizziness to the ground. The medical inspection over, I slipped a small dose of antidote into the ear vein and within two minutes the animal was on its feet, eating food and glaring suspiciously at me once more. It looked as if M99 was going to be the answer to the terrible problem of doping elephants.

Two months later the telephone rang. It was Billy Smart junior. Gilda, one of his elephant troupe, was having trouble with a strange lump on her hind leg. Apparently the lump, the size of a large apple, had been there for about a year, but over the past three weeks it had begun to grow very rapidly and was now as big as a melon. I drove down to Leicester where Smart's Circus was playing and went into the elephant lines. Sure enough, Gilda was the elephant I had seen in the photograph in Cyprus. The swelling in her leg was hard but apparently painless. Its base was deep below the skin in the great thigh muscles.

'What do you think it is?' asked Billy. He had had years of experience with elephants and with the abscesses, cysts and skin diseases which are commonly seen in the species, but he had never seen a lump behaving like this one.

'It doesn't look like an abscess or cyst to me,' I replied, exploring the consistency and shape of the thing with my fingers. 'I think it's a tumour.'

Billy had trained the elephants himself and thanks to his remarkable rapport with them I was able to push a special biopsy needle deep into the lump in order to sample the tissue without the animal reacting or making a fuss. Billy just stood at Gilda's head talking firmly and kindly to her and stroking her trunk while she gazed devotedly down at him. The speck of flesh on the end of the biopsy needle was sent to the laboratory for microscopic examination. A few days later the result came back that it was a tumour, with areas of cancerous change. A major operation to remove it was imperative.

This time the anaesthetic would be M99. My experiences with it in the African elephants and other animals had impressed me, but I travelled down to Leicester again with a slight feeling of apprehension. Everything had been beautifully arranged in the elephant tent for the operation. Deep straw had been piled on the ground and covered with new canvas sheeting. The other elephants had been moved far away to the other end of the tent, where they stood with necks bent and eyes popping inquisitively as they watched with an air of disapproval what we were preparing to do to their companion. Gilda had not been given any solid food for twelve hours prior to the operation and was grumbling a bit about this as she was led onto the canvas sheets. She tried to grab bits of straw from the bedding as an illicit snack and became irritable when Billy Smart stopped her.

'I think I'll bring Burma over to stand by her,' said Billy. 'It will give her more confidence.'

Burma is the gorgeous old matriarch of Smart's Circus elephants. The first elephant that the famous Billy Smart himself bought, very big, looking always uniquely old and wise, she is the most intelligent, gentle and patient elephant I have ever met. She is just the sort of companion you want next to you in time of trouble, reliable, a rock. The Smart family worship her and see that at Christmas, weddings and other festivals, or if she looks a little peeky, she receives a bottle or two of her favourite tipple, neat Bisquit de Bouche cognac. The presence of Burma near a nervous, distraught or ailing elephant always seems to bring calm and confidence to the sufferer. I have often been glad of her help when treating sick or injured animals in the Smarts' winter quarters at Winkfield.

Burma came and stood impassively and quietly next to Gilda, who seemed immediately reassured. It was not necessary even to drop the anaesthetised elephant onto the floor. Billy simply gave Gilda the command to lie down (this is just one of the advantages of working with circus as opposed to zoo elephants) and the elephant obediently lay down with the tumorous leg uppermost. I could almost hear Burma murmur in approval. It was easy to inject just two c.c.s of the M99 solution painlessly into Gilda's ear vein, and within half a minute and without any problems she passed from conscious rest into a deep and satisfactory sleep. It took me about an hour and a half to cut out the great growth. Although elephant skin is tough, it is nothing like as thick and awkward to work with as, say, rhinoceros skin, and ordinary scalpels cut through it with the greatest of ease. The time-consuming part was the tying-off of all the blood vessels that supplied the hidden depths of the tumour.

When at last the mass had been totally dissected out (I had been at great pains not to leave even one particle that might multiply into another tumour) there was left a gaping hole in the thigh which had to be closed. The skin was virtually impossible to slide across the hole, the gap was so large and I had been forced to remove such a great expanse of skin. For a moment I was frightened. The hole had to be closed, but how? Using double lengths of the thickest stitch material I had, a sort of plaited nylon fishing line with a breaking strain of 250lb, I inserted 'relaxation sutures', which go through the skin far behind the wounded edges and take the main strain. I put dozens of them in place and gradually tightened them. Slowly the wound began to close. As the first relaxation sutures went slack I tightened them and reinforced with more. At last it was finished. The hole was sealed, although the operation site looked like a spider's web of interweaving green nylon. I prayed it would be strong enough to withstand the pressures when Gilda moved about. After tidying up the wound I filled my syringe with the anaesthetic antidote, injected it into the ear vein and looked at my watch. Thirty seconds later Gilda sighed deeply, switched her trunk and rolled her eyes. Then she heaved herself over onto her brisket and with a little grunt rose to her feet. No wobbling, no dizziness. Gilda looked round, touched trunks briefly with Burma and then grabbed a tuft of straw protruding from beneath the canvas. She stuffed it hungrily into her mouth. The stitches held.

There was no further trouble with Gilda and her growth. The last sign of it was the faint white scar which could just be detected the following Christmas when I sat with Shelagh and watched Billy Smart's Circus on television. The audience in the big top and the millions of television viewers undoubtedly enjoyed the scintillating and colourful display as the elephants carried clowns and glamorous girls about the ring. But the glimpse of that thin and fading line on the prancing grey hams of an elephant made me the proudest person on earth that Boxing Day afternoon.

Chapter Fourteen

S O LITTLE research has been done in exotic animal medicine compared to other branches of veterinary science that a zoo vet must seize on any scraps of information which might help him in his work. Thus it was that I took my first lessons in the care of the camel from the manual of the Royal Army Veterinary Corps. Not much has been published about the health problems of camels, but somewhere I had found an ancient copy of this work and among the masses of information on unlikely things such as how to dispose of dead horses at sea and how many miles a pack mule can be expected to go on so many pounds of groundsel, I found what the Army knew about camels and their problems in days when military men considered such knowledge essential.

A camel in the Manchester Zoo which had been in England for almost three years was becoming thin and debilitated for no apparent reason. Try as I might I could not find any firm cause, and tonics, pick-me-ups and vitamins were not having much effect. After some weeks of illness swellings began to appear on the camel's sides and legs. The tissues in these regions were soggy: if you pushed your finger in you left a dent that stayed for hours as if in putty. The camel was developing dropsy. I checked and re-checked the heart, took urine samples for more tests of kidney function, and sent blood to the laboratory for analysis of liver function. But no, the dropsy was coming from none of the expected sources. There did not seem to be much wrong with heart, liver or kidneys.

The case puzzled me. I read what little I could find in the pathology books I had available without getting much further. One day I remembered that the Army manual had talked about certain important diseases and I vaguely recalled something about surra, a kind of sleeping sickness similar to the well-known tropical disease of humans and caused by a trypanosome parasite which is carried by biting flies. It attacks camels in Africa and Asia and other animals including the horse, buffalo, elephant and tapir. Surra does not occur naturally in Europe. I searched for the manual but could not find it, indeed I never found it again, but I had remembered enough to set out on a new trail. Surra produced lumps or bumps of some kind. I went to the Medical School library in Manchester to consult the books on protozoology. There it was. Surra: trypanosomiasis of camels. Caused by a rather elegant protozoan parasite in the blood. Common in Egypt, Africa, etc.

Could this be a case of typical trypanosomiasis in darkest Manchester? I examined the camel once more and took more blood, this time to make smears which I could examine myself for the presence of the parasite. Not a thing. No parasite. More blood, more smears. Still nothing. I sat at the microscope with my eyes aching and my hopes of a clinching diagnosis receding. I decided to take more blood from the animal but at a different time of day, since some of these parasites are creatures of habit and only seem to go promenading in the blood at certain times of day. I took blood at night. Still nothing. Then I tried a sample first thing in the morning. The camel, miserable as it was, was becoming thoroughly fed up at the repeated jabs from my needle. I was having trouble washing the smell of camel puke from my hair. The latest sample was stained in the usual way with dyes to bring out contrasting colours in the blood corpuscles and anything else that might be there. I scanned field after field through the lenses until little red discs filled my eyes. Suddenly there it was! A beautiful object to look at, coloured by the stains at the moment of its death and preserved for ever, a sinuous twist of lilac and purple veil. A trypanosome. You only need one to clinch it. I had a case of surra.

When I rang up ICI and asked for what I needed the man at the other end of the telephone thought I was pulling his leg.

'You're D. C. Taylor of Rochdale and you've got a case of camel trypanosomiasis?' He paused. 'Rochdale in Lancashire, you mean?'

'Yes,' I said, 'and I believe you make a drug to cure it.'

The ICI man said he would have to have a word with somebody and I could faintly hear the comments as he left the telephone and recounted the gist of my request to the office at large. There was some guffawing and something about somebody having somebody else on. The man returned to the phone.

'Well, how many doses will you need? We only sell it for export normally. It's in packs of a hundred doses.'

'I only need enough to treat one camel,' I replied. 'Can you split the pack?' Rochdale doesn't see many camels. I imagined having difficulty getting rid of the other ninety-nine doses.

ICI turned out to be most co-operative. They sent me a specially packed single course of treatment for my surra case. The animal had obviously been infected with the parasite when it first came to Britain nearly three years previously. All that time the bug had been slowly nibbling away inside it. At least things turned out well: the anti-surra compound worked as efficiently in Manchester as it is said to do in Africa, the dropsy subsided and in due course the camel regained a plump, healthy weight.

Camels are fascinating animals, tough, uncomplaining about work and beautifully and functionally built, but the contents of their stomachs seem to have an affinity for suede leather. Once together the two cannot be parted. This I discovered when, clad in an expensive and much prized suede jacket but unprotected by an overall, I examined my first camel. I knew as we all do that camels spit but I did not realise what little it takes to make them spit. Camels will spit for the slightest provocation, real or imagined, they

201

will spit pre-emptively to start trouble or defensively even if only looked at in the wrong way. What is more, the word 'spit' conjures up a picture of relatively limited quantities of frothy saliva, the sort schoolboys eject, whereas camel spit is in fact a bottomless well of smelly, green, partly digested stomach contents that are sprayed as a broadside or aimed in a single noxious blob of flying soup. This makes examining camels something of a specialised art. Putting an old jacket over the camel's head is said to help but I have known a wily beast spit accurately down the sleeves of the garment.

Camels can also kick in any direction with any or all of their legs, if necessary at the same time, and they try to heighten the effect of spitting by making awful gurgling noises and extruding a heaving pink sausage, part of the lining of the mouth, from between yellow teeth. They can bite very severely and with purpose and Moses, a magnificent but stroppy male Bactrian camel at Manchester, is one of the most dangerous zoo animals I know. I saw what he did to a kindly old man who, without permission, went into the camel pen to stroke him. Camels can build up a pressure cooker of resentment towards human beings, then the lid suddenly blows off and they go berserk. In Asia when a camel gets to this high pitch of bottled-up tension the camel driver senses the brooding trouble and takes off his coat and gives it to the animal. Then, rather like the Japanese workers who are provided with special rooms where they can work off their frustrations and resentments by beating up models of their executives, the camel gives the garment hell. He jumps on it, rips it, bites it, tears it to pieces. When it is all over and the camel feels that it has blown its top enough, man and animal can live together in harmony again.

Andrew and I had ample opportunity to study the contrariness of the species at close quarters when we went twice in the same day from Manchester to Prague to pick up a consignment of Bactrian camels. The camels were from Asian Russia, semi-wild and grumpy. Some had vicious rope halters running tightly round their heads and through holes bored in their ears. They had been branded on the cheeks with hot irons months or years before and had been fitted with the halters when quite small. As the camels had grown the halters had cut deep into the flesh and in some places had disappeared completely beneath the skin. Before loading in Prague our first job was to cut off these evil devices but, even so, for one poor creature it was too late. The dirty rope sawing away interminably at its head had introduced tetanus germs into the body and it was showing the first symptoms of lockjaw, a terrible disease to witness. At least when we got it back to Manchester we were able to give it treatment and relieve the agonising muscular spasms, but the unfortunate animal died.

Everything went well with the loading at Prague. A communist soldier stood guard outside the aircraft's lavatory door to ensure that no-one stowed away in there, while the poor veterinary surgeon from Prague Zoo who handed the animals over to us was not even allowed to set foot inside the cargo hold or cabin at all. He would dearly have liked to see his charges settled down in the plane but the authorities were not taking any chances that he might somehow disappear amongst the grunting, shuffling crowd of Bactrians. Instead we gave him a bottle of whisky and some bottles of a superb new zoo animal anaesthetic and he gave us in exchange some Czech aerosols for treating skin diseases.

The camels behaved themselves perfectly. Once aboard the aircraft almost all of them sat quietly down and we did not need to use a single dose of sedative. The flight back to Manchester was uneventful, with not so much as a peep out of the animals. We landed at Ringway Airport where transport and lots of keepers from the zoo were waiting to help us unload. By this time all the camels were sitting down and relaxing. They were superb air travellers. Now we had to get them onto their feet to walk them down the ramp into the special fly-screened quarantine van that would take them to the zoo. Camels and their relatives, the llamas, alpacas and vicunas, are easily offended. They sit down for a variety of reasons such as annoyance, disgust, boredom, fright or just to be unco-operative. Sometimes, of course, they sit down for the pleasure of it. When sitting

203

down they may insist on rising for the same reasons. The general rule is that they will do the exact opposite of what the humans round them want them to do. This was a typical case: the complete cargo of camels in the aircraft decided, as one camel, not to get to their feet. Presumably they felt that they had done us enough favours that day in allowing themselves to be loaded so easily and then transported across Europe and that it was time for them to give us a bit of stick.

We tried shouting, slapping, lifting tails, blowing down ears and prodding with a stick. Nothing worked. Camel spittle began to fly around. Not one solitary camel was prepared to budge. They sat quietly resting on their briskets as if bolted to the floor. In the end they won. Each one had to be lifted by hand and carried bodily down to the van. It breaks the backs of five or six men to pick up a mature camel in this way and we had fifteen on board and another fifteen in the second consignment waiting in Prague. At last it was done. We flew back to Czechoslovakia and collected the rest. Again they travelled perfectly but, once they had landed at Manchester, became completely unco-operative and had to be carried out like the first bunch. It made the sweating keepers curse when some strapping great bull, who had just insisted on being borne out like a pitiful stretcher case, stood up voluntarily when deposited in the quarantine van and projected a gurgling stream of stomach contents at his erstwhile bearers.

Once in quarantine in Manchester the camels had to be observed carefully for any sign of disease. As usual we found on the skin of several of them dry scaly areas where the hair had fallen out. They had mange, a very common complaint caused by a minute mite which burrows into the skin. That meant giving the camels special shampoos, spraying every square inch of their body surfaces with a stirrup pump. It is not easy to be sure that the animal is totally wetted by the shampoo but if it is not, a few mites may escape destruction and survive to spread rapidly over the body during the next few weeks. Ideally the camels should be made to swim through a deep dipping tank and their heads dunked under the surface briefly to ensure

204

complete application of the anti-mange chemicals, but very few zoos have that facility.

Another problem Andrew and I found in the camels was the appearance in the droppings of a bacterium related to the tuberculosis germ. We arranged with Cambridge University to perform a delicate and accurate test on the droppings which would spot these germs, the cause of an illness named Johne's disease even when present in only minute numbers. Johne's disease, or paratuberculosis as it is sometimes called, can attack cattle, sheep and goats. Little is known about the effect of the germ on exotic ruminants, so when we began to find large numbers of the bacteria in some of the camels we became rather worried. The camels were not showing the typical symptom of chronic diarrhoea. Were they just carrying the germ harmlessly? Then after some weeks one of the animals began to lose weight and condition steadily. Despite intensive investigation and treatment it became a walking skeleton, but the only thing we could find were clusters of the Johne's bacterium in its droppings. Virtually nothing had been written about Johne's disease in species other than farm animals but we did stumble across a Russian scientific paper which said that the disease had been recorded in a substantial proportion of Bactrian camels and that it could cause death. Our camel in Manchester became in the end so weak and emaciated that it could no longer rise to its feet and the keepers had to bottle-feed it with gruel. One morning it was found dead. An autopsy found the wall of the intestine to be extensively damaged, and the microscope showed lying in the wall the little red rods that are Johne's bacteria.

So Johne's disease was able to treat camels with as little respect as it does domestic cattle. What was worse was that I soon spotted what looked like another case of the disease, this time in a rare sitatunga, a beautiful but very nervous antelope from the secluded swampy forests of Africa. Again there was no persistent diarrhoea as might have been expected but the other symptoms were highly suggestive and we found the germ lurking in the droppings. By now we were very alarmed. Through how many species could this tiny red rod that looks so insignificant under the microscope spread its havoc? No-one had ever seen a case of Johne's disease in sitatunga before. What other new ground were we doomed to break?

One major snag was that there was no certain cure for Johne's disease and vaccination was still being developed. We decided to try an experiment. The germ looks like and indeed is a close relative of the human tuberculosis bacterium. What if we did something not normally feasible for economic reasons in domestic cattle or sheep affected by Johne's disease and treated the sitatunga with a long course of drugs designed to combat TB in humans? We had no choice. Tragically, one of the sitatunga, a youngster bred in the zoo, had died and we had found his bowels riddled with the complaint. The others must all go onto the treatment immediately.

Sitatunga panic violently for the slightest reason so handling them provides many headaches. Open the door into their paddock or startle them by some unusual noise after lights-out and they may dash frantically about, colliding with walls or fences and damaging themselves severely. The pop of the dartgun and the slap of the flying syringe are asking for trouble so to examine the sitatunga closely, except in urgent emergencies, I use crushed tranquilliser tablets mixed with their food. Like all antelopes and similar creatures, sitatunga require a far larger dose than a human being of twice the weight or more. To treat the sitatunga with daily doses of streptomycin or even twice-weekly shots of viomycin as used for TB was simply not practical. We would have to rely on rather more old-fashioned anti-tuberculosis chemicals mixed daily in the food.

The treatment seemed promising at first. Symptoms of the disease faded, but although the numbers of bacteria in the droppings diminished it was impossible to eradicate them altogether and even after months of treatment the animals were not fully cured. The entrenched germs meant that recurrences were likely to occur – sadly, they did.

The finding of this disease in two zoo species prompted us to screen other likely candidates for possible unsuspected infection. More tests at Cambridge found it in a few other ruminants in the zoo. The management at Manchester, who always supported enthusiastically any health programme for the good of their stock, were keen to find out the extent of this hidden problem. In order to compare the position in Manchester with that elsewhere we obtained samples from animals in other British zoos. In a remarkable mumber of samples from a range of antelope, deer, gazelles and exotic cattle we found the germ.

Although all the zoos had been most willing to co-operate in supplying the samples, the reaction of a few zoos when we found evidence of Johne's disease was surprising. Ostrich-like, they stuck their heads in the sand. They were actually piqued that we had provided evidence that their stock had a potentially dangerous infection in its midst. There was nothing wrong with their stock, they protested. The whole thing was absolute nonsense. It must have been some other harmless bug picked up from the grass and simply passed out through the intestines into the droppings! This latter possibility had been provided for in the test developed at Cambridge and we were certain that we were not dealing with cases of bacterial mistaken identity. Despite this, and although we had seen the bug chewing away at the bowel tissues of camels and sitatunga, some very respectable zoological collections dropped the whole matter like a hot potato. They could not contemplate the possibility that all was not well with the animals in their care. There is quite a grapevine in the zoo world and from time to time I hear of animals dying in some of the parks where we found positive samples. The post-mortem findings, so it is whispered, strongly suggest Johne's disease.

☆☆☆☆☆☆☆☆☆☆☆☆☆☆☆

Chapter Fifteen

☆☆☆☆☆☆☆☆☆☆☆☆☆☆☆

I MISSED the end of the conference because Shelagh phoned my hotel the next evening with news of an accident at Belle Vue. Pedro, the smallest of the zoo's bull giraffes, had been wounded in the neck. He was eating and drinking all right, but dribbles of food and water were running out of the wound when he did so. I took a taxi to Schiphol airport and caught the next plane back to Manchester.

It was past midnight when I met Matt Kelly (the stocky little Irish head keeper) outside the darkened giraffe house. 'Looks nasty to me,' he said, clicking his teeth. 'We'll have to be careful goin' and puttin' the loights on.'

When zoo animals are put down for the night, they expect to be left undisturbed. Suddenly breaking the routine by switching on lights and making a noise can startle the resting or often snoring inhabitants, with disastrous results in that confined space both to panicking animals, and to any humans who happen to be in their way. After 'lights out' you go back into an animal house very carefully.

We went up to the door. Before opening it, Matt began to talk just loud enough to be heard inside. Gradually he increased the volume, whistled a bit, tapped on the woodwork and finally turned the knob. Very slowly pushing the door open a crack, he addressed the animals pulling themselves to their feet and flaring their nostrils in the blackness. 'There, there. How're ye doin', me beauties? Oi'm sorry to be disturbin' ye.' He moved a hand to the light switches, put on one bulb, paused, then lit another, paused and lit a third. We moved unhurriedly into the house, both billing and cooing softly towards the knots of zebra, giraffe and wildebeest that stood alertly, all with eyes upon us and ears pricked, ready to panic. After a few moments inspecting us, the animals relaxed: there was no mistaking the familiar friendly tones of the head keeper.

Pedro, the giraffe, was standing in a corner. He seemed unconcerned about the ugly, six-inch long tear, caked with blood, in the left side of his neck.

'How did it happen, Matt?' I asked, as Pedro wandered over to the railings, craned over and curled a rough grey tongue round a twist of my hair to give my scalp a painful tug.

'We're not too sure, but it looks as if he got his muzzle jammed in one of them water bowls up high on the wall, panicked and threw himself about and crashed against the iron hay-rick. It came away from the wall and a bracket went through his throat.'

Matt pulled an apple out of his coat pocket and offered it to the giraffe, who took it willingly. Pedro chewed it, drooling saliva down onto us, and swallowed. We watched the sinuous waves of the gullet muscles carrying the mashed-up apple towards the stomach. As the waves reached the neck wound, a pink finger of foam welled out of the bloody hole and then, to my horror, soggy white pieces of apple pulp flecked with pale green slivers of peel emerged from the wound and dropped onto the straw-covered floor.

'Bejasus!' exclaimed Matt.

There was no doubt about it. Pedro had punctured his gullet, a rare and serious injury, particularly in an animal like a giraffe.

There was nothing to be done that night apart from shooting a couple of dart-syringes containing penicillin into his buttocks. The formidable prospect of trying to close the wound would have to wait until daylight. I drove home to Rochdale with my head full of questions. How to lay hands on the big beast in a place that was smooth walls on three sides and iron bars on the fourth? What type of anaesthetic to use on the most notoriously unpredictable of zoological patients? The operation itself: how badly damaged was the gullet? Repairing such a wound might present problems never encountered in the day-to-day cobbling together of skin and muscle injuries. Giraffe again, I thought. One of the most difficult of all zoo species to treat, and one which seemed lately to be needing a lot of my help – such help as I could give. At least things were busy, but the cases were rough.

'Well, you can always go back to speying cats and vaccinating poodles,' Shelagh said provocatively next morning as I worried over the turn of events.

'Don't be daft,' I retorted, stabbing at a fried egg that was not looking for trouble.

As I arrived at Belle Vue I was no nearer finding the answers which had haunted me all night. Matt was already in the giraffe house, looking worriedly at Pedro, whose appearance had altered distinctly in the past six hours.

'Would ye look at that, Doctor,' said the head keeper, pointing. 'He's gettin' fatter somehow.'

Sure enough, Pedro did look plumper. It was not that he was bloated with air or excess food in his belly, but he seemed simply to have enlarged. There was no question that his neck, chest and forelegs were fatter. Ominously, the giraffe had stopped eating and was looking depressed and miserable. Sticky froth had made a trail down his neck from the puncture wound.

'I'll need to examine him, Matt,' I said, 'But how?' There was at that time no proven reliable anaesthetic for giraffes, no swinging gate or funnel-shaped 'crush'.

'What d'ye want to do exactly?' Matt asked.

'First, I'd like to feel him to see why he's so much bigger than last night, then if possible get a finger into that neck wound.'

'It's goin' to be tricky. Let's try a door and some straw bales.' He shouted to a bunch of keepers, 'Lift the elephant house door off its hinges, and look sharp about it!' The elephants were already outside for the day and had no need of their night-house door.

After a few minutes the keepers tottered into the giraffe house, straining and sweating under the weight of the massive, iron-studded door which must have weighed five or six hundredweight. The idea now was to take it into the giraffes' quarters, having moved out all the animals except Pedro, and then gradually press him against a wall by using the door as a portable barrier.

All went well at first. The door was introduced quietly and slowly. Pedro began to pace about nervously as the men under Matt's command advanced cautiously, carrying the door in an upright position. At least if the giraffe lashed out with one of his feet to deliver the powerful blows that can brain a charging lion, the solid wood should afford the keepers some protection. Gently cornered at last and unable to turn round, Pedro began to 'stargaze' – holding his head up so that his chin pointed directly at the ceiling – a sign of profound mental agitation. I told the men not to press the door actually onto the animal, for under such circumstances anything could happen. Pedro might try to climb the wall, jump amazingly upwards on four legs like a spring lamb, throw a limb over the door or even, seemingly, try to fly. Such remarkable displays always ended in torn muscles, fractures or even worse.

Matt piled up some bales of straw on our side of the door and I gingerly climbed up them. Now I was high enough to put my arm over the top of the door and do a bit of prodding around. 'Coosh now, coosh,' I murmured, the words that Pennine farmers would use when approaching a prickly-tempered cow. I lightly stroked Pedro's neck. Niggled, he swung his head to and fro and then lunged down awkwardly, trying to butt me with the hard pegs on his head. 'Coosh, coosh, boy.'

Pedro became accustomed to my touch on his skin, which flickered and jumped beneath my fingers. I prodded carefully. Scrunch! Scrunch! It was just like pressing shredded cellophane – I could hear as well as feel the crackling beneath the skin. This was not fat, nor was it the

211

soggy fluid of dropsy. It was gas, gas collecting in thousands of bubbles under the animal's hide and puffing him up like the Michelin man. If the gas was being produced by bacteria that had entered through the wound, Pedro really was in trouble. Gas gangrene is usually lethal and runs a quick course, but somehow he did not look poorly enough for that. I looked at the neck wound from a few inches away and listened intently. As Pedro moved his head about I could hear the faintest sucking sound. A bubble of serum would appear at the hole, swell, shrink and vanish. That was it: movement of the neck was drawing air in through the wound, which acted as a valve. Once inside, the air was gradually working its way through the subcutaneous tissue. Another day or two of this and Pedro could be like a zeppelin right down to his hind feet.

The operation to repair the gullet and close the overlying tissues would put a stop to all that. As long as I continued to provide an antibiotic 'umbrella', the air under the skin would be absorbed by the blood capillaries and harmlessly dispersed. Ready for trouble, I moved my fingers up towards the wound. I touched the crusted blood, then, ever so delicately, pushed my index finger into the ragged hole. Pedro swayed about. I swayed with him, letting my hand ride with his neck. I felt my fingers pass through a thin layer of split muscle and slip on the smooth lining of the gullet. The gap in its wall was as big as a plum.

I turned my head to look at Matt. 'There's a bloody great . . .' I began but then all hell was let loose. Pedro had had enough. Kicking mightily sideways with a fore leg and a hind leg in concert, he connected with the door with a crash that shook the building. The heavy slab of wood fell away from him, taking me and my pile of straw bales with it. The men buckled under the tumbling mass and collapsed to the ground. A yelling, struggling heap of keepers, plus one startled veterinarian, saw the great door come toppling down onto them. Only Matt Kelly had managed to skip out of the way. Luckily the straw bales in which we were tangled took much of the impact and saved us from being utterly flattened.

Unconfined once more, Pedro stalked haughtily from his

corner and actually walked over the door beneath which we were sandwiched. The momentary addition of his weight resulted in a broken collar bone and a bloody nose for one of the keepers, and made my ear swell up like a tomato. When we emerged from our press we found Matt hopping about in a mixture of amusement and agitation like a red-faced leprechaun.

As our wounded were borne off I explained the situation and told Matt to prepare for an operation. At that time few attempts had been made to anaesthetise giraffe, and those who had tried it had found grave difficulties in coping with the tall beast: its peculiar circulation system seemed to distribute anaesthetics in an unpredictable way. Slowly induced anaesthesia resulted in dizziness, panic and awful accidents, while fast knock-out shots were dangerous, tricky to administer and brought the animal crashing straight down from its height of seventeen or eighteen feet.

213

In the rare cases where the operation was completed satisfactorily, a giraffe might well refuse to get up on its feet ever again and there was the strange business of individuals which developed grotesquely twisted necks for some reason. Zoo vets had one recurring nightmare: that a giraffe might need surgery.

Even chiropody was a headache. In captivity giraffe hoofs sometimes grow long and curl upwards, but the difficulty was doing anything to remedy the situation. I had had some success in putting the patient into a specially built travelling box, removing the bottom plank on one side and working through the slot, but it was a dangerous technique. The horn, particularly in dry weather, can be hard as iron. A hoof-knife as used on sheep or cattle was useless, and there was not room to apply a blacksmith's hoof-clippers with the foot planted firmly on the ground and maybe a ton or more of weight resting on it. It was a painless operation but the giraffe usually resented his tootsies being fiddled about with, so it was difficult to decide which was best: to sweat away with a saw, waiting for the inevitable, lightning-fast kick to shatter the metal blade; to chip with a chisel and mallet and risk a broken arm or the chisel smashed into one'e teeth; or to use a fast, electric portable saw and maybe amputate the giraffe's ankle when it suddenly struck. Just before leaving my old practice, though, I had used an injection of acepromazine, a sedative made for farm and domestic animals, on an old bull giraffe at Dudley Zoo that had had terribly overgrown feet for years. It had worked well. The drug had left the animal standing but droopy-eyed, relaxed and uncaring. There had been no problems in darting the bull or cutting the horn and there seemed to be no after-effects to the acepromazine.

I had not wanted to use the drug just to examine Pedro, but for the operation on his throat I reckoned that the best and safest thing to do was to use acepromazine, put the patient behind the door again and then numb the operation site with plenty of local anaesthetic.

Even with the decision about the anaesthetic resolved, there were still the surgical problems. Left untreated or

214

simply dressed with ointments or plasters, the hole would never heal as saliva and food passing through the orifice would encourage the formation of a permanent link, a fistula, between the gullet and the outside of the neck. I would have to close the gullet with special stitches that rolled the wound edges inwards, so that the mucous membrane lining the tube could knit together, and I must not cause an obstruction to swallowing by narrowing the tube too much. I had opened ostrich gullets in the past in search of metal foreign bodies which they had swallowed but which we had located with army-issue mine detectors, but I had never had to operate on a mammal's gullet. Even in dogs it is rarely necessary – gullets get blocked some-times, but they normally emerge from accidents unscathed. The rest, closing the muscle and skin, and thus putting an end to the air-sucking, would be simple.

The first step was to give the sedative. As usual, I worked out the dose by taking the average of three estimates of his weight, mine, Matt's and the senior giraffe keeper's. Then I assembled one of the aluminium flying darts with its ingenious, explosive-activated plunger and selected a needle appropriate for the buttocks of an adult giraffe. Finally I charged the dart with the calculated volume of acepromazine, a beautiful golden-coloured liquid. There should be just enough to make this giraffe as peaceable and amenable as the one at Dudley.

With a soft 'phut', hardly loud enough to startle the animal, the dart flew from my gas pistol and homed perfectly into the giraffe's rump. So fast and surely do these devices travel that there is far less sensation for the recipient than there would be if a hypodermic needle were punched in manually. Pedro seemed unaware that he had been slipped a Mickey Finn.

I looked at my watch. Usually the first signs of drowsi-ness appear after five minutes or so. We all waited.

Six minutes went by. The giraffe started to droop his upper eyelids, instead of his normal alert expression he looked rather dumb, and his muscles visibly relaxed.

'Get the door, lads,' I said, 'and approach him nice and easy.'

As I spoke, Pedro gave a great sigh, keeled over as if struck by invisible lightning, and crashed onto the thick straw. I was stunned. The giraffe lay flat out, legs flailing and eyes rolling wildly.

Matt and I dashed over, and I put my ear to his chest, listening to the slow thud of the mighty heart.

'Get up, Pedro, get up!' yelled Matt, slapping the animal ineffectually on the flanks, his teeth grinding with tension.

I felt the pulse in the giraffe's femoral artery. It was soft and weakening.

'Come on, everyone. Prop him up on his brisket. Two of you hold his head up!' I shouted, and the keepers crowded round. 'Head up at all costs,' I repeated, and rummaged in my bag for syringes and needles.

Thoughts whirled through my mind. Certainly I had taken the correct drug from the correct bottle. Dose? We had all agreed that he weighed around sixteen hundred-weight, and I had given 5 cc, a low to moderate amount. I looked at the dart to check. Yes, it was a 5-cc dart and could not have held more. It could only be a side-effect of the acepromazine: heart failure had been reported occasionally in domestic animals, and it was recognised that one effect of the chemical was to lower the blood pressure.

As Matt and his men pushed the now unconscious giraffe into some semblance of a normal sitting position, with the head propped on one fellow's shoulders, I drew a quantity of noradrenaline into my syringe, fast. I bent to pick up a skin swab and heard Matt's words as if in a dream.

'He's gone, Doctor. He's gone,' he said quietly.

I went over to the giraffe, cold sweat breaking out under my shirt. I gently touched the cornea of one eye. I jammed my head against the warm chest and listened. Matt was right. Pedro had died. Just like that. The acepromazine had over-expanded the blood vessels, Pedro's blood pressure had plummeted and his vital brain cells had been starved of circulating oxygen. 'Damnation,' muttered Matt. The men all stood back and let the giraffe's body slip onto its side.

'Unpredictable things, giraffes. Bloody terrible to treat,' I said. It sounded like an apology.

No-one said anything further as we collected our gear. Matt left silently to phone the knackerman.

I drove home in despair. Only a fool would take on the agony of zoo medicine, I thought. Pigs, cats, cows we understand; giraffes can only bring heartache.

Shelagh knew what had happened with one look at my face when I entered the house. She also knew that it was best to stick the lunch in the oven; I would not be eating. I went to my office to sit and think, go over all the possibilities, to try to get an inkling of what had gone wrong. The thought that one day there might, there would, be another giraffe was like iced water in my brain.

Shelagh brought me a cup of tea. 'Come on,' she said. 'The cup that cheers. By the way, there's been a veterinary student on the phone a couple of times. He wants to know something about lobsters. His name's Greenwood, Andrew Greenwood.'

'You can tell him what he can do with his lobsters, love,' I replied, and stared unseeing out of the window. The gangling, long-necked creature that the ancients had called a camel-leopard, *Giraffa camelopardalis*, was becoming my jinx.

On the way to Harderwijk for the conference which Pedro's accident interrupted, my old friend Mr van den Baars had invited me to Rotterdam to look over a mixed bunch of animals belonging to him which had just arrived from East Africa. One of his keepers took me round the live cargo: giraffes, antelopes, a hippo and zebras.

'You should be interested in this one,' the keeper said, pointing to one slatted crate. 'It's a young zebra.'

My heart leapt as I put my face to a slot in the woodwork and looked inside. A beautiful, nine-month-old zebra colt was looking directly towards me with his ears pricked forwards and his eyes glistening like cobs of coal. There were three spots on his forehead. It was Tatu!

I was ecstatic. Tatu had survived. Blind and concussed in the heat of the bush eight months before, he was now a stroppy individual with glancing, arrogant eyes on his way to a zoo in Poland.

'Spirited little devil,' said the attendant. 'He kicks and bites as soon as look at you.'

'But does he look?' I asked. 'You've not seen him bump into things or miss objects, have you?'

'Definitely not,' came the emphatic reply. 'See this blue dent in my wrist? That's where he grabbed me a couple of weeks ago when I was mucking out. He saw all right.'

I was content. No doubt Tatu could have done better with a pair of bifocals or even contact lenses if such things had existed for wild animals, but he was biting folk accurately enough. That was just what I wanted to hear.

Pedro's death drove all thoughts of Tatu from my mind, and it was only some days later that I remembered to tell Shelagh about my reunion with the young zebra. She was thrilled.

'What's for dinner?' I asked when I had finished my tale.

'Can't you smell it?' Shelagh replied.

It was true there was a strong fishy smell about. 'Herrings!' I said, my mouth beginning to water in anticipation of baked rollmops with mashed potato and mustard sauce.

Shellagh shook her head. 'Wrong. It's mackerel today'.

'Fine by me.'

'And it's mackerel tomorrow, and the day after and Friday, Saturday, Sunday . . .'

'Whoa! Hold on!' I interrupted. 'What are you going on about?'

'Mackerel – twenty stone of it. It arrived on the front doorstep this morning, sent by Pentland Hick of Flamingo Park. He wants you to check its quality. He's bought a killer whale in Seattle and hopes to fly it over in two or three weeks, so he's been talking so merchants at Billingsgate about fish supplies. Oh, and that student, Andrew Greenwood, has been on about his lobsters again.'

Never mind lobsters – a killer whale! Determined to make his Flamingo Park Zoo in Yorkshire the finest in England, Hick had built one of the country's first dolphinaria and had become fascinated by the potentialities of the cetaceans – whales, dolphins, porpoises and the like. Harderwijk in Holland had had the first European killer a

218

few months previously, but it had not survived long before dying, it was said, of a brain haemorrhage. Now with any luck I was actually going to touch one of the most awesome marine mammals, probably handle its medical problems.

A frisson of excitement ran down my spine as I thought about it. Since my first contact with Flamingo Park, capturing an escaped nilgai antelope for them, I had gradually seen more and more of Hick's growing empire of animals. I telephoned him immediately.

'Yes,' he said in his deceptively soft and sleepy voice, 'I'd like you to go to Seattle next month. Bring back a killer whale. Think about it. Check everything. Talk to the Americans by phone. But remember' – his voice took on the menacing tones of the Godfather – 'nothing, but nothing, must go wrong, David.'

My contemplation of the momentous news was interrupted by Shelagh's more mundane but highly pressing problems as owner of 280 pounds of mackerel, a fish renowned for its lack of keeping quality. It was all over the kitchen, ousting my beer bottles from the refrigerator and filling the sinks. My daughters, Stephanie and Lindsey, peered somewhat mournfully from behind a stack of fish boxes which we had to climb over to get out of the kitchen.

'Lancastrians don't seem to eat mackerel,' Shelagh complained. 'I've managed to give away about ten pounds to the Schofields, old Fred the other side and even a pair to the postman, but look at the rest! I'm not going to waste them by dumping them in the dustbin, but what are we going to do with them before the house stinks of rotting fish?'

For the moment, though, they were beautiful fresh fish, youngsters about seven inches long. I inspected a selection, checking gills, eyes, skin, oil content, smell, parasite load, muscle firmness; they were perfect. It seemed safe to order this for the new whale, but just in case there were invisible bugs in the fish I took samples from half a dozen for bacteriological culture and for analysis for heavy metals, an increasing worry as the seas become polluted by man and his industries.

That evening I was to be found bearing unsolicited fishy gifts wrapped in newspaper to friends and even mere nodding acquaintances all over Rochdale, and for the next week my enthusiasm for the hobby of cooking was put to the test as I experimented with the mackerel.

On the Sunday night, as I called the family to the supper table, Stephanie asked apprehensively, 'It's not mackerel again, is it Dad? How have you done it this time? We've had it boiled, with white sauce, barbecued, as kedgeree.'

'And don't forget when we had it in cider, and with cucumber, and with tomato,' chimed in Lindsey, who was also approaching the table with less than her usual enthusiasm.

Shelagh pointed at the cat. 'Even poor old Lupin doesn't look like he could face a mackerel again for ten years.'

I knew I had plumbed the depths for this evening's meal but put a brave face on it. 'Tonight,' I declared gaily, 'my pièce de résistance – curried mackerel.'

With the groans of the family in my ears as I retreated to the kitchen to bring in the dishes, I began to doubt a killer whale's famed intelligence; after all, he would swallow a hundredweight of this stuff, day in and day out for years – and raw, without benefit of my sauces!

Before I had time to make serious preparations for my visit to America, I was summoned by the manager of the Garden of Eden, a sleazy night-club in Manchester, to sort out one of the alligators which had a 'funny tail'. My only previous contact with the establishment had been to treat an eye condition in the python who was the working partner of Miss Seksi, the striptease dancer there: I had never actually set foot inside the place and could not imagine what alligators were doing in such surroundings. Props in some exotic, erotic burlesque sketch – Tarzan and nude Jane, maybe? Perhaps they made alligator steak flambé out of them. After all, people rave over the rather indifferent soup made from that other enchanting reptile, the turtle – a dish which Shelagh insisted we never ate because of the cruel way the gentle animals are killed to titillate the palates of gourmets far away.

Reptiles form one of the most difficult and neglected areas of zoo medicine, and there are not the funds or the scientific facilities available for much research into the special problems of a group of animals that are rarely worth more than a few pounds apiece. So the more reptile practice I got, the better: as a student I had watched Matt Kelly first slip a leather or rope noose round an alligator's jaws, thus putting the more lethal end out of action, then jump boldly onto the thrashing muscular tail and eventually force the reptile over onto its back. With the beast in that position Matt had begun to stroke it gently and repeatedly in a straight line down the middle of its body, beginning at the point of the jaw and going right down the underbelly to the vent. After six or seven passes of this kind, the animal had become immobile and perfectly relaxed in a hypnotic trance. As a mere nuisance of a student I had not been allowed to participate in or get too close to these mysteries, but this Garden of Eden case might be my big chance. I had seen it all and was sure I was up to it, even if my alligator patient was a fine nine-footer like the ones at Belle Vue which had laid eggs in captivity – the first to do so in any European zoo. Noose, jump onto the tail, whip over and begin the Svengali bit. Taylor the Zoovet will emerge with flying colours this morning, I thought, as I pulled up outside the night-club.

There was no mention of alligators among the collection of curling photographs of fishnet-covered flesh on the billboard by the entrance, a small black door set in a grimy wall in a back street, but I could not help musing on the cosmopolitan spice in a zoo vet's life that is rare in the general-practice world of say, a James Herriot.

Nothing inside the dimly lit basement room recalled in the slightest the first Garden of Eden, unless it was a reek of original sin. There was not even a plastic apple tree. The place was tatty, smelling sourly of stale beer, yesterday's cigars and cheap perfume. Groups of small tables, with crumb-dusty, wine-stained covers, and guttered candles stuck in empty Sauternes bottles, surrounded a minute dance floor. The whole garden of delights was illuminated coldly by blue fluorescent strip-lights which made the dandruff on the manager's jacket sparkle like snowflakes as he led me to my patient. Around the edge of the dance floor

221

there was a narrow, water-filled channel perhaps twelve inches wide and six inches deep. The water was turbid and oily. Floating on the surface were cigarette butts, bits of cork and other scraps of debris.

'He's in there,' said the manager. 'There's three of 'em altogether. Quite a gimmick, don't you think?'

I scanned the grey water. Sure enough, three pairs of green-gold eyes just broke the surface. Yes, the Garden of Eden had alligators, each about one foot long and as lean as hazel twigs – not quite the monsters I had hoped for.

'That's the one, I think,' said the manager, pointing towards one of the three. 'They don't have names. There's something wrong with his tail. I wouldn't have troubled you myself but one of those bloody Eytie waiters seems to have got attached to the little perishers and said he'd report us if we didn't do something. I mean, I could understand if it was a dog or something, but well . . .' He sniffed disdainfully.

I plunged my hand into the channel and brought out the

small alligator by the base of his tail. Four inches of his length was tail and half of that was brown, lifeless and rotting. It had obviously been gangrenous for weeks.

'What do you feed the alligators on?' I asked. Not only was the creature rather small, but the death of tissue without sign of infection, particularly on an extremity such as a tail, might well suggest something lacking in the diet. And the creature was rather small.

'What do you mean, feed them?' replied the manager.

I thought back. Perhaps I had phrased my question awkwardly. No, it seemed to make reasonable sense. 'What do you feed the alligators on?' I repeated. 'What food do you give them?'

The manager seemed perplexed. 'Food?' he mumbled. 'We don't exactly feed them at all. That's up to our customers.'

'What do you mean by that?' I felt the first stirrings of understanding and anger.

'Well, you know. The customers, the punters. They feed the little fellows. That's part of the gimmick – dancing with crocs all round you, throwing 'em bits to eat. Thrills the ladies no end. We're the only club in the North with the idea.' He smirked proudly.

'But what do the customers give the alligators?' I persisted. 'And how much?'

'Well, that'd be difficult to say. Prawns from the prawn cocktails, bits of steak, cheese of course, bits of melon – we do have quite a name for our Ogen melons filled with port wine you know, you ought to come some time and bring the missus – oh, and of course they get potato crisps and peas and scraps of lettuce.'

'Is that all they get in the way of food?' I asked, tight-lipped.

'Well, yes. But the people at the tables closest to the dance floor throw plenty in. They like to move 'em round a bit. Trouble is, they do throw fag ends in as well. Never seen 'em eat those, though.'

'Have you ever seen them eat anything that's thrown in?' I looked at the carpet of decaying food remains and filth that lay on the bottom of the channel.

The manager reflected for a moment or two. 'Can't say I ever have, to be honest. Being so near the band puts 'em off, I suppose. Maybe they eat after closing. That's it – they're nocturnal, aren't they?'

'What do you think they normally eat in the wild?'

The manager frowned, then sniggered. 'Wogs, I imagine, natives, black boys, eh?' He gave me a jolly poke in the ribs. 'No, seriously, I reckon when they can't get human flesh they, well, they, er, graze on weed or chew reeds or something. Anyway, our food's very mixed, and the vegetables are good. They must get better fed here than up some mud creek among the fuzzy-wuzzies.'

Despite having to keep myself from punching this unlikely paradigm of zoological erudition in the eye, I was eager to hear more. 'How long have the alligators been here?' I inquired, gritting my teeth.

'Three years, about. They've grown a bit.'

'How big were they when you bought them, then?'

'Oh, about nine or ten inches, I'd say.'

It was appalling. The little reptiles had grown only two or three inches in three years. The reason was plain: eating little and very rarely, in cool water and a confined space, cold-blooded creatures like alligators grow barely at all. These should have been eight times their actual size. The wonder was that they were alive at all.

I inspected the tail of the little alligator closely. It was my first such case but I felt sure that the basic cause of the disease was vitamin B_6 deficiency. What was more, the bones of all three reptiles seemed unusually soft and pliable, so there was the complication of rickets too. The whole mess was one of gross neglect and malnutrition.

The manager paled when I asked him to hold the alligator while I amputated the gangrenous portion of its tail. 'Oooh! I couldn't possibly,' he said. 'Can't bear to touch the slimy beasts. Can't stand blood, really I can't. So sorry.' He edged away, muttering something about accounts to attend to and wine to order.

As it was the middle of the morning there was no-one else around. I took off my jacket and slipped the alligator inside head first, leaving just the tail protruding. Holding the wriggling reptile through the sleeve with one hand, I managed to inject a ring of local anaesthetic around its tail. Giving time for the anaesthetic to act, I prepared scalpel, suture needles and nylon thread. Meanwhile the alligator, alarmed at the prospect of imminent surgery, disappeared completely down my jacket sleeve. When I was ready, I pushed my hand down to feel for my little patient. As my fingers reached him, he bit down hard and painfully, seizing two of my fingers in a miniature gin-trap of spiky teeth. In agony, I withdrew my hand, bringing with it the tenaciously engaged alligator. I did not want to break the little fellow's teeth so I slowly used the blunt end of a scalpel in my other hand to prise open his mouth and release my punctured digits. That done, I wired his jaws securely together with an encircling strand or two of nylon.

At last the operation could begin, but without any helper I had to hold the animal, cut and stitch. The problem began when the tail had been amputated, a fraction closer to the body than the line where the rotting tissue ended, and I was attempting to suture the wound neatly. How was I to tie the knots in the nylon? The slightest relaxation of my grip on the alligator's body and he prepared to scuttle off. I turned him upside down on the nearest table and stroked his tummy in the style of Matt Kelly, the croc mesmerist. He seemed to like the tickling sensation and lay still. When I thought he had gone properly into a trance, I released my hold on him. Quick as a flash, he flipped onto his feet and fled over the dirty tablecloth. I cursed the Garden of Eden and its fallen angels. Retrieving my bolting patient, I held him up to my mouth with one hand. I would have to use my teeth. I passed the needle and nylon thread through the edges of the scaly skin with my other hand, caught and held them between my teeth while I slipped a knot round with my bleeding fingers. Right under my nose, the soggy rear end of the alligator smelt distinctly unpleasant. Slowly, one by one, I 'toothed' surgical knots across the tail stump until it was completely sealed. Then I gave all three alligators stiff shots of vitamins and liquid minerals.

My final job was to deal with the manager and I went to his office.

'I've operated on the alligator,' I told him, 'but the Garden of Eden is a bloody disgrace. You've kept those animals for three years in abominable conditions and with no provision for proper diet or care.'

The manager stood up abruptly from behind his desk with a look I imagine he normally reserved for clients requiring the attentions of his bouncer. There was no bouncer at hand.

I continued. 'You know nothing at all about these creatures, you've been neglectful and cruel and you're not fit to keep tame bluebottles!'

'Now look here, young fellow, I don't know who you think you are, but . . .'

'I give you one week to donate those alligators to the zoo, otherwise I blow the whistle. *Manchester Evening News*, police, Cruelty to Animals Act, the lot – you get my point?'

The word 'police' seemed to quieten the manager down immediately. 'Yes, er, quite, quite,' he said. 'Now how about a drop of short stuff before you go?'

'Thank you, no. But please remember my advice about your donation to the zoo.' I had made him make an offer he could not refuse.

Sure enough, the manager did remember, for three days later the local newspaper carried a publicity shot of Miss Seksi, she of the python and the striptease, presenting Belle Vue with the trio.

' "Do take care of them, we're so fond of them," said Miss Seksi,' read the blurb beneath the photograph.

The three alligators from the Garden of Eden were named Adam, Eve and Abel by Clive, Belle Vue's reptile keeper, and under his care they began to grow long and fat. When Belle Vue closed in 1977 they were all around eight feet long and they went off to sunnier climes in the new Zoo de la Casa de Campo, Madrid, where I still see them.

Chapter Sixteen

☆☆☆☆☆☆☆☆☆☆☆☆☆☆☆

I F THE chambers of Sir Arthur Conan Doyle's great detective had been situated in Hyde Road, Manchester, instead of Baker Street, London, he would have laid down his violin, lit a pipeful of rare Albanian Latakia and surveyed the evening fog rising round the speedway stadium beyond the window. 'I think, Watson,' he would have said presently, 'that this singular matter should be entitled The Case of the Italian's Peanut Butter.' 'A capital suggestion, Holmes!' the good doctor might have replied. 'For that, I recall, is how it all began.'

Belle Vue had occasional circus acts on site during the summer season. June had been unremittingly grey and rain-swept that year when, towards the end of the month, a team of footballing boxer dogs arrived from Italy to play for a month in a candy-striped mini-circus tent set up near the funfair. The owner, Signor Vamponi, arrived with one caravan for himself and his wife and one as quarters for the footballers.

The quarantine rules of Great Britain are strict and with good reason: rabies, arguably the most horrific disease known to man, hasn't been seen in these islands since 1902. The Vamponis had come from the continent, where the virus is steadily increasing its hold on the wildlife of many areas, so they had to quarantine their dogs like any other visitor, but the Ministry of Agriculture arranged for a building within the Belle Vue grounds, in which the two caravans would stand, to be designated as a quarantine area for the duration of the Vamponis' stay. It was inspected by Ministry vets and strict controls put into operation. No-one but the owners, Ministry officials and the Belle Vue vet could enter the premises. The dogs could not be taken outside except to go straight into the nearby circus ring which was reached by a tunnel of canvas. All the dogs' exercising and bodily functions had to be performed within the designated quarantine premises.

I inspected the animals weekly on behalf of the Ministry, counting the dogs and checking each for signs of illness. After the first inspection, Signor Vamponi and his wife invited me to have a coffee and a glass of grappa in their untidy caravan. They were a picturesque couple, he small and swarthy with a Groucho Marx moustache and an addiction to snuff that had stained his nostril region brown, and she a tall blonde who had once been a Bluebell dancer until she had lost an eye in a bad car accident and had its place filled by a glass eye of electric blue; the impact of this unseeing, unmoving, gleaming sphere was increased by the fact that Signora Vamponi's good eye was brown as mahogany. Both spoke excellent English and regaled me with the latest gossip from the continental circus world: how an artiste had recently been strangled to death by a python he was working with in front of five hundred people (everyone thought he was hamming it up splendidly when he went blue and collapsed), how the glorious old Circus Bouglione building in Paris was still the same, and so on.

The Vamponi dogs were a cheerful bunch, keen players of the ball who were divided into two teams when in the ring, one wearing blue jerseys and the other red. The teams were kennelled at opposite ends of their caravan. 'Professional rivalry,' the Vamponis explained. 'They are highly competitive and have real team loyalty both on and off the field. If there is any squabbling among the dogs, it's always reds versus blues. Worse than Celtic and Rangers in Scotland, Doctor!'

228

As usual with circus acts at Belle Vue, food and certain other provisions for the animals were drawn from the zoo stores under the supervision of the redoubtable head keeper, Matt Kelly. Vamponi collected beef and some dog biscuits every day. Matt also came up with some fish, vegetables and a little fruit for the Vamponis' little pug who acted as referee in the circus act and suffered from mild diabetes that was controllable with careful diet.

One morning I was at the zoo to check on the progress of a young wallaby whose Achilles tendon I had repaired after an accident. The little marsupial wasn't recovering as strongly as I'd anticipated and I wondered whether some invalid food and peanut butter in the diet mightn't help to fortify it. I asked Matt for a jar of the peanut butter we kept in stock for such purposes. He shook his head.

'Bad cess to it,' he grumbled apologetically in his warm Dublin brogue. 'Wouldn't ye know ye'd ask for it today, Dr T. The Vamponis took both the pots Oi had this mornin'. We'll get more by this afternoon, though.'

I asked Matt if he thought the Vamponis were using the peanut butter to spread on their own breakfast toast. If so, they were definitely breaking the rules. The stores were for victualling the animals only. True, the boxes of bananas, pomegranates, melons and apricots, bundles of asparagus and broccoli, nets of onions and nuts, the trays of shrimp, sprats and herring on ice, all selected personally by Matt from the early-morning Shudehill market, wouldn't have looked out of place in the kitchens of the Midland Hotel. But a zoo must cater every day for a wider variety of tastes and palates than any chef de cuisine – carnivores, herbi-vores, insectivores and fruit-eaters, gourmands who will gobble anything and gourmets who are as fussy as an Egon Ronay inspector. The table d'hôte menu ranges from hundreds of bread loaves and gallons of molasses for the elephants to steak tartare followed by a fruit salad of apple, pear and chopped cherries for the iguanas. An entrée of cabbage heads and white mice must be prepared for the ostriches alongside snacks of hard-boiled eggs, locusts and nuts for the monkeys and more steak tartare, but this time flavoured with a few drops of formic acid, for anteaters who naturally insist on food which has the authentic aroma of ant. The danger is that such a cornucopia of goodies will tend to end up in human rather than animal stomachs if not carefully controlled. The keeper who munches the occasional grape taken from some dish he has prepared can soon progress to taking home a basket of greengrocery and a shoulder of lamb, and I've known places where an employee took enough each week to fill all his neighbour's larders. Apart from the financial loss to the zoo, the more dangerous effect is on the health of the creatures in his charge: malnutrition, even starvation, can develop while the office records still show a theoretically adequate amount of food being bought and fed to the animals. At Belle Vue it was up to Matt as head keeper to set up anti-filching countermeasures.

'The peanut butter moight be for that sugar-diabetic dog of theirs,' suggested Matt. It was possible. We agreed to overlook it this time.

A week later, still depressed by having lost my wallaby from a heart attack while I was removing the sutures in its leg, I was again at the zoo stores talking to Matt. The current problem was a weakly sitatunga calf that needed bottle-rearing. I had anaesthetised its mother in order to milk from her a few teaspoonfuls of the essential colostrum that the beautiful antelope calf had to have in the first day of life if it was to stand much chance against infant infections. Now I would give it to the baby by bottle and follow up first with protein solution and then with watered-down cows' milk.

'Let's use the normal human-type rubber teat,' I said to Matt, 'but with the squeezable plastic bottle. I think it will need encouraging to suck.'

Matt opened the door of the cupboard where we kept our special feeding equipment – premature baby bottles, stomach tubes, intravenous fluid sets and drenching flasks. We had the necessary tackle to pump bucketfuls of gruel into a convalescent elephant or provide artificial nectar to a humming-bird on the wing. He took down the box containing teats of various sizes, from baby mouse to baby hippo. Looking inside, I found that our stock of the size I needed was unexpectedly low.

'I thought we had more than these, Matt,' I said.

The head keeper muttered under his breath and screwed up his puckish face. 'Ah well, now. Vamponi borrowed some teats the other day for his dogs, after the shops were shut. He said he'd replace them. Oi'll see him about it.'

'The Vamponis again? Peanut butter and now teats? Have they been drawing anything else for their animals?'

'Well, just the usual meat and biscuits. Some milk. Oh, and some fruit and veg for the pug.'

'We can spare the odd apple, cabbage and what-have-you for the diabetic, that's legitimate. But I'm not having him nick our teats. Suppose we have an orphan cub tonight. Anyway, what does he need the teats for?'

Matt scratched his pate where it shone through the sparse covering of hair. 'Sure, Oi couldn't say. He said something about one of his dogs bein' still on the bottle. Oi was goin' to go and see 'em but you know the quarantine rules.'

'Rubbish! Those dogs are all full-grown. I'll mention it when I do my inspection tomorrow.'

Next day I was at the zoo early to take dropping samples from the sitatunga calf and then I headed for the dispensary inside the zoo stores to prepare a drench for the patient. Entering the stores, I almost collided with Signor Vamponi who was coming out carrying a large box full of bananas, apples, leeks and carrots.

'Oh, scusi,' he said, smiling, as I stood to one side to let him pass. He continued on his way without pausing.

'A fair bit of fruit there for your footballers!' I called after him. He said something that I didn't catch and kept walking. Ellie May, one of the elephants, deftly helped herself to a hand of bananas as he went by her paddock.

It was Matt's day off. In the store I found Len, the assistant head keeper. 'What's Vamponi doing with all that fruit?' I demanded. 'He had enough for a conclave of Vegans.'

'Claimed that they're for the animals, as per the contract with Belle Vue.'

'But a pug dog with diabetes doesn't need that much. I believe our Italian friends are scoffing the stuff themselves.'

'Maybe, Doctor. But what can I do? I'm not allowed to take the food into the quarantine area, nor is anyone else. If he says they need it, who am I to argue?'

When the sitatunga had been given its medicine I walked over to the buildings in which the two caravans were quarantined. I knocked on the Vamponis' door and the wife opened it.

'Prego, Dottore,' she said with a flashing smile. 'Come in, you are just in time for an espresso.'

Signor Vamponi was standing in the little kitchen area. He was working a coffee machine and gave me a cheerful 'Benvenuto'. The interior of the caravan was a scruffy chaos, reigned over by statuettes of saints and pictures of circus heroes. Clothes were piled everywhere. Unwashed crockery and glasses stood on tables and window sills. The floor was littered with bits of carrot and slivers of fruit peel and the pug scampered about in the debris.

'Please excuse the mess and take a seat while Alberto does what he can with this terrible chloriney Manchester water,' said Signora Vamponi, sweeping some filthy towels off a chair to make room. The air was stuffy and heavy with the odours of dog, coffee and butane gas.

'You'll find the boxers in perfect health, Dottore,' said Vamponi when we sat drinking his brew of aromatic Mocha.

'And you are keeping them indoors? No walks in the zoo grounds after dark?'

'No, no, Dottore, of course not. We understand.'

'How is the little pug with his diabetes?'

'Oh, still the same. Unless he steals a biscuit from one of the boxers or Laura here gives him a chocolate there is no sugar in his urine. But we carry the zinc insulin injections with us in case they are necessary again.'

'You can control him purely by a low carbohydrate diet?'

'More or less, Dottore.'

'Matt Kelly sees that you get fruit and vegetables for him, I understand.'

'Yes.' The Italian's face became abruptly unsmiling and mask-like. His wife stared out of the window and toyed nervously with the Ankh pendant hanging at her breast. They seemed suddenly tense.

'He seems to eat a lot,' I continued. 'Do the other dogs like fruit too?'

'Ah, si si. You know, Dottore – a little vegetable and fruit each day is good for a dog. It gives plenty vitamins and, how you say, rough stuff for the intestines.'

True, and there are even cranks who believe in total vegetarian diets for dogs and cats. Such people find cats awkward converts to non-carnivorous diets but claim that they can be weaned into the right and proper path by titbits of cucumber, melon and fruit cake.

'So your footballers like bananas and leeks?' I went on.

'Love them, Dottore.'

'Cooked or raw?' I knew the stores were providing twenty cans of cooked meat per day and there was none of the typical smell of simmering stew in the caravan. Raw bananas might be acceptable to a dog but raw leeks?

'Yes,' said Vamponi. He was now plainly uncomfortable and began to tap a nervous tattoo on his knee with his coffee spoon.

'Raw?'

'Si, the bananas.'

'The leeks?'

'Yes . . . well, no . . . they are cooked.'

'You cook them and add them to the canned meat?'

'No . . . yes! Si, we cook them, don't we, Laura?' He addressed his wife petulantly in rapid Italian. She turned her head and looked at me icily, her eye of blue glass like the beam of a laser.

'Si, Dottore, cooked like Alberto says. Boiled, then mixed with meat, biscuits and fresh fruit. Is healthy, no?'

I changed my tack. 'Kelly says one of your dogs is still on the bottle but there isn't one under two years of age. Have you been over-generous with the grappa in his direction?'

Signora Vamponi gave a harsh, mirthless laugh from a mouth now trap-like and unsmiling. 'Madre di cielo, the man's mad. I borrowed a couple of rubber teats from him

233

the other day for my friend, Rosa. She came to look round the zoo with me and brought her new baby. Rosa used to be with the high-wire Carvellos, but she married one of the Tower Circus clowns and lives in Blackpool now.'

I changed the subject. Slowly, warily the Italian couple relaxed again. So they'd been fiddling some food and some cheap teats from the stores. I could understand them being shifty. But their manner had puzzled me; I sensed it sprang from something more than such petty greed unmasked.

'Come, Dottore,' said Signor Vamponi eventually. 'Let us go to the dogs so you can write your report.'

The boxers were indeed in good health. No signs there of the weakness or tense hyper-sensitivity that can be the first indications of rabies virus newly arrived and rampaging in the brain cells. While I was going round the kennels in the dogs' caravan I sent Vamponi to bring me his copy of the import permit. As soon as he had gone, I pulled out of my pocket a banana and half an apple that I'd taken earlier from the stores. Quickly, before the owner could return, I broke the fruit into pieces which I pushed through the wire mesh to the boxers. Each dog sniffed the offerings and then utterly ignored them. Not one fragment was licked, let alone eaten. I couldn't imagine that they would have treated leeks any differently.

Back at the stores later I spoke to Len again. 'Stop providing fruit and greenstuffs for the Vamponis. They're free-loading on the zoo. If they want fruit for themselves they must buy it at the shops.'

No more greengrocery was drawn by the Vamponis in the days that followed but I was soon to hear of them again. I was driving towards the Dee estuary on my way to the Welsh Mountain Zoo at Colwyn Bay when a message came through over the radio-telephone. Would I please phone Boots the chemist's shop in Manchester concerning a prescription? I pulled up at the next telephone box to make the call.

The duty pharmacist came on the line. 'Dr Taylor? I've had an Italian couple in asking for an antibiotic – chloramphenicol suspension. No prescription. They said they were part of a circus at Belle Vue and have got trouble with one of their dogs. I explained that I'd need a scrip from a vet or in emergency a phone call. They got most upset when I wouldn't supply them with the stuff and said it was very important. So I rang the zoo and they put me on to you. Will you confirm the prescription?'

'No I won't,' I replied irritably. 'I know of no sick dog – anyway they're all in quarantine. Any sickness has to be notified to me and it hasn't been. I'll look into the matter.'

I thanked the pharmacist and went back to the car to continue the last few miles to the pretty hilltop zoo where a pair of Przewalski's horses awaited their regular hoof manicure under anaesthetic. After that I would call in at Belle Vue to see what the Vamponis wanted the chloramphenicol for.

Italy is one of those countries where anyone can buy anything, barring heroin perhaps, at the chemist's shop without prescription. I have a hypochondriac friend living in Rome who whenever he feels a cold coming on shoots himself up with an incredibly dangerous mixture of antibiotics including the controversial chloramphenicol, corticosteroids, vitamins, antihistamines and analgesics, all contained in one ready-filled syringe and purchased without a doctor's note from the local pharmacy. It's madness, of course. I could understand that the Vamponis might think that drug controls in the United Kingdom were similarly lax. Not so. There is enough over-use of powerful antibiotics with gay abandon by the medical and veterinary professions without laymen being encouraged to do the same.

'The Eyeties have been in again on the cadge,' said Matt when I got back to Belle Vue. He was bundling the week's harvest of fallen peacock feathers that had been gathered up from the park grounds by his keepers. The long plumes with their phosphorescent eyes would be sold to flower arrangers for £1 each.

'What have they been after this time – medicines?' I asked.

Matt looked up in surprise. 'How did ye guess? But so it was. Wanted some drugs for diarrhoea. Oi said they'd need to see ye first.'

I took some sample bottles from the dispensary and went over to the Vamponi encampment. The red team were running loose in the quarantine building while the blues, still locked away, barked disconsolately. Signor Vamponi, whistle in mouth, was giving the reds some coaching in leaping with all four feet off the ground for the shiny white ball. His wife sat on the steps of their caravan, fitting the pug out with some newly tailored black and white kit. Both greeted me with something less than effusiveness.

'Good day, Dottore. The medicine, have you brought it?' Alberto inhaled deeply over the back of a clenched fist and a small pyramid of brown powder vanished up his nose.

'I have come to see you about it, Signor. Why didn't you phone me if one of your dogs is ill? You are obliged to do so under the licence conditions, you know.' A boxer in hot pursuit of the ball cannoned off my legs and I found myself in the middle of the action with slavering, yelping players swirling all around me.

Vamponi lifted both hands level with his joke-shop moustache, palms turned outwards in supplication to heaven.

'But, Dottore, it isn't for the team. Is for Laura!' He swept one arm melodramatically towards his wife.

'Your wife? But you talked of a sick dog when you were at the pharmacy. Why?'

'Maledetto sia!' he cursed quietly. 'We thought we could buy some medicine for Laura, for her water trouble – how you say – cystitis? But when we asked the farmacista he says we gotta have a presc . . .'

'Prescription.'

'Prescription from a dottore. I say no but I know Dottore Taylor at Belle Vue. He will give me prescription for dog diarrhoea, no problem. Gotta keep the Italian dogs healthy, keep the British government happy, no?'

'So no dog is ill. No diarrhoea?'

'No'.

'But your wife has cystitis?' She looked perfectly fit to me, but that didn't mean she wasn't suffering from that common female complaint.

'Si, si. You understand?'

236

'Why not go to the medical doctor? It's free on the health service in England.'

Alberto frowned and I saw his wife look up, glower in my direction and shake her head. 'No is possible, Dottore. No time, so many shows today. Anyhow, she knows what she needs, what puts her right. Some liquid like the dottore in Italy gives her, chloramphenicol or terramycin. Laura can't swallow tablets.'

'Well, I'm sorry, Signor Vamponi, but I can't help. You'll have to see a doctor if you want that sort of treatment. I'm sure you could arrange for Dr Brown, the Belle Vue wrestling stadium MO, to visit. Now, I'd like to inspect your dogs. Will you kindly blow the whistle for half-time and call the lads in.'

The Italians were beginning to annoy me with their hotch-potch of little lies and half-truths for the sake of a box or two of fruit, some rubber nipples and now some antibiotics. I had difficulty in distinguishing the true from the false in their Alice-in-Wonderland affairs. Penny-pinching, sly, dissembling – they acted more like gypsies than circus folk and to what end? I felt sure it wasn't mere stupidity. What I increasingly suspected was that there were more dogs in the Vamponi squad than I or the Ministry licence knew about. I counted all the red team and then went into the caravan to count the blues: twelve boxers in all. The pug referee made thirteen, all present and correct and apparently in tip-top shape, and with no sign of diarrhoea. But why would the Vamponis go to the trouble of not declaring extra dogs when they could have come in on the same licence? Unless they were ill – that seemed the likely answer and would explain the need for medicine and maybe for an invalid diet of peanut butter.

The building in which the two caravans stood was a mere shell of brickwork illuminated by a single window. No place to hide dogs there. If a contraband animal existed it must be in one of the caravans. The dogs' caravan where I was standing had been stripped of all its normal furniture and fittings; even the bathroom had gone. The interior was bare except for the kennels, one for each boxer, six painted blue at one end and six red at the other. The pug lived with

237

the Vamponis, perhaps because a referee must always be seen to be impartial. The dogs' kennels were simple constructions of plywood and wire. I looked carefully at their dimensions as Vamponi brought one animal after another to me for inspection. False backs or bottoms in animal crates and boxes are commonly used by smugglers of livestock. I have seen six squirrel monkeys secreted behind a consignment of as many macaws, and rare snakes in a hidden compartment beneath a chattering cageful of monkeys. A favourite ploy at one time was to smuggle valuable or prohibited small creatures concealed behind more lethal creatures such as cobras, big cats or crocodiles that the customs man and Min. of Ag. veterinary inspector wouldn't investigate too intimately. The only one of such smuggling incidents that I approve of was when a respected animal inspector now working at a safari park in West Germany brought his wife out of East Germany behind a group of very stroppy elephants who violently crashed the doors of their transport closed with their trunks whenever the communist border guards tried to look inside. You don't push your luck with opinionated elephants facing you head on!

Sadly, many of the animals illegally imported in such nefarious ways die in their cramped hidey-holes, not always because of lack of air or water or because of delays but from over-dosage of knockout drops given by the unscrupulous dealers in Bangkok, Kinshasa or Asuncion to keep them quiet when going through checkpoints. Could the Vamponis be playing at that dirty game? And for what – a litter of pups? Another footballer perhaps, some canine Pele, a star that they feared had a bad illness but couldn't bear to leave behind?

The kennels plainly couldn't have concealed anything much bigger than a flea. With one layer of plywood all round, each was built exactly the same. It must be the Vamponis' caravan then. The now taciturn and edgy Italian wasn't likely to invite me in for coffee and grappa this time.

'You go in ten days,' I said when we had finished the roll-call. 'It is necessary to begin preparing the export documents in good time. Is there somewhere I can sit down to do the writing?'

Vamponi scowled. 'Si, come into my trailer.'

I followed him into the other caravan and sat at a table in the lounge area while he searched for the necessary papers. There could have been space under the seating where a dog or two might be hidden away but there was no sign of any air-holes that might have afforded ventilation. Perhaps any ventilation was to the outside or under-surface of the caravan; I must try to look when leaving.

'I'll just pop into the bathroom if I may,' I said, and went over to the narrow door that was decorated with a ceramic plaque of le mannequin pis. A lavatory, shower, sink and tiny washing-machine were crowded into the minuscule room. I couldn't see how one could possibly attend to the call of nature, wash or clean clothes in such a press, let alone find space for a smuggled pooch. If, and I was beginning to have doubts, there were a sick dog or dogs in this caravan, they must be under the seating, either in the lounge or beyond, in the sleeping area. I flushed the toilet and went back into the lounge where I sat down heavily on the seating, making the framework shake. There was no hint of any scrabbling noise underneath me, but it was difficult to listen with a cassette player in the galley blaring Verdi.

While filling in the official forms I chided myself for playing amateur sleuth complete with *Boy's Own Paper* theories of skullduggery, dog-runners and secret compartments. The Vamponis were surely nothing more than a couple of strangers in a strange land. If there had been a little misunderstanding, the odd fib, that didn't make them mafiosi. They would be gone in a few more days, anyway.

Two days later I did indeed feel ashamed at ever doubting the Italians' explanation of their request for antibiotics. Matt informed me that Signora Vamponi had been taken ill and admitted to hospital for tests. Still, I reasoned, it wasn't my place to have given her chloramphenicol for her bladder trouble: leave that to Dr Brown. But the same evening, as I sat at the Keighley office going through the literature in an effort to find some information on the analysis of sitatunga milk (the baby wasn't putting on weight and I needed to change the formula of the bottle feed), I received another telephone call about the Vamponis. This time it was from the bacteriology department of Manchester Royal Infirmary.

'We've got one of the Italian circus people from Belle Vue in for observation,' said my caller, a bacteriologist. 'We've grown a culture from her and I thought you might be able to give us some information.' Cystitis isn't rare in dolphins and occasionally occurs in other zoo creatures, but the condition in female humans was outside my ambit, so I was doubtful. 'We've come up with a Salmonella bacterium,' he continued.

Salmonella isn't a germ particularly associated with the urinary system. 'That's surprising, isn't it?' I said. 'I know she has a history of cystitis.'

'Cystitis? She's not in here with cystitis. She was admitted with acute gastro-enteritis, suspected food-poisoning. We've grown Salmonella java from her sample.'

'How can I help you?'

'The source of the bug is concerning the public health boys. They're looking at some salami and mortadella that she'd eaten portions of and I've sent the original cultures to the central reference laboratory at Colindale for typing. You've had Salmonella in the zoo at times in the past, haven't you?'

'Yes. Last time in an elephant. Salmonella typhimurium, probably from rodent droppings contaminating the hay. It died overnight before having a chance to show diarrhoea and despite a big shot of ampicillin.'

'You haven't any cases there at present?'

'None that I can find. The elephant was two years ago. I regularly screen each of the animal houses for background infection in the mouse population by hanging Tampax sanitary tampons in the drains for a week or two and then culturing them. No Salmonella found recently.'

'Could you take some swabs from the dogs they've got in quarantine? There might be a carrier there and we're keen to trace the source.'

'Sure. I'll do them first thing in the morning.'

When I telephoned the laboratory forty-eight hours later,

I was told that all the samples I had taken from the dogs, and the salami and mortadella, had proved negative for Salmonella. 'No clues where the bugs originated,' said the bacteriologist. 'We must have missed something somewhere though I'm darned if I can think what it is. She hadn't eaten any shellfish, ice cream, meat paste or anything of that sort in the week before she became ill.'

'What did Colindale find?'

'No reply yet. Maybe tomorrow.'

Colindale's report when it did eventually arrive was a startling one. Signora Vamponi's Salmonella was no common or garden variety. It had been identified as type 01451227HB126, a variety so far unrecorded in Britain or Italy or anywhere else in Europe. 01451227HB126 was known to be resident at that time in the island of Borneo and to be causing a spate of intestinal infections in inland villages among the peasants. The physicians attending Signora Vamponi at Manchester Royal asked her about any possible connection with the Indonesian area. It turned out that she'd never heard of the place and had never in her life been farther east than the heel of Italy.

'Unless they're conning us again for some inexplicable reason,' I mused. The Vamponis were beginning to irk me once more.

Three days to the Vamponis' departure and it was time for the final health inspection of the footballers. Signora Vamponi was out of hospital, starting to work again with the act. 'I won't be sorry to see them go,' I said to Matt as we watched the sitatunga now drinking unaided from a bucket of artificial sitatunga milk.

'Oi agree. There's somethin' that isn't kosher there.' The Irishman lowered his voice. 'Personally, Dr T., Oi think they've been breakin' the quarantine rules. Havin' folk who shouldn't be there at all in the quarantine zone – maybe playin' with the dogs.'

'Why do you think that?'

'Your theory about smuggled dogs was off beam, Dr T., but suppose they've got an illegal immigrant tucked away!' Matt's expressive eyes were wide with anticipation. 'Charlie Entwisle, the security guard, reckons he's seen a kid in there. Looked through the window of the quarantine on his rounds last night and saw a youngster in the Eyeties' caravan!'

Entwisle was a tall ex-soldier with a shiny face of angry red crowned by a stubble of coarse yellow hair, and although his voice was loud and fearsome he couldn't run fast enough nowadays to back up the terrible imprecations that he hurled at the dozens of young boys who daily climbed the walls or ran through the gates behind delivery vans. He looked up as I tapped on the glass of his security hut by the main gate, and opened the window. 'Mornin' Doctor,' he said in his broad Oldham accent: 'Owt sick today?'

'No. What I wanted to ask you about was your seeing a child in the dog quarantine area. Is it true?'

The red face glowed brighter. 'Absolutely no doubt about it, Doctor. Saw the little beggar plain as a pikestaff in the Eye-talians' caravan skennin' through t'winder. Reet ugly little chap an' all. A proper little carrot-top 'e were, but pale-faced like a lot 'o these sallow continentals. Unhealthy, Doctor. All that foreign food – spaghetti, macaroni, garlic an' that. Ugh!' Entwisle knew all about Abroad; he'd been there with the Eighth Army.

I was about to ask what time he'd seen the child when something flashed, bright as a magnesium flare, at the back of my brain. The lies, the things obtained from the stores, the medicine, the child, Signora Vamponi's illness – all the bits and pieces suddenly came together. Stunned at what I had deduced was the only possible explanation, I asked Entwisle to pass me the phone. Puzzled, the security man brought the telephone to the window and I dialled the Ministry headquarters in Preston.

That afternoon, when the Vamponis were in the middle of their football game before a crowded audience, I stood with a Ministry vet, a policeman and an officer of Her Majesty's Customs and Excise inside the quarantine building. The customs man was applying a gleaming stainless steel crowbar to the door of the Vamponis' caravan. With a metallic clang the door flew open and, led by the constable, we all entered. I was feeling troubled, to say the least, but my suspicions were stronger than ever. The Ministry man had shared them and had set up the dramatic break-in.

'The seating you think, Doctor?' said the customs man. He grabbed the nearest cushion and pulled it up. Underneath was a space filled with bedding. He moved along under the window and expertly dismantled the upholstery. More storage areas were revealed, filled with books, clothing, household items, fragile crockery packed to withstand travelling – all the impedimenta of travelling folk who needed to use every square inch economically, but nothing out of the ordinary. Dismayed, I watched as the search moved on to the sleeping area. Up came the seating, out spilled the blankets and pillows, night-dresses and pyjamas, even a pretty Victorian chamber-pot, but again no sign of stowaways.

The constable coughed a stage policeman's self-important cough. 'It seems apparent to me,' he said in his official voice, 'that we have been summoned here upon a misapprehension, a wild-goose chase.'

'Hold on, mate,' replied the customs man. 'I haven't even begun yet!' He went into the bathroom and pried with his crowbar at the base of the shower. It lifted and he got down onto his knees, bottom stuck through the doorway, and flashed a torch into the gap revealed. 'Nothing there but cockroaches,' he reported. Standing up, he looked around and then opened the refrigerator door. 'Wouldn't be the first time I've found one of these to be just a false front,' he murmured. But the refrigerator was a refrigerator and it contained only butter, eggs and some San Pellegrino water. Next he searched the cupboards but, apart from discovering where Signora Vamponi kept her jewellery in a secret drawer, unearthed nothing of note. A meticulous examination of the floor followed and likewise drew a blank.

The customs man was now looking as gloomy as the rest of us. He bent down, opened the door of the stove and flashed his light inside. No fire, just old ashes – but then it was supposed to be summer. Taking his crowbar again, he tapped the fire-brick at the back of the hearth. I heard him mutter something to himself and then he stood up, fished a retractable metal tape-measure out of his pocket and began taking measurements of the outside of the stove, the chimney-breast and pipe and the breadth of the caravan. He tapped several times on the stove-pipe and we heard its metallic resonance. Suddenly his calculations seemed to indicate something of significance for his expression brightened and he snatched up the crowbar yet again. He put the sharp bevelled tip into the joint between stove and chimney-breast and, grunting at the effort, swung on the bar. Slowly the stove moved away from the wall. We all pushed forward to look into the cavity his labours had exposed.

Three little orang-utans blinked back at us.

The Vamponis were heavily fined and the three orangs were confiscated by the authorities. All three were found a home in a good zoo where their Salmonella infection – the diarrhoea that the Vamponis had been hoping to cure with chloramphenicol and which Signora Vamponi had contracted in a more acute form through handling the animals – could be eradicated. Any home would have been better

244

than the black recess behind the stove with only the stove-pipe as its ventilator, where the little orangs had spent twenty-three hours a day for God knows how many weeks, only being let out in the evening and early morning to be surreptitiously fed milk from a bottle as well as fruit and vegetables and, when one became sick, peanut butter. If the Italians had bought the peanut butter, fruit and the teats at one of the shops just outside the zoo gates on Hyde Road they wouldn't have drawn our attention to them in the first place.

Smuggling great apes is a highly profitable business and it still goes on. Corrupt officials, many at the very height of the government, are everywhere in Indonesia. Everything from Komodo dragons to birds of paradise (exported as 'pheasants' with their tail feathers cut off and dyed black) can be obtained for the right price. Gorillas and chimps continue to come in considerable numbers out of African countries where only lip-service is paid to the principles of conservation, and their importation into European countries such as Belgium and Spain is virtually uncontrolled. Other European countries, Britain included, now strictly regulate what comes in and to whom it goes but there are still wealthy private collectors, some nutcases and a few disreputable zoo directors and circus proprietors who are only too pleased to pay several thousand pounds in cash, no questions asked, for a young great ape whose parents have been murdered to obtain it in Zaire, the Central African Republic or Sumatra.

Vamponi claimed that a buyer in England, whose name he never revealed, had welshed on the deal. If he wasn't lying and hadn't just brought the little animals to England on spec in the hope of finding a market, I'd dearly like to know who his mysterious client was. I'm inclined to think that on this point he told the truth. Somewhere among us is a scoundrel, probably well-to-do, who deals in living creatures as if they were krugerrands or cocoa futures.

Perhaps, I reflected when it was all over, a more appropriate title for the case of the three ginger-haired orang-utans, if Sherlock Holmes had not already used it for one of his most celebrated investigations, would have been

'The Red-Headed League'. After all, as I said to Matt later, the Vamponi affair had largely been 'Alimentary, my dear Kelly.'

☆ ☆ ☆ ☆ ☆ ☆ ☆ ☆ ☆ ☆ ☆ ☆ ☆ ☆ ☆

Chapter Seventeen

☆ ☆ ☆ ☆ ☆ ☆ ☆ ☆ ☆ ☆ ☆ ☆ ☆ ☆

I VISITED many marine-mammal vets and all the major marinelands in the United States before turning my attention to the dolphin-catching side of the business. Just as a zoo vet must understand the housing, handling and transport of his charges if he is to deal competently with their health problems, so it seemed to me best in this aquatic arena to try to find a water-borne equivalent to head keeper Matt Kelly from whom I could learn the nitty-gritty of the non-veterinary side of dolphins. I found him one March day in Fort Myers, Florida. He made his living catching dolphins in the Gulf of Mexico, his name was Gene Hamilton and with him I had some of the most exciting days of my life.

Like Alice I decided to begin at the beginning and asked Gene if he would take me out with him. A tall, lantern-jawed individual with a taciturn but kindly nature, he agreed, provided that I did exactly what I was told. His catching boat, with low sides and a cutaway stern for pulling animals on deck, could touch sixty miles an hour skimming over the shallow Florida waters, and it could turn on a sixpence at almost full speed. It was no place for novices who got in the way when the hunt was on.

The first thing I learned about catching is that wind is one's prime enemy and patience the greatest virtue. Even a slight breeze, which was welcomed by the yachtsmen and sweating sunbathers of Fort Myers, was enough to put a chop on the water that extended to the horizon. Under such conditions every triangular wavelet could be a dolphin's dorsal fin. The ocean seemed filled with dolphins or, looking at it another way, totally devoid of them. After an overnight storm, the water would be opaque, full of stirred-up sand, and the spotter plane which worked with us as our airborne pointer could not see the groups of dolphins hunting fish shoals under water. So if there was wind or had been wind, and that was most of the time, we sat cutting fish on the rickety old jetty where Gene moored up and put a fortune into the pockets of Mr Schlitz, brewing beer far away in Milwaukee.

When we did have a calm and glassy sea we would be off early, sometimes before sun-up, to the shallows where the waking dolphins might be collecting a breakfast of mullet, blue runner or butterfish. As the sun climbs out of the grey water we hear the crackle of our spotter plane's radio. In the first good light of the day he has located a group of twelve dolphins feeding quietly ten miles to our north. The pilot, experienced at estimating size and age from a height of several hundred feet, tells us how many animals of the right length, not too young and not too old, not pregnant and not suckling babies, are there for the taking – if we have luck.

We make for the area while Gene's two assistants, bronzed teenagers in frayed jeans shorts, check the catching gear. This is a mile of lightweight, fourteen-foot-deep net which has been carefully folded into zigzag layers and sleeved onto a long bamboo pole which projects over the stern The top edge of the net is attached to a series of floats and the end nearest the water carries a small sea anchor. The sea anchor is watched carefully. If it were to fall into the ocean before the appointed moment, one mile of net would be unfolded in seconds and it would take an hour or more to retrieve it, sort it out and reposition it along the bamboo pole. While we sail for the catching zone I stand at the wheel talking to Gene, taking lungfuls of cold, morning sea air and munching my share of a bizarre but delicious breakfast of fresh clams, fried frogs' legs and doughnuts, washed down even at that hour with cans of foaming Schlitz.

248

Before long we hear the buzz of the spotter aircraft somewhere overhead, and the pilot tells us the latest position of our quarry. Cutting the engine speed down to avoid alarming the feeding dolphins, Gene takes the boat towards the school of animals while the spotter keeps up a continual commentary. Suddenly I catch the first thrilling glimpse of a low, dark-grey dorsal fin breaking the water surface for a second as its owner takes in a gulp of air. Then we see another and another. Gene at this point relies almost completely on the aircraft. The pilot, seeing the dolphins' reaction to our approach, for their sensitive ears would have picked up our engine noise miles away, gives instructions that put us in a favourable position for our sweep. To us at almost water level the directions do not seem to make sense, but the pilot is looking down on the chessboard from on high and has a perfect view of all the players in the game. With luck, the dolphins will assume we are just another of the many pleasure boats in Florida's teeming waters. Nevertheless, some of the cowboys who sail such craft are known to indulge in the 'sport' of using dolphins for rifle practice. It has made many old bulls wary of any sort of vessel, and the bullet scars that some of them bear are the reason why.

Today all goes according to plan for once, and the spotter plane tells us we are in an ideal position, with the dolphins quietly browsing a hundred yards to our right at two o'clock. He then leaves the scene, and the hunt from now on is conducted solely by Gene. His first action is to tell me, 'Sit squarely down on the deck, grab hold of something firm and hold on!' Then he opens the throttle to the full, and the boat leaps forward with a deafening roar and with a punch that leaves the thrill of a ride on Belle Vue's roller coaster in the novice class.

Over the sparkling skin of the water we charge, the boat heeling over as Gene cuts a trench of frenzied foam that arcs across the path of the leading dolphin. The g-forces play musical chairs with my innards and I cling on for dear life, certain that at any moment I will be catapulted through the air like a human cannonball to join the dolphins. The boat stays flat out and the arc continues into a full circle. Gene

takes us completely round the school of dolphins and keeps the wheel locked over for a second circuit. Peeping tensely over the gunwales, I can see the animals bobbing and blowing puffs of rainbow-shot vapour in the centre of a broad ring of white water. Gene's aim is to confuse the dolphins by encircling them with a continuous wall of sound from the powerful engines. We have encountered one or two wiser, pluckier leaders of schools (not always bulls, sometimes redoutable matriarchs) who have made a high-speed beeline run for it, leading their weaker brethren straight through the noise wall and away safely into quiet water, but today the animals are hesitating and milling in the water, uncertain of the best plan of action. Gene observes their indecisive movements, tightens his circular run still further and then roars to his boys, 'Shoot!'

At his command one of the boys throws the sea anchor overboard. Gene continues to carve out yet another circle, and all the while the mile of net is being dragged off the bamboo pole like an express train. Round we go, leaving the net floats bobbing in a great curve in our wake until, having completed the full 360 degrees, we come back again to the sea anchor and first float. Gene kills the engines and peers anxiously towards the now fully cast ring of netting, one mile in circumference. There has been no last-minute dash by his quarry, he has not misjudged the water depth, and the nets are deep enough to stop escapers diving underneath; in the centre of the circle a cluster of dark-grey dorsal fins swirl about.

At this stage in the proceedings I was able to stand up again and start to be useful. The first thing was to scan the line of net floats. Evenly spaced, they should all be visible on the water surface. If one or two were submerged it might well mean that the net at that point was being dragged down by some heavy object – like a dolphin enmeshed several feet below and in imminent danger of drowning. 'In y'go, Dr Taylor,' Gene would say if we saw such warning signs, and with goggles and a short snorkel tube I would drop over the side into the cool, dark water and make for the spot where the floats had disappeared. Once there I would make an awkward duck dive and pull myself down to where a grey shape might be struggling to free itself from the net. As I glided down I would sometimes hear through the water the alarmed, high-pitched communication squeak of the trapped dolphin. If the animal was not too severely entangled I might free it by hand; otherwise Gene's treasured net had to be cut with a diver's knife.

Trapped dolphins were not the only cause of the net floats sinking. My first experience of other accidental catches came one sunny afternoon off Key Largo when Gene dropped his nets in a perfect 'set' round six or seven immature adult dolphins. The line of floats dipped at two points and, while one of Gene's boys dived to investigate one, I went down to look at the other. Kicking myself under, I followed the net down to where the expected grey form thrashed furiously twelve feet under the surface. Through the fuzzy shadows I could tell that the beast was caught by its head in a hole in the net. It should not be too difficult to pull it back by hand and release it so that it could surface for a welcome gulp of air. Coming closer, I saw to my horror that I was within inches of a seven-foot shark that was lashing its tail to and fro and gnashing its rows of razor-like teeth. I identified it as a black-tipped shark, a species strongly suspected of attacking humans. Should I release it? What would Gene do? Would it attack me if I freed it? Looking at it held in the net by its pectoral fins, I decided to risk a few cuts with my knife before going up again for air. Surely it would be too relieved at its near squeak to try tangling with me. I reached for the knife in my belt and then I saw the second black-tipped shark. Bigger than its companion, it was weaving figures of eight two yards to my left and below me. That made my mind up. In a flurry of bubbles I kicked for the surface and pulled myself thankfully up onto the boat.

'Don't ever fool around with those guys,' Gene said when I had told him my story. 'If he ain't dead when we pull the nets in, I'll kill him. Hate those guys. Sometimes get a hammerhead or two in with the dolphins messin' up the nets. Ain't no good for anythin' 'cept bait.'

'What are blacktips like around here?' I asked.

'Cain't trust 'em,' he replied. 'Know a dolphin catcher up near Steinhatchee lost a couple o' pounds o' thigh muscle from a blacktip. The doctors who stitched him up knew it was a blacktip by the pattern o' the tooth marks.'

That was not the last time I went down to entangled sharks, but whenever I found one I came up fast and left it for Gene to deal with later. I often watched one or another of Gene's boys make similar hurried exits from the water while he laughed and shouted, 'Sharks down there? Well, get on your Jesus shoes and walk on the water, fella!'

After clearing the nets of trapped animals, Gene would supervise the slow and meticulous pulling in. The area of the circle was decreased gradually to stop the dolphins panicking and entangling themselves en masse. Little by little the group of captured animals was brought closer to the boat until finally, with one or two men in the water to help, they could be hauled up onto the stern decking. Unsuitable animals were released while those that were to be kept were placed on foam mattresses amidships. There, while the other men pulled in all the net, I had my first experience in handling one hundred per cent wild, drip-

252

ping wet, fresh dolphins. The older animals usually lay resignedly, chirping plaintively to one another but not objecting to my touching their bodies. I got, and still get, a sheer physical thrill from contact with the flesh of animals that a few minutes before had been masters of a virtually limitless three-dimensional world where man is a feeble, groping amateur.

When the net was finally aboard and Gene started the engines ready for a fast cruise back to the holding pens at Fort Myers, another unwanted kind of captive often caused us problems and pain as we tended the dolphins. These were stingrays. This flat relative of the shark, which flies through the water like some marine bat and carries a poisonous flick knife at the base of its whip-like tail, abounds in Florida waters. Very often a number of these fish, even a hundred or more and some weighing up to twelve pounds, would be pulled in along with the dolphin haul. We would throw them back into the sea after picking them out of the net, but some of the slippery, plate-like creatures would fall onto the deck and flip about, unsheathing their poisonous spines and making it perilous underfoot. Occasionally we were inundated with the stingrays, and dead ones would lie all over the boat as we made for home, but even up to many days after its death the poison spines of the fish remain highly active. Once we had the net in, I put on rubber boots to cut the risk of being stung, but the spine of a big ray could easily go through the rubber covering my leg and would go through jeans with no trouble. Gene did not make it any easier for himself by working at all times barefooted, relying on his nimbleness and quick reactions to keep out of the way of the spines that would click up into the armed, offensive position in the twinkling of an eye if a ray was touched or even if it just felt ornery.

It was Gene who gave me one of my most important lessons about the extraordinary ways of the dolphin. It was a bitter but salutary experience; at the end of it a dolphin was dead and I had killed it.

We had caught a young dolphin which was on the point

253

of weaning. It had been captured along with its mother, and both were destined for a famous marineland in California. The youngster struggled and fought when brought aboard and, most significantly, stopped breathing.

'Right now,' commanded Gene, 'listen good. Young critters like this one will commit suicide by holdin' their breath if you don't watch carefully. Once they're out of the water you gotta time their breathin'. If they go for a maximum, a maximum of two minutes without breathin', we put 'em over the side in a turn or two of net as a sling and let 'em be in the water again. Then they breathe.'

'And what then?' I asked.

'Then we pull 'em on board again after a short while and try 'em some more. If they do it again, we dunk 'em again and so on. Usually by the time we get back to Fort Myers and put 'em in the holdin' pens they're OK.' Gene wagged a leathery, sun-blackened finger at me. 'Now your job, Dr Taylor, while I get us home lickety-split, is to do nuthin' but watch that little feller and your wrist watch. If he goes more'n two minutes, give a holler and we'll stop and dunk him.'

We set off and I sat close to the agitated baby, timing its respiration and pouring sea water over it from time to time to keep the skin from cracking and the body temperature from rising too high. Two minutes went by without the little blowhole opening to suck and blow.

'Whoa!' I yelled, and Gene slowed the engines and came back to help me sling the dolphin and immerse it in the sea. Hanging over the side I watched the youngster breathe normally once it felt the ocean around it. Gene told me that he never had this trouble with bigger specimens.

After two or three minutes we pulled junior back aboard and continued on our way. He took one good breath when he was settled on his pad again, and I noted the time. Two minutes passed with no further breathing. I stopped the boat a second time and we repeated the ducking. Once more the young animal went back to a normal respiration rate of four per minute. Back in the boat again he took a breath and Gene returned to the wheel.

I stared at my watch, following the movement of the

second hand, and reflected silently as I squatted by my charge. The breeze streamed through my hair and the sun scorched my naked back. Suicide, Gene had said. Could any animal commit suicide? The mystery of the mass self-drowning of lemmings was a different matter. Could an individual animal just stop breathing and die? Some canonized Catholic virgin was supposed to have taken her life in this way, but normally in mammals the brain simply forces its owner to breathe when the body senses a deficiency of oxygen and an increase of carbon dioxide in the blood. Will power, design, psychological state do not come into it, and shock is a separate thing that produces collapse of the circulation and unconsciousness before death. This little dolphin, though obviously agitated, was conscious and alert and, as far as I could tell from its colour and pulse, its circulation was good.

The seconds ticked by. One minute fifty. I sat on. I knew dolphins' brains ignored high levels of carbon dioxide in the blood when they were diving, but they needed oxygen, demanded it, in the end. That is why eventually they have to surface for air. That is why they drown if trapped in nets. So some involuntary mechanism must make this dolphin breathe and soon.

One minute fifty-nine. I wondered why Gene had said 'Two minutes.' Surely this was just a good estimate – no, more likely it was a dolphin catcher's unscientific bit of mythology. I watched the second hand pass the two-minute mark and decided to let it carry on without calling Gene yet again. As the watch ticked out the third minute, I knew that orthodox, reliable physiology would prove Gene wrong. It was the unbreakable rules of oxygen deficiency versus the crude rule of thumb of the dolphin catcher.

Four minutes. Still no breath taken by the dolphin. I began to sweat slightly and bite the tip of my tongue. Gene was busy navigating through the shoals. He probably did not know whether two minutes or twelve had gone by. Four and a half minutes. I felt my heart pounding but still trusted the laws of physiology which are common to all mammals from tiny vole to giant elephant. An arrogant voice still whispered, 'Oxygen demand must prevail.' Four minutes forty-five. The baby dolphin became as still as a plastic model and the pulse faded. My idiot resolve broke and I yelled to Gene, 'He's stopped breathing!' The boat came to a stop again and Gene came back to help me lower the dolphin into the water, but it was obvious that this poor creature would never breathe again. It was limp. The eyes were glazing. I had murdered it.

In deep misery I told Gene what I had done. He grimaced but said nothing. Then, as he knelt by the gunwale to release the corpse from the net and let it fall away into the gloomy depths where the sharks patrolled, his knee touched a stingray that had been dead for some time. The erect spine pierced his leg and the barbed point delivered its poison into the vein. White and sweating with pain, he had to endure the worse agony of me withdrawing the spine against the direction of the barbs. Using one of the rubber tubes of my stethoscope as a tourniquet, I bandaged the wound, but within minutes the pain worsened and Gene became very ill. The tough dolphin man stood the wracking agony without uttering one sound, and I made him comfortable on a foam pad while one of his boys took us the rest of the way in. Gene was in bed for nearly a week after that. Dolphin catching was off and all I had to do was to sit on the old jetty, throwing bits of stick into the water and staring miserably out over the dark green expanses of the holding pools, where a big female dolphin dipped and rose without her young son by her sleek side.

When the newly caught dolphins destined for Europe were fully acclimatized and feeding well in the holding pools, they were judged fit to make the long journey over the Atlantic. I had much to learn about this important aspect of dolphin management, too, and the best way to learn was to go with the animals from start to finish, from the sunny coast of Florida to New York and then on to London, Scarborough, Cleethorpes, Nice, Hamburg, Antwerp or Stockholm. Everyone thinks that accompanying dolphins by air from Florida to Europe must be an ideal way of earning one's living. It is not. It is hard, boring, wet, smelly work and it can last for two or three days, particularly if, as

256

happened this time, the first leg of the journey from Miami International to JFK New York is delayed and a missed connection means a twenty-four-hour lie-over in the Big Apple. You cannot take a pair of dolphins along to the nearest Holiday Inn and stick them in your bathroom. If they stay in a cold and windy warehouse in mid-January, you stay too – night and day.

First comes the road journey to Miami with the animals smothered in vaseline or lanolin which gets on your clothes and makes everything tacky. At the airport are the loading and paperwork formalities. I was to find that experienced dolphin handlers avoid excess weight charges by emptying all the water from the crates and removing the recirculating spray pumps and their twelve-volt batteries just before checking in at the freight warehouse. The animal and crate are then weighed and the weight entered on the papers. Now everything can be loaded. On the way to the aircraft the handler nips quickly round the corner, turns on a tap, runs tens of gallons of water into the crate and replaces the spray equipment and batteries. The dolphins then go onto the plane with the whole load weighing several hundred pounds more than the amount accounted for on the way-bill. The alternative, I was told, is to carry water at a cost of five dollars a gallon for the trip. Another source of free water is the washroom on board the cargo planes. The trouble is that if this is overdone the crew of the aircraft complain later that they found no water on board for their needs during the flight and there might be inquiries made.

Batteries for the pumps have a nasty habit of failing at some crucial point along the way. If you are prepared to go completely without sleep in the uncomfortable cargo hold, the constant squirting of water through a large rose spray helps to solve this difficulty. The equally tiresome alternative is to try to buy eight twelve-volt car batteries in the middle of the night somewhere near Kennedy Airport. At that time of day, if you can find a handy garage that is open, the disbelieving guy on duty is likely to demand a fistful of dollars and to regard an American Express card with the enthusiasm he reserves for four-dollar bills.

The endless flight to Europe in what resembles the inside

of a giant cigar tube has none of the amusements enjoyed by travellers on passenger flights. Damp and grease go through to your skin. There is the perpetual chore of un-clogging the holes in the spray system which become choked with circulated dolphin droppings, and on bumpy flights the shifting positions of the dolphins in their crates means constant vigilance and a handy supply of cotton-wool pads in case of wounds, eye damage or bedsores. Meanwhile the crew sit forward in their snug cockpit and once in a while pass back a liverwurst sandwich or a beaker of Seven Up as you shiver in your duffle coat and try to find a comfortable squatting position for a minute or two on the treacherous ball-bearings which stud the floor of the cargo hold.

Probably the worst part of the whole journey will be the arrival at London Heathrow. It is not uncommon for a dolphin to wait in the bonded warehouse there for a couple of hours while the customs men take their time about sorting through the mass of paperwork. Rarely will they agree to let the long-suffering beast get on its way while you stay behind to sign all the necessary documents and answer any questions. It is not as if they ever inspect the animals thoroughly for diamonds or contraband hooch, even though it would be quite possible to slip small packages into a dolphin's stomach and the animal would tolerate them for months. No, however much suffering it causes the animals, the customs men work by the book and the dolphins must do likewise.

My first experience of the Heathrow customs was when I went there to receive a giant Pacific octopus from Seattle that arrived, all fifty angry red pounds of him, neatly packed in water, ice and oxygen. This finest of all octopuses is extremely difficult to transport because it tends to pollute the water in which it travels and eventually poisons itself with nitrates produced by its own excrement. Anxious to resuscitate my giant octopus and to give it the chauffeur-driven limousine treatment at express speed all the way to the Yorkshire zoo that had bought it, I had gone out of my way to co-operate with customs.

'There's nothing in my book of duty rates concerning

giant octopus,' said the official sternly as the minutes ticked by, 'but I can't let it go without classifying it. I've got to fill in the right tariff.'

'It's a mollusc,' I insisted, 'like oysters, snails and so on.'

The official glowered at the massive, scarlet, tentacled creature in its plastic bag and insulated box. 'You mean it's edible?' he queried.

'Well, no, but to make it easier you can classify it as an oyster if you like.'

'Oysters are on my list, but he doesn't look anything like an oyster, or a snail.'

'Don't you eat little squid, calamares, in Spain or Italy ever?' I asked. The octopus was getting madder and redder and passing more droppings. I had to get it out of there and away with new water and oxygen.

'Nope,' said the customs man, 'don't like nasty foreign food. Squid? Yuk!'

'Please, please,' I said, 'take my word for it. It's the same family as oysters. Look that lot up in your tariff book and charge me at the same rate.'

At last commonsense prevailed. My octopus was entered on the import documents as 'One unusually large shell-less whelk'. The customs man had had the last word, and what did it matter to me if he considered this scarlet kraken a variety of the humble whelk which is so good with vinegar, salt and pepper? At least I had got away.

As a direct result of this experience, when I returned with the Florida dolphins I did my first and only bit of animal smuggling. I was bringing back an unusual present for Belle Vue's aquarium in the shape of a bunch of horseshoe crabs, primitive, helmet-shaped creatures that abound in the canals and round the shores of Florida. I put a dozen adults, each ten inches across, in the water beneath a dolphin slung in its crate. Coming to count the single 'fish', the customs officer noticed the spiky, rod-like tails of the large crabs projecting above the water surface as the creatures shuffled about below.

'Whassat?' asked the official.

'Horseshoe crabs,' I replied.

'Crabs? What for?'

Oh dear, I thought, not again. I bet my bottom dollar that this unique descendant of the trilobites, a group whose other representatives became extinct two hundred million years ago, would not be in the tariff book.

'Er, the crabs are for the dolphins. Animal food for en route,' I lied.

'Oh, fine. Of course,' said the customs man. 'I suppose they've got to have a nibble on the way like us.' The crabs and I had won through.

Arrived at their destination, the dolphins were lowered into a shallow pool, their first feel of salt water in days. Even then, my work was not done. Stiff and sore from the journey, the animals had difficulty balancing themselves in the water. This went on for a further eight hours, but until they were able to swim freely and safely, I had to go in with them. Though dog tired, I would walk them round and round their pool, guiding them by holding onto their dorsal fins. No, dolphin transporting is not much fun.

One of the dolphins I brought back from the Gulf of Mexico was destined for the London Dolphinarium on Oxford Street, a place where dolphins, sea lions, penguins and beautiful girls put on non-stop shows in a converted theatre. There were marvellous sound and lighting effects, and professional actors presented the shows. Behind the scenes, beneath Soho Square, there were holding pools and facilities where I crammed in among leggy chorus girls and kept the dolphin stars up to scratch under intensely artificial conditions. It was a good training ground for me in working against the odds in show business, preparing for the days when I would go to Paris to examine dolphins in the glass pool at the famous Moulin Rouge, the only dolphinarium where the management has ever informed me that 'When 'e 'as finished, ze veterinarian can take a shower weez ze girls eef 'e wishes, like ze French vet used to do.'

Unfortunately, although brilliantly conceived, the London Dolphinarium was built in the shopping area of the West End where passers-by were more likely to seek coffee shops than wander into Flipper shows in their breaks between bouts of buying and window gazing. The Dolphinarium was eventually forced to close, but before it did I had driven down from the north at least once a week to sort out one problem or another with the animal and occasionally with the human performers. When the dolphins started roughing up some of the girl 'aquamaids' swimming with them in the water, I was called in to help. The girls were getting bruised and alarmed by the dolphins' boisterous attentions, the shows suffered and some of the ladies talked of resigning. I found that the animals were detecting minute quantities of pheromones, sex chemicals, in the water during the days that the girls had their monthly periods. The attacks turned out in fact to be vigorous amorous advances, triggered off by the chemicals. Once the dolphin roués had been given shots of a drug normally used to turn the minds of human sex criminals to higher things, peace and good shows returned to the Dolphinarium.

One day, Clyde, the dolphin at the London Dolphinarium whom I had accompanied across the Atlantic, fell severely ill with liver inflammation. I struggled with the case, sleeping for a couple of nights beside the pool on a makeshift bed of an upturned rubber dinghy, and gradually Clyde began to pull round. He would need a massive dose of vitamin B complex by intravenous injection, so he was taken from the water and laid carefully on a thick mat of plastic foam. With two men holding the dolphin firmly, I slowly pressed a new, fine needle into the tail. A dark gout of blood welled up. Vein. I improved the flow by edging down a fraction more and stared intently at the blood. It was blackish, surely all of it de-oxygenated blood from a vein. Then I noticed the finest hair-thin wisp of pillar-box red. I recalled Dr Sam's 'Watch out, buddy' at Point Mugu. Probably the needle was drawing from veins and from the central artery. I pulled the needle back a whisker. Now all seemed blackish blood again. I must be in a vein and a vein alone. Trying not to alter the needle's position, I carefully connected the loaded syringe, sucked back to check all was well and then gently depressed the plunger. The vitamin B went into Clyde's circulation, he was returned to the pool apparently unperturbed and continued to make a fine recovery over the next forty-eight hours. We were all delighted.

Then, three days after the intravenous shot, I received a worrying phone call. A strange mark had appeared on Clyde's tail, a pale streak that was long and showed smaller branches, rather like a fern. Clyde was showing signs of pain and irritation in the area, an area as important to the motive power of the dolphin as a propeller is to an ocean liner. I went to look. Sure enough, the fern-like mark was distinct but only on one half of the tail, the half where I had given my shot, and it began at exactly the point where I had introduced my needle. For the first time in my life I had given at least part of an injection by mistake into an artery. Glumly I knew that the vitamin B, an irritant chemical, had gone whipping along the artery and into its tributaries. Thrombosis had occurred, the tissues supplied by the artery beyond my injection had died and I could expect them to drop off. It was a classic case of iatrogenic gangrene or, in honest layman's terminology, a real screw-up by the vet. There was little I could do. Dead tissue is dead tissue. I could encourage it to slough off, prevent secondary infection and wait. The nub of the question was how much tissue did that artery supply and so how much had died? If half the tail dropped off eventually, how would Clyde swim? I lay awake during those nightmare hours between two o'clock and five o'clock in the morning when only ill humours are abroad and sweated as I imagined the prospects.

As the days passed the pale, fern-like area became an ugly yellow colour, expanded and began to soften. At last after a week it was clear that I could see all the dead area; it had stopped expanding and the rotting tissue was beginning to peel away. A broad band ran down the centre of one tail fluke, but to my relief it seemed very unlikely that half the tail was going to fall off since the rest of the fluke looked healthy and was apparently well furnished with blood. What had seemed to be the main vessel supplying the tail fluke must have been backed up by other, smaller arteries which were not its tributaries and had been undamaged.

262

Dolphins were obviously designed marvellously in yet another respect, to keep erring veterinarians from screwing up their engines.

After many anxious days, Clyde's tail eventually cast off all the dead tissue, leaving a deep wide trench which had gone right down to the fibrous core of the fluke. Still, the tail worked. Clyde jumped, somersaulted and spun. My job was to get this gaping hole filled as quickly as possible. Twice a day I arranged for it to be coated with a healing cream and then thickly plastered with Grandmother's water-resistant denture fixative. After a month Clyde had completely healed and I could sleep dreamlessly again, but a long, fronded snow-white scar remains to this day to remind me whenever I see him that 'mainlining' a dolphin is one of the most hazardous of procedures.

Chapter
Eighteen

☆☆☆☆☆☆☆☆☆☆☆☆☆☆☆☆☆

H AVE YOU ever seen a black polar bear? The first
one will be worth a fortune, and it looked as though
Belle Vue might have struck lucky. The coats of
their polar bears were becoming darker and darker, giving
a fair impression of bottle-blonde barmaids who had been
slack and let their hair-roots grow through the bleach.

One summer Sunday Shelagh and I watched delightedly
with our two daughters as two newly-born cubs played by
the edge of their pool.

It was Shelagh who first noticed the bears' colour. 'The
babies are lovely,' she said, 'but the others are just plain –
well – filthy!'

My daughters agreed and wagged admonitory fingers at
me. 'The polar bears are turning brown like Mum says,'
chirped five-year-old Lindsey. 'Why don't you give them a
good bath in Omo?'

'In my view,' opined Stephanie, with the solemnity of a
nine-year-old newly embarked upon biology studies at
school, 'they're mutating into brown bears.'

I had to admit that there was something in what they
said. Only in picture books are polar bears portrayed as
being white as snow; in their native Arctic they are actually
a creamy colour. But compared with the shining pearly
coats of the bears I had seen at other zoos, and even
allowing for the Manchester atmosphere, our bears were

not the right colour. I raised the matter with the zoo's director, Ray Legge.

'Funny you should mention it,' he said. 'I've watched this darkening of the fur for a couple of weeks now. I wondered if my eyes were playing tricks.'

'My girls said the colour reminded them of caramel cream.'

'That's it,' Ray replied. 'Caramel describes the shade exactly. What's more, it gets deeper every day. At this rate, within two months you won't be able to tell them apart from the real brown and black bears.'

What could be the reason? The animals had a deep pool of sweet water in which they swam during daylight hours and they were hosed down regularly. Surely this was more than just grime.

'Let's dope one of the most café-au-lait individuals,' I suggested, 'and have a look at the skin.'

On close inspection, the skin of the slumbering beast appeared to the naked eye to be healthy, the coat was thick and shining and the animal was generally in tip-top shape, yet without doubt the hairs were more like those of a seal-point Siamese cat. I took a small bunch of hair clippings for microscopical examination, and in due course these revealed, loosely speaking, that the polar bears were growing seaweed! Under the microscope thousands of minute brown plants could be seen clinging to each hair. These algae, the sort of primitive vegetation that forms the green scum on pond water, are the smaller relatives of the various types of seaweed. In the case of the polar bears, they were not invading the hair and causing disease as, say, ringworm fungi do; they were just camping out and multiplying in the warm, moist forest of the bears' coats.

It was the same little plant which made the stone steps at home as slippery as oiled ice in damp weather. Shelagh tried to keep it at bay with scrubbing brush, chlorine solution and copper sulphate crystals, but her methods were never successful for very long and anyway could not be applied to living animals. After a long hunt I found a chemical manufactured in the USA which was lethal for algae but completely non-toxic for every other living

265

animal or plant except, oddly, rice sprouts. As there are no paddy fields in Belle Vue I felt safe in using the stuff, which we sprayed over the bears and added to their pool water. Within three weeks our Manchester polars looked as if they had just come back from the laundromat. It is not true that bears are pure white only in picture books; maybe in the Arctic they are not white as snow, but they were for a time in the icy wastes of north-west England.

A small, whitewood coffin lay on the back doorstep. The sunlight glinted off the brass knobs, brass handles and oblong brass plates with which it was fitted. I stood looking down at the doleful box, my hand frozen in mid-air on its way to pull my keys from my jacket pocket. The family had appeared hale and hearty at breakfast a few hours before, as far as I could remember I had never brushed with the Rochdale branch of the Cosa Nostra if it existed, and my wine-merchant would have had difficulty in fitting my

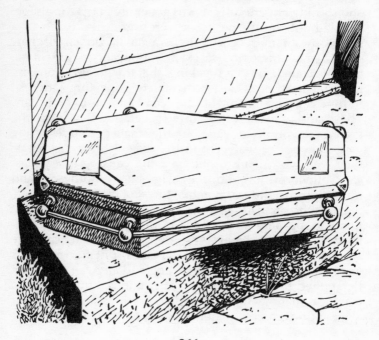

monthly order into the rather shallow sarcophagus even if he had for some reason started to deliver his wares in so funereal a fashion. The brass plate on the coffin lid was unengraved but the corner of a piece of white paper had been slipped under it. Stooping down, I read the words scribbled in pencil on the protruding part: 'Having a drink at White Lion. L. Fazakerly, Undertaker.' I was intrigued. Shelagh was out shopping, the girls were both at school. I decided to go down to the pub for a beer and find out why Mr Fazakerly had taken to leaving samples of his craft on my back doorstep.

The snug of my local pub, the White Lion, was almost empty when I entered. Mr Fazakerly, whom I had heard of but never met, was instantly recognisable as he leaned against the copper-topped bar with a pint of bitter before him. Black jacket, faintly striped dark grey trousers, white shirt and black tie, the whole outfit clothed a slight and stooping figure surmounted by the pale face of a Low Church ecclesiastic and the Brylcreemed hair of a British Rail buffet car attendant. Coal-black eyes flanked a waxy, pointed nose.

'In nomine Patris, Filii . . .' the unmistakable undertaker was intoning as I walked over. I saw that he had a saucer of mussels in front of him, and that with one hand he was shaking drops of tabasco sauce from a small bottle over the plump bodies of the molluscs.

'Mr Fazakerly?' I asked.

The undertaker nodded but continued his invocation: '. . . et Spiritus Sancti.' When he was satisfied that each mussel had been splashed with the red sauce, he picked one up between black-gloved fingers and popped it into his mouth. Then he beckoned to the landlord before turning to me with a thin smile as delicate as hoar-frost on a thread of gossamer.

'Dr Taylor? Will you have a drink? How about a mussel?'

'Thank you,' I replied. 'I got your note on the, er, the box. What's it about?'

Mr Fazakerly wagged one glistening leather finger at me and drops of tabasco and mussel juice ran down onto his curling shirt cuff. 'Casket, Dr Taylor, casket, I beg you.'

'The casket, then, the one on my doorstep,' I went on correctly. 'Is it meant for me?'

The undertaker's whole face miraculously reformed itself into the spitting image of a saint or martyr as conceived by an Italian Baroque artist: the diagonally uptilted face, the lowered eyelids, the half-open, inverted crescent of pale lips, it was all there. He pressed his gloved palms gently together and breathed his next words towards me. 'The bereaved gave me your name, Dr Taylor. Normally we would not need assistance, but as this is a, well, rather unusual loved one . . .'

'Something's died?' I whispered awkwardly over the rim of my tankard.

'Some*one*, yes indeed. Sorely to be missed, I'm sure. A good, a loyal, an abiding friend.'

'Who?'

Mr Fazakerly cleared his throat and looked at me solemnly. I expected any moment that he would reach out, grasp my shoulder resolutely and support me as he delivered the sad tidings. 'Phillips – Lumbutts Lane . . .' He hesitated for a moment as if to give me a chance to take it all in, then he went on, 'The dear spaniel, Fly by name, I believe.'

Fly Phillips; so that was it. The epileptic spaniel with an incompetent mitral valve, who had uncomplainingly gobbled down each day a shower of multicoloured capsules, digitalis, tocopherol, primidone and phenytoin, was dead. Half of my remaining canine practice had passed on.

'How did it happen and how do you fit in?' I asked.

Mr Fazakerly looked about to break into tears. 'The loved one . . .'

'The dog,' I interrupted tetchily.

'. . . died suddenly in its sleep this morning. Mr and Mrs Phillips called you but you were not at home, so they contacted us.'

'To bury him, I presume?'

'No, Dr Taylor, to prepare him.'

Now I was stumped. As far as I knew, the Phillipses were not any sort of religious eccentrics. They were devoted to their pet, but I had never heard them mention anything special that should happen to Fly after he died. They were well-off, and I could imagine them forking out the cash to have the dog properly buried, but what was this about preparation?

I wondered if Mr Fazakerly, despite all this solemnity, was playing some sort of joke, fuelled by the White Lion's best bitter. Grinning, I thumped my companion in the ribs. 'Come on,' I said, 'you can't be serious. What do you mean by preparing him?'

Mr Fazakerly did not allow his pious expression to slip so much as a millimetre; there was no hint of a smile, no relaxation of his frown. 'Dr Taylor, the loved . . ., that is the dog, Fly Phillips, is to be buried in a plot at Mumbles on the Welsh coast, where he used to run on the cliffs as a puppy. Mumbles is over two hundred miles from here. My firm has been asked to embalm him.'

'Embalm the dog!' I exclaimed. 'You must be pulling my leg.'

The undertaker sighed and looked round conspiratorially to make sure that he was not being overheard. 'Not at all, Doctor. He is to be embalmed in a running position, albeit lying on his side, with his ears tastefully disposed as if blowing in the wind as he gaily bowls along.'

Astounded, I could still detect no chink in the undertaker's grave countenance. To give myself time to collect my thoughts, I invited him to have another pint.

'No, thank you. We can't possibly discuss matters further here. Let's go to your home. I'll meet you there.'

We left the pub and I climbed into my car. As I pulled out onto the main road moments later, I glanced into the driving mirror. A few yards behind me was cruising a highly polished Daimler hearse with Mr Fazakerly at the wheel.

Back at the house, the coffin was still lying on the doorstep. Soundly asleep on top of it was Lupin, my cat. There was nobody about although Henry, our pet goat, with his head as usual poking inquisitively through the market-garden gate, did seem to be straining his ears in our direction. The undertaker eyed Henry and motioned me away out of the goat's earshot.

'The dog must be embalmed, as I explained. I have all my equipment and materials with me, but as you will appreciate, my, er, subjects are normally humans. Of dogs I have no anatomical knowledge. That is why I need you to help me achieve a perfect closed circuit.'

'Closed circuit?'

'Yes, indeed, the touchstone of one in my profession, Dr Taylor: absence of bubbles.'

Mr Fazakerly had lost me again. What had all this flatulent talk to do with circuits and dead dogs? I decided to push on and tackle the bubbles when they appeared.

'So you want me to help you at the embalming?' I said.

'Yes.'

'Where is the body?'

'In the casket.'

I looked across at Lupin, blissfully unconscious with his head resting on the twinkling brass plate.

'Couldn't we have done this at your premises?' I asked. Fazakerly's Chapel of Rest was a sizeable building near the Town Hall.

The undertaker looked alarmed and tut-tutted. 'Oh, I'm afraid not, dear sir. We have our other loved ones and their bereaveds and their bereaveds' feelings to think of. I mean, if I got around the Freemasons and the Catenians and all the rest of our clientèle that Fazakerly's wasn't exclusively for, er, homo sapiens . . . Oh no! Quite out of the question. Hence the need for some degree of secrecy.'

A few minutes later Henry the goat watched soberly as Mr Fazakerly and I carried the coffin into the shed that I was planning to use for autopsying the cadavers of exotic birds, reptiles and small mammals which would, I hoped, soon begin to arrive by post from all over the world. Mr Fazakerly went back to the hearse and returned with a large black box which he placed on the floor near the examination table. Then he unscrewed the brass knobs of the little coffin, took off the lid and brought out the body of the cocker spaniel. I was intrigued, and waited expectantly for the undertaker to begin his arcane rites.

Fazakerly opened his black box, which was split into two equal halves. One side contained two large glass flasks, one empty and other full of clear, pink liquid; there were also coils of rubber tubing and a shiny, dagger-like instrument. The other side of the box was crammed with cosmetics, creams, powders, make-up sticks, eye-liners, rouges.

'Leichner,' said Fazakerly proudly, when he saw me staring at his collection. 'We always use Leichner – nothing but the best for Fazakerly's.' He fished in the box and pulled out a lipstick. 'The latest spring fashion – crusty pearl. May I offer this as a present for your wife, Doctor? Or would she prefer some gunmetal mascara?'

Hastily, I made up some story about Shelagh being allergic to the stuff.

Fazakerly returned the cosmetics to their compartment, then put the two flasks, the tubing and the dagger instrument on the table near the body. 'In order to preserve the loved one's appearance and presentability for the inspection of the bereaved between now and the interment in Wales,' he began, 'I shall now replace all the loved . . . the dog's blood with this pink solution of formalin in water coloured with cochineal. In humans I would set up an airtight closed-circuit pumping system by attaching one rubber tube via a glass cannula to an ankle vein. This tube leads into the empty flask, and a second tube links the empty flask to the one containing pink fluid. A third runs from there to this trocar' – Mr Fazakerly picked up the dagger-like instrument – 'which is inserted by a deft thrust through the upper abdomen and diaphragm into the left ventricle of the heart. By squeezing this rubber enema pump clipped into the system, I can cause blood to enter the empty flask and be replaced via the heart and arterial system by the suitably coloured preserving fluid in the other container.'

Mr Fazakerly's enthusiastic exposition of his art had left him slightly breathless. He turned to me. 'So now you see why you are required, Doctor. Since my anatomical knowledge extends only to the human, you must find me an ankle vein on the dog and more importantly, the left ventricle. I needn't say how vital it is that the loved one isn't mutilated unnecessarily.'

I thought about it. The 'ankle' vein would be no problem,

and it took only a second to attach the first tube to a blood vessel below the right hock joint. The precise point at which to insert the dagger-like trocar was far trickier. Fazakerly was right. For his pumping system to work efficiently without air entering the system, the trocar had to be placed absolutely correctly; anywhere else and the strange post-mortem circulation of liquids just would not take place. The problem was that a dog's heart is quite small, and the left ventricle forms only one quarter of the heart. Its position in the living animal is fairly precise, but it is much less easily located from outside after death and least of all with a big instrument designed for the larger human species.

After much careful consideration I selected a spot and inserted the undertaker's grim weapon. He connected all the tubes, checked for obvious leaks and began to pump vigorously. I watched the two flasks with fascination, feeling a bit like Igor, Dr Frankenstein's idiot assistant.

Some dark blood fell into the empty flask, while the level of pink fluid in the other fell slightly. Then, with a friendly chuffing sound, the empty flask began to fill with great big pink bubbles. All the tubes began to gurgle and vibrate.

'Holy Harry!' exclaimed Fazakerly irritably and pumping ever more furiously. 'Look at those bubbles. The circuit's faulty. You've got it wrong!'

It was not much use explaining that cardiac punctures on stiff and lifeless cadavers were hardly everyday work for veterinarians, so I began to fiddle with the tubes, made sure the connections were tight and adjusted the position of the trocar. My anatomical expertise and reputation were at stake.

The undertaker pumped some more and the froth multiplied. Bubbles danced prettily and inexplicably through the pink embalming fluid which was now certainly not going down. Mr Fazakerly positively growled at me. He couldn't have looked more deadly serious. He pumped on with wild abandon. Suddenly, the flask containing the fluid hiccupped and blew its lid off. Smelly formalin ran over Mr Fazakerly's black boots.

'There – you see! Look at that! That's never happened in

all Fazakerlys' seventy-eight years!' He lowered his voice to a passionate whisper. 'Imagine what our bereaveds would say if that happened in the home!'

My future as a mortician's apprentice had never looked bleaker, but try as I might, I could not re-adjust the trocar in a way that started the exchange of liquids. Air was entering the system somehow. We both waggled the tubes, pushed and pulled, but it was no use. Eventually the undertaker reluctantly suggested that I operate on the dead animal, correctly place and sew in the trocar and then stitch everything up neatly beneath the long hair. For the first time since I was a student I practised surgery on a dead animal, but an hour later I had managed to link up Fazakerly's confounded plumbing system and the fluids began to flow. Fly was embalmed.

Mr Fazakerly was by now a trifle less indignant. He bent down to his black box again and rummaged among the cosmetics.

'You're not . . .' I began incredulously.

'I am indeed,' he replied, straightening up with a fistful of tubes and waxy sticks. 'Fazakerlys' are rightly appreciated for their thoughtful and realistic attention to every detail.'

Still keeping his gloves on, he began to reflect the lips of the dead spaniel and to reinforce the pale pink tinge produced by the embalming fluid with a liberal application of coloured cream. A glazed, partly-open eye was given a liquid glint by dropping in some glycerine, and the dried-up nose was freshened into the counterfeit dampness of health through the vigorous application of Nivea cream.

When my companion was satisfied with his artistry he stood back to admire the overall effect. 'Hmm. That seems fine,' he said. 'D'you see how I've got the shading of the tongue just right?' It was indeed a glorious salmon pink. 'I've done the make-up for Littleshaw Amateur Players for years, you know.'

Not with the same black boxful of cosmetics, I hoped.

It was time to box Fly's remains, now eternally glorious. The little coffin was neatly lined with white satin. We placed Fly inside. 'Now for the final effect,' said the undertaker. He flapped the two ears up over the head and, straining with all his might against the hold of rigor mortis, gradually persuaded the fore limbs to creak forwards and the hind limbs to groan backwards. Fly was silently galloping over the heath.

'There,' said Mr Fazakerly. With a sigh of satisfaction, he put the lid on the coffin and tightened the screws. 'The bereaveds will be satisfied and reassured, I think,' he said solemnly. 'Now, Doctor, would you be so good as to help me carry the casket out in proper fashion? In case there's anybody about, I don't want Fazakerly's to be thought capable of levity or lack of propriety.'

I guessed correctly what he meant. With Mr Fazakerly at the front and me at the back, the coffin was hoisted onto our left shoulders. When the undertaker gave the word the cortège trooped out of the shed and, at a pace that Fazakerly's over seventy-eight years had no doubt found appropriately sedate and impressive, bore its burden towards the waiting hearse. Only Henry looked on as we slid the coffin in and Mr Fazakerly gravely shut the doors.

'Well, good afternoon then, Doctor,' said the undertaker, shaking my hand and leaving my fingers smelling of pickled mussels, formalin and greasepaint. 'I'll leave you my card. Perhaps Fazakerly's can be at your service some time.'

After he had driven off at a sedate speed, I gave the business card to Henry, who quickly gobbled it down. 'Do you think that might have been some sort of ill omen for the future?' I asked the old goat.

Henry said nothing but his wise eyes, with the pupils like ever-open letter boxes, twinkled. No, it was going to be all right.

☆☆☆☆☆☆☆☆☆☆☆☆☆☆☆☆

Chapter Nineteen

☆☆☆☆☆☆☆☆☆☆☆☆☆☆☆☆

T HE FOLLOWING summer was exceptionally busy.
It was the height of the craze to open safari parks,
following the lead of places like Woburn and Longleat. Every duke, earl or impoverished fellow who fancied
he had a teaspoonful of blue blood in his veins, and who
was certain of the jaundiced tinge to the Inland Revenue
inspector's eye whenever the stately pile cropped up in
conversation, was scattering lions and giraffes around the
Nash terraces and along the rosewalks. Capability Brown
was turning in his grave and being dug up to make room
for dolphin pools.

The safari parks undoubtedly saved a number of aristocratic residences from having to be taken over by the
National Trust and contributed a great deal to our knowledge of keeping wild animals in captivity. Jimmy Chipperfield showed at Longleat, Woburn and elsewhere that
properly acclimatised tropical mammals, with their built-
in heat-regulating systems, could prosper in the depths of
an English winter without fancy heated housing. Town
folk got a taste of the African bush without driving far from
London or Liverpool. Species such as the cheetah, notoriously difficult to breed in traditional zoos, began to
reproduce at an increasing rate.

There were problems, however. The wide open, grassy
spaces of the parks, with an abundance of food lying

around, encouraged rodents and other pests to move in, join the fun and import troublesome diseases. Parasites thrived comfortably in the semi-natural terrain. Animals were not as easily inspected and handled as in the closer confines of a zoo.

Not all of the problems were purely veterinary ones. The controlling of social groups of creatures like lions, zebras and baboons in extensive parkland presented many challenges for the pioneers. I found myself one of those pioneers when, through my connections with the Smart circus family, I became involved in helping them to set up a safari park at one of the finest sites in Britain, on a hillside looking towards the Royal castle at Windsor.

Baboon reserves are one of the commonest and certainly one of the most entertaining features of a safari park, and the baboons were some of the first animals to take up residence at Windsor. They, and their cousins in other parks, gave us a heap of headaches in the early days, mainly because of their obsession with escape. Compared to baboons, prisoners of war with their wooden horses and other feats of mental and physical ingenuity were mere beginners. If they could talk, some of the baboons I know and respect, with names that sound like hoods in a Cagney film – 'Scarface', 'Tin-Ribs', 'Wart' and 'Squint' – could confidently drawl, just like Cagney, 'The jail hasn't been built that can hold me!' and mean it. At Windsor the baboons were originally corralled, or so we fondly thought, by a high wire fence with a sheet of smooth, slippery plastic on the top. The idea was that they could not get a grip on the plastic; that was what was going to keep them in. The baboons solved this minor problem by climbing up the wire until they reached the bottom of the plastic sheet and then, like a troupe of circus acrobats, forming a baboon pyramid to by-pass the puerile device. Sitting on the top edge of the fence, the first escapers would then reach down, if necessary with someone holding their ankles, and give a hand up to their mates who had been the sturdy-shouldered base of the pyramid.

To make the baboon pyramids unstable and unwork-able, we stepped the plastic sheet inwards a foot or so from the fence. Back went the baboons to the secret drawing-board. The next schemes involved either unpicking the slippery green sheet with the persistent patience of a few dozen Counts of Monte Cristo or mounting diversionary attacks on the Alsatian dog that guarded the gate to the reserve whilst the main bunch of escapers slipped out on his blind side.

In the end the Windsor baboons opted for a peaceful life within their compound, mainly because their successful break-outs led either into the tiger reserve, where they got the fright of their lives and quickly 'escaped back in', or into less lethal parts of the park where meal tickets were hard to come by; meals in their reserve were plentiful and toothsome. Also there were lots of fun things to do inside, like dismantling cars. The baboons could take the trimmings off a moving car far quicker than any automobile worker on the production line could put them on. As I discovered to my cost when I first drove my own car into the Windsor baboon reserve to visit a patient, Citroën saloons were bristling with lamps, bits of chrome and other trimmings that French workmanship had neglected to make monkey-proof. Having dealt with my sick baboon, I returned to the car to find the exterior denuded of everything portable. Aerial, screen wipers, lamp glasses – all gone. It was not as if the animals wanted to do anything useful with the articles that they stole. Like their human counterparts with birds' eggs, butterflies or beer mats, they just collected them for collecting's sake.

I at least knew where I might find the looted bits of my car in a day or two. Along with the baboons in the reserve at Windsor lived a lugubrious coven of Egyptian vultures. These harpies never caused anybody any trouble and were remarkably diligent in building nests, not nests of twigs and sticks in the manner approved by the ornithological rule-books but jazzy, glittering, pop-art bowers, comfortable lattice-work constructions made from screen wipers and radio aerials gathered from the ground after the baboons had knocked off for the day.

At a safari park which I visited in Spain, the wire fence of the baboon reserve was topped not by slippery plastic but by a strand of electrified wire of the sort used to corral cattle. Here the baboon POWs adopted a method of escape which might have been copied from the way soldiers are supposed to deal with barbed-wire barricades. One individual would fling himself onto the wire and lie there, twitching and jerking, whilst the others would quickly scurry over the bridge made by his gallant little body. When all had gone, he would drop back exhausted. It would be his turn to go out with the next batch, when someone else would act as the insulator.

Unlike the prisoners of Colditz, the baboons did not need to fudge the numbers at roll call to give fugitive comrades valuable time to get well clear of the camp. Keepers and curators do make regular checks of the stock list, but by their very nature the shifting, fidgety bands of baboons in a spacious reserve are as uncountable as a flock of sparrows. So some who 'make it' are not missed for a long time and their disappearance can remain permanently undiscovered or forgotten as numbers are built up by breeding or as the keeping staff change. I know one deep wood of birch and fir trees, fringed with palisades of brambles and wild roses that are heavy with juicy hips and blackberries in the late summer. Its inner fastnesses are carpeted from June with succulent red-cap boletus mushrooms, and edible blewits can be found even in the first frosts. White truffles sleep just below the beech mast. There are breaks in the trees where the grass grows tall and is speckled with vetches. Shallow, reedy pools tremble as water beetles, caddis-flies, water snails and frogs go about their business. In the depths of that wood live at least three baboons with long and glossy coats. They supplement the harvest of food, which each season naturally brings and which hunger, curiosity and intelligence revealed to them, with occasional forays for eggs, vegetables and discarded goodies from the gardens of cottages just outside the wood.

There was another baboon, a female, in the fugitive band but she was caught in an illegal gin-trap and died miserably. I was brought her emaciated and multilated corpse. At autopsy I found the pieces of insect carapaces, seed husks, toadstool stems and bone fragments from small creatures that revealed how she and her comrades feasted in their woodland territory. And there is an abandoned badger sett, which I found at last after days of searching, where the gang holes up, dry and snug, during the dripping chill of winter.

I would not reveal the location of these English baboons for a king's ransom; unlikely to be able to trap them, but fearing claims for damages from folk who have been relieved of a few apples or radishes, their former owners would send in the shotguns. Like slaves in ancient Rome, these doughty creatures have earned their freedom; they have been on the run for more than a year and a day.

One of the first parks I visited in Europe was the superbly designed and beautiful zoo at Kolmården, on the Baltic coast of Sweden. I was there to study, among other things, their well-built baboon compound. High fences with their top sections angled inwards, deep foundations to thwart tunnellers, electrified mats at the exits and entrances – this was surely a maximum security unit. But they said that about Colditz.

Beyond the baboon compound was a lovely wooded reserve of pine trees in which a number of bears ambled about. The ground was covered with delicious pine kernels. The baboons could see and smell the tantalising morsels through the wire, but how were they to get at them? The 'goon squad' of keepers at the gates were very alert. The first attempts were not up to the expected standard: they tried stowing away on the roofs of coaches or sneaking along beside a car, keeping the vehicle between themselves and the guards and then, as the car reached the electrified mat, jumping up, holding onto a door handle and keeping their feet clear of the ground until they were safely through. Using a pair of guards, one at each side of the mat, soon put a stop to that. The Escape Committee had to put their heads together. It took time but in the end they came up with the answer. As a coach approached the exit gate, the baboons would nip smartly between its wheels and with both hands and both feet latch onto the chassis. Best of all, on some models they could pull themselves up into secluded recesses in the bodywork or behind the mudguards. Out went the coach with its stowaways, who dropped from the undercarriage like autumn leaves when they reached the pine trees. The answer to that one was to equip the guards with angled mirrors on the end of long poles. Before each coach left the reserve they inspected its underside carefully for contraband apes, just like the stony-faced East German border guards at Checkpoint Charlie.

Baboons are a hardy breed, and the group at Belle Vue needed my attentions only once in about eight years. Manchester air and the carefully planned diet agreed with them and they, a peaceful, well-balanced social group, agreed among themselves. At the safari parks, on the other hand, I was kept busy patching up the bruises, cuts and knocked-out teeth of the day-to-day squabbles which regularly arose from disputes over marital and territorial matters, from greed, jealousy and the eternal clash between youth and age. To watch them at it reinforced my opinion that the naked ape in New York, London, Ulster or Moscow is barely a step ahead of his simian cousins in the evolutionary race.

Although my baboon friends did not pose any exceptional veterinary problems for me, I did meet a certain baboon, named Wunn, who had had a whole bundle of surgical problems heaped on his little shoulders by mankind. Wunn was an experimental baboon in a University laboratory involved in advanced transplant research. After being captured as a youngster in Africa, he knew no home other than the small galvanised box with a metal grille at the front, one of many identical one-man cells that stood in rows in the antiseptic, green-tiled room. He grew well enough on a scientifically perfect but unutterably boring diet of monkey pellets with the occasional half-orange, and, when his turn came around, was experimented upon. Bits were taken out and put back in, plastic tubes were inserted to replace portions of his natural ones, miniature electronic gadgets were buried in his flesh to record this and that and always, always he was being sampled – a biopsy today, blood tomorrow, urine catheter the day after.

280

For years Wunn bore it all stoically and displayed a gentle and warm nature towards the laboratory staff. Eventually the series of experiments came to an end. The men and women in white coats were pleased, and moved on to tinker with other baboons that Wunn could not see but only smell and hear.

Wunn had made his contribution to medical science. Now, instead of an OBE, there was only one remaining thing: death. According to the strict vivisection laws which operate in Great Britain, a laboratory animal which has played its part in a series of experiments must be put to sleep. There are no exceptions, no question of finding it a good home like a retired greyhound or redundant pit pony. The Home Office is adamant.

The girl laboratory technicians who had worked all along with Wunn had become particularly attached to the sweet-natured baboon. With the tacit approval of the surgeons involved, and with even the august head of research turning a Nelson's eye, they contacted me. Could I find a zoo where, without any chance of Government snoopers finding out, Wunn might for the first time in his life rattle about with a troupe of other baboons just like baboons are supposed to do? I was all for it. The secret of the bionic baboon would never be leaked to the Government but there was one possible snag: baboons live in strictly organised social communities where everyone knows his place. Singleton strangers are rarely tolerated and at worst are beaten up and driven off or killed.

Windsor Safari Park agreed to accept Wunn, and we decided to put him first in the baboon reserve in a cage normally used by nursing mothers. Wunn could see and be seen by the other animals but was protected from them by the wire. They became used to his presence and his smell. But what would happen when the newcomer was eventually let out into the main bunch? When should we try it? It was my decision, and I knew that if I saw Wunn at the receiving end of a lot of punishment from the other adult males, I would have to dart him and put him painlessly to sleep.

After Wunn had spent three weeks in his separate cage,

281

during which time he had aroused a certain but not inordinate amount of curiosity from a few of the other baboons, I decided to release him. My heart was in my mouth as a keeper opened the cage door and Wunn shuffled out into the grassy reserve. Now for it, I thought. My dart-gun was ready and loaded in case of a mugging. Wunn went a few yards, sat down and blinked towards the sunlight. He picked idly at this funny but tasty green matting all around him. His eyes followed a great grey and white cloud moving gently across the blue sky and then flicked across to where the cloud was suddenly pierced by a 707 climbing out of Heathrow airport. Slowly, nonchalantly, the baboons began to gather round him. To my surprise, instead of marching up to him and demanding to see his credentials, or beating up the stranger first and asking questions afterwards, they drifted up in twos and threes diffidently and almost respectfully. As would happen were a white explorer to stumble into the camp of a band of nomadic tribesmen, the first individuals to come right up to Wunn were the children. Within minutes, one or two of the smallest baboons were climbing over his hairy mane as if he were their long-lost favourite uncle.

We were overjoyed. So far, so very good. After the kids, one of the dominant male baboons cautiously approached the stranger, sniffed at him from a couple of feet away and then walked off unconcernedly. Wunn gazed benignly after him. I had already noticed that Wunn's testicles were abnormally small, probably because of his lifetime of acting as a surgical swap-shop. Perhaps he did not give off enough of the masculine scent to provoke the males; if so, I thanked God he was so poorly endowed. A few of the females came closer, emboldened by the first male's display of disdain. They gave Wunn the once-over, but from their reaction it did not seem as if the baboon equivalent of Richard Burton had arrived. It was all going far better than I could ever have hoped. The main group moved off and carried on with their foraging, feuding and courting. Wunn was left peacefully alone to begin doing amazing, novel things like sticking a finger into the soil or finding his first discarded screen wiper.

Not once in the days that followed did we see Wunn get into trouble. The kids liked him and a gang of them were constantly in attendance on him. The women continued not to be turned on by his charm, but then there was obviously more of the philosopher than the philanderer in his sage countenance. And the bellicose, butch leaders of the pack ignored him; the newcomer, they had concluded, was not going to make any waves. Gradually, as the months passed, Wunn was absorbed smoothly into the troupe. He seemed, and still seems, one apart, a member of the society but with no precise place in the hierarchy. The important thing is that he enjoys the sunshine and the rain, chasing the vultures, climbing over the rocks, taking handfuls of warm meat and vegetable stew in the winter and riding round the reserve on car bonnets during the summer. Two recent events have given me the utmost pleasure: Wunn has acquired a timid and devoted lady companion who grooms him whenever he feels lordly; and I have watched him deftly steal the chromium-plated wheel-trim from a coach – a coach carrying a visiting party of eminent surgeons.

It was at Windsor that summer that I was approached by 'Mac' McNab, the head keeper there, a plump, genial individual and a dead ringer for film comedian Oliver Hardy. 'We're going wallaby catching,' he announced. 'Do you know much about them?'

The honest answer was 'No'; I had already found these mini-kangaroos from down under to be unco-operative in responding to the medical ministrations of a Pommy veterinarian. With the aid of a certain brand of mint which these animals adore, a tip that I had picked up from my professor of surgery whilst at university and the only piece of exotic animal know-how I had been given as an under-graduate, I had been able to come into close contact with the timid marsupials from time to time but had found the early diagnosis and effective treatment of their ailments difficult. They are particularly prone to infection by a germ called actinomyces, which is carried into the jawbone and later to deeper parts by the tiny, barbed awns of grass on which they graze. The awns get jammed between their teeth and gradually work their way down into the gums. It was not an easy condition to tackle: the wallabies' struggles while they were injected often overstrained their hearts fatally and the surgical attempts I had made to cut out diseased areas of bone had been dogged for many years by the animals' unpredictable reactions to the only anaes-thetics available.

'Not really, Mac,' I told him, 'but I'd dearly love to come on the catching.'

'Right,' he replied. 'We're going down to Hampshire. Leonard's Leap, a private estate, has a surplus of the little beauties. We've got to grab them ourselves, though. It'd be best if you came along in case they need doping.'

Although McNab's words made it sound as if I were a key member of the hunting team, I had a feeling that I was being invited for the sake of appearances, more as a professional scapegoat than as an insurance against mis-hap. My old partner, Norman Whittle, had warned me early in our days together of how often the zoo vet finds himself playing this role.

With an assortment of wooden crates and three vehicles we set out from Windsor and drove down to Hampshire. Leonard's Leap is buried deep in the countryside and is to be found by strangers only with much difficulty after wending through a maze of leafy, un-signposted lanes that fork a hundred times. Not only that, but wallabies at the time were hard to come by, yet the owner of Leonard's Leap, a gentleman apparently quite unaware of the going rate in the zoological business, was asking a ridiculously low price for his animals. No wonder McNab, a wily Scotsman, went to great pains to keep the source of the bouncing bargains a close secret. The keepers who drove the vans carrying us and the crates were given maps in case the convoy became split up. The maps had been carefully drawn by the head keeper and bore only the barest details necessary for arriving at our destination. When all three vehicles finally reached the estate, a network of small valleys thickly scattered with large rhododendron bushes, McNab dashed round retrieving the maps from the drivers and put a match to them. It was all rather melodramatic but to this day, although I have got the name right, live within forty miles of the place and have occasionally driven around on a summer Sunday trying to find it, I have never been able to locate the hidden haunt of the wallabies. McNab is an ex-gamekeeper and knows a thing or two.

The rhododendron bushes at Leonard's Leap have dry and hollow centres where the wallabies could be found, snugly holed up and proof against the elements. All that McNab, I and the keepers on the expedition had to do was to chase the wallabies out of their rhododendron hide-aways and into a funnel-shaped trap which the estate gardeners had made with wire-netting at the head of one valley. This was the athletic side of a zoo vet's life. All through that hot afternoon we panted and puffed, running up and down the grassy slopes, crashing headlong through bushes and hurling ourselves in futile rugby tackles at the lithe, grey-brown bundles of fur that sprang silently over the ground as we approached. By late afternoon we had at last bagged our quota. Although not as winded and worn out as we were, the wallabies had begun to pant and their heart rates were almost too rapid to count. I decided to give each animal a shot of tranquilliser before crating it so that it would be able to relax on the long journey home.

McNab held the wallabies by the base of the tail while I gave the injection and checked to see how many of the females were carrying babies or 'joeys'. Of the twelve wallabies we had caught, ten were females and eight of them had sausage-sized infants firmly attached to the milk teats in their warm pouches. Safely on board the vans, the animals settled down quickly and without fuss in their boxes. I felt confident that I had done a good job in helping to catch the wallabies, and that my little drop of tranquilliser had set a seal of professionalism on the proceedings. McNab had told me that previously wallabies had been captured and moved with drugs being used. Sometimes an animal or two had died, probably of heart failure. Get this load back alive and well and McNab would undoubtedly appreciate the superior virtues of modern veterinary science in the zoo field. We set off home, map-less, following our noses towards a main road.

Back at Windsor, as the light began to fade, the wallabies were released into their grassy paddock. Ten, eleven, twelve: I counted them out. They were all alive and looking fit, and immediately began jumping uncertainly around their new compound. They bounced nervously along the perimeter and glanced with darting dark eyes at all the strange surroundings, at the humans peering through the fence and at the giraffes strutting in the adjoining paddock. They cocked their heads to listen to the sound of roaring lions, the screeching of bus brakes on the road outside and the thunder of jetliners making their final approach into London. McNab and I watched them, but suddenly he cursed and leaned forward. As the wallabies hopped, wriggling pink lumps of what looked like denuded mice fell onto the ground from the pouches of some of them. Within a minute or two, eight helpless baby wallabies, still with the foetal appearance of marsupial young, who are normally ejected from the womb to spend the latter half of 'pregnancy' in the pouch, were blindly writhing on the grass.

'Jeez, will ye look at that!' exclaimed McNab. 'Every mother's lost her young 'un!'

Quickly but carefully, we began to collect the hairless infants. They felt red-hot in the palm of my hand.

'Why, why d'you think that could have happened?' mused the head keeper as we stood looking at the adults springing quietly around us.

Suddenly the answer came to me: my wretched tranquilliser. It had done the trick all right on the mothers during the journey, but a proportion of it must have passed from their blood into their milk. Taken in by the babies, it had made them slightly drowsy and, when their parents were released at the park and began to leap about, they had lost their hold on the teat in the pouch and had been thrown out. I had given them each an indirect Mickey Finn.

I explained my theory to McNab, who nodded grimly. 'Hrrumph. Never did like the idea of all these new-fangled chemicals. Too much of it. Far too much of it,' he growled.

His opinions had been confirmed, but there was no time for further recriminations. Something had to be done – fast. The awful thing was that all the babies looked alike in their shiny, frail nondescriptness and so did all the mums. There was just no way we could tell which infant fell from which pouch, but back into someone's pouch each would have to go. McNab called in some keepers and the job of re-catching the wallabies began. Carefully, and with fervent silent entreaties to the gods to forestall what might turn into a joey holocaust, I stuck a couple of fingers into the pouch of each female. If I found a damp teat from which a drop of milk could be drawn, I plugged on one of the rudely evicted innocents.

Back in the security of a pouch, each joey latched firmly onto its allotted teat and snuggled down, but the chances that I had paired the right mother and offspring in each of the eight cases was something like one in five thousand. What if wallabies were like many other mammals and identified their own babies by scent, rejecting all imposters? In that case there would be de-pouched youngsters on the ground again in a little while and the deadly game of snap, using flesh and blood creatures instead of cards, would have to be played over and over again. Please God, let them be like caribou cows who willingly accept infants not their own, I prayed.

'Let's put them all in the night-house now,' I suggested to McNab. 'That way, at least they won't be bouncing around and it will give more time for any tranquilliser still in their systems to wear off.'

He agreed, and we released the nursing mothers into their indoor quarters. Now there was nothing more to be done except to leave them in peace for a few hours and hope that St Francis was listening. There was no point in saying anything to Shelagh about the affair when I telephoned her that night. I felt wretched enough as it was, without re-hashing everything. Nothing even she might have said could have provided any mental loophole through which I could wriggle away from the brutal fact that I had put the joeys' lives at great risk.

After a sleepless night I went down to the safari park early. It was seven o'clock. McNab and the rest of the staff would not be in for another hour. My heart was bounding as I went to the wallaby night-house and opened the sliding door an inch. Peeping in with my stomach anxiously churning, I scanned the sawdusted floor. There was no sign of any still, pink sausages. I went over every square inch again, straining my eyes till their muscles ached: not a joey in sight.

Only then did I raise my head a little to look at the crouching wallabies. All twelve of them seemed in good order, but there was no way of knowing how things were going in their pouches. Maybe the flattened corpse of a joey was underneath one of them or hidden under a layer of bedding. I pulled the door right open and gently shooed the animals out onto the grass. Nothing fell out of them as they hopped off into the morning sunlight. On hands and knees I meticulously picked through the sawdust, the bedding and the droppings, sweeping clear every inch of the floor with my bare hands. Saints be praised! Not one single baby could I find.

I went outside and watched the wallabies moving about, busily cropping the short grass. All seemed perfect. I hurried off to see if McNab was in yet and to give him the good news. In the days that followed, frequent inspections by McNab and his keepers turned up no evidence that any of the willy-nilly adoptions had failed. To my delight, it gradually became obvious that all eight babies were none the worse for mum-swapping; after a few more weeks furry brown heads began to peep out of the pouches on sunny days.

'Well, Mac,' I said, when it was clear that the wallabies were out of danger, 'it seems that they must be very civilised and tolerant creatures. One kid's as good as the next to those little ladies.'

'Yes,' he murmured, 'but no thanks to your tranquillisers, David. How many millions of years have wallabies been happily bringing up their young without 'em?'

He had a point, and a good one, but it struck me then how generally accepted on the zoo scene the veterinarian had become. Of course some of the old prejudices still lingered on, and calamities like the wallaby affair did not help, but most zoo men appreciated well enough how veterinary science could make their jobs easier and raise the standard of zoo care by – and this was the fundamental and important thing – improving the health, diet, handling, breeding and day-to-day welfare of the animals. I thought back to my early days at Belle Vue, when I despaired of my medical knowledge ever matching the wisdom and experience of Matt Kelly, or of showing him that modern drugs and other developments could go hand in hand with his innate animal-craft. Now even old hands like Kelly and McNab would grudgingly admit that perhaps my potions, flying darts, autopsies and analysing did have something to offer. That battle was all but won at last, I felt, and it would be together that we would tackle the numberless problems that lay ahead.

Chapter Twenty

ALTHOUGH THE fascination of tending exotic animals is endless, it is not every day that a vet is faced with a life and death emergency. What may start as a comparatively simple task (if such a thing may be said to exist in a zoo vet's work) can develop into a situation calling for rapid action if a valuable animal is to be saved. For example, a new hippopotamus, Hercules, arrived one afternoon at the zoo in Manchester. He had been sent from Whipsnade in a massive crate made out of thick wooden beams reinforced with steel bands. The hippo is not a creature to be trifled with. He can hurl himself forwards or spin round on his hind feet with remarkable agility, he is as unstoppable as a tank and he delivers a fearsome chomping, crushing bite. To be on the safe side, Whipsnade had given Hercules a dose of phencyclidine before sending him off and had strongly recommended that he should receive a further shot just before he was uncrated in Manchester. They feared that otherwise, once the door of the crate was opened, a highly irascible hippo might emerge and make his way like an express train, walls and so on notwithstanding, towards the city centre.

Hercules' crate was open-topped and by climbing up the side I could look down on the steaming armour-plating of the big hippopotamus. He was standing calmly enough without any sign of agitation and showing little sign of the effects of the sedative. I had not unloaded a hippo before. My inclination would have been to forgo the second phencyclidine injection but Whipsnade, with much more experience of these matters at the time, had made the point strongly. They had even sent a measured dose of the drug. I filled my syringe, bent down over the side of the crate and slapped my stoutest needle through the hippo's rump. Hercules reacted by slamming my wrist hard against the wooden side of the crate. I was trapped securely. Hercules maintained the pressure against my wrist with all his might. He wiggled his hips a bit and ground my hand excruciatingly into the wood. Biting my tongue, I slapped vainly at the hippo's bottom with my other hand. It was some minutes before he conceded to pull away and I could retrieve my extremity, now numb, black and horribly scuffed. Twenty years later I still have no feeling in that part of my wrist.

After a quarter of an hour Hercules was still standing but his ears were drooping slightly and there was a string of saliva hanging from his jaw. I decided to let him out. The bolts were removed from the reinforced door and the door was opened wide. We were using the rear door to make him back out so that he would be less likely to charge. Hercules did not budge. No matter what we did, tapping his nose with a stick, tempting him with food or slapping his back, he was not inclined to go into reverse gear. So we cautiously opened the front door, revealing fully the bucolic features of Hercules for the first time. He stared blandly at the inside of the tropical river house where he was now to live, sniffed disdainfully and blinked his drowsy eyelids. Then he saw the shining pool of warm water for him, its surface wreathed in misty vapour. Very sedately Hercules began to move forwards. He emerged from the crate, paused briefly, then walked slowly towards the pool. He went down the ramp at the side of the pool as if on tiptoe, sniffed at the water, found it to his liking and very gracefully slipped in. Through the clear water, not yet sullied by hippo droppings, we could see him settle peacefully on the bottom of the pool and then, gradually it seemed, fall asleep. The second dose of phencyclidine,

together with the soothing warm bath, was having an understandable but potentially lethal effect. A conscious hippo can hold its breath underwater for many minutes but will eventually come to the surface to take in a fresh gulp of air. A doped hippo might very well be a different matter. Suppose Hercules inhaled blissfully while dreaming on the bottom of his pool? A cluster of icicles formed in the pit of my stomach.

'It looks as if he's going to sleep,' I told the keepers around me. 'Get some ropes – fast. We could be in big trouble!'

Some of the men dashed off. The zoo director and I stood at the water's edge looking anxiously down at the recumbent form of the hippo three feet below the surface. When the ropes arrived there was only one thing for it. Stripping off to our underpants, Matt Kelly and I jumped into the water and dived for the submerged hulk. It is no easy task to feel one's way over a hippo's anatomy without the benefit of a pair of goggles and towing a length of thick rope. Spluttering we both surfaced for a quick discussion on a plan of action.

'You try to get a rope on the back legs, Matt,' I said. 'I'll see if I can get one round the neck.'

Matt dived again and I followed. Hercules slumbered on, unaware of the visitors struggling clumsily about his submarine bedroom. I would not dare to such liberties with a hippo in full possession of its senses. After much effort and repeated returns to the surface with bursting lungs we managed to place the ropes more or less as we wanted them. The keepers hauled on the ropes and to my relief Hercules, most un-Venus-like, rose to the surface. The great nostrils opened as his head cleared the water and he exhaled gently. His eyes were half closed and there was a pleasant softening of the hippo's usual grim smile.

It was impossible to drag the heavy creature onto land. There were not enough of us, hippos have no convenient handles, and I was afraid that the excessive use of ropes on Hercules' limbs and neck might injure him. In water he weighed much less, so we would have to support him in the pool by passing ropes under his belly until he was no longer under the influence. We kept the crucial head up by wrapping towels round it and slinging it to a beam. Hercules looked for all the world as if he was suffering an attack of toothache and had taken to the whisky bottle to alleviate the pain.

After some hours Hercules began to wriggle on the supporting ropes. His eyes opened fully and he surveyed the strange scene sombrely. When he realised that his towel bandage inhibited chomping he became restless and we decided that he had come round enough to look after himself. After being untangled he retired to the bottom of the pool from which secure position he looked up at us lugubriously. Several minutes later I watched him come to the surface to breathe deeply. Hercules was going to be all right.

Hercules was indeed all right. He immediately fell in love with his pool set in an imitation tropical jungle with waterfalls, islands and luscious vegetation. His arrival,

293

however, spelt disaster for some other denizens of the Manchester jungle. Sharing his habitat were tapirs, capybaras and an assortment of exotic birds. These Hercules proceeded to stalk, and, if possible, eat. He would play the crocodile, lurking beneath the surface of the water now dark with his droppings, and using his protuberant eyes as mini-periscopes. When a tapir came down to drink or a bird perched on a rock at the water's edge, Hercules would glide stealthily in like a killer submarine. With a sudden charge when he was within inches of his prey he would seize it in his jaws and kill it instantly with one powerful crunch. Then Hercules the hippo would feast until not a scrap remained. So much for vegetarianism: Hercules fancied meat and he still does. Sometimes when he is off colour I stand on the rocks by his pool and toss him loaves packed with pick-me-ups or stimulants. I have to watch carefully for the pair of gleaming eyes that just about break the water surface and come slowly but steadily towards my feet. At such moments I skip smartly backwards.

Hercules would seem to relish a taste of vet's meat to break the monotony of his orthodox diet, and perhaps it is for the same reason that zoo animals so often swallow unusual objects. Sometimes these things are ingested accidentally but at other times there may be special reasons for them being taken in voluntarily, as in the case of the sealion, which in the wild can often be found carrying a few stones quite harmlessly in its stomach. These stones act as ballast to help the animal dive, rather like the weighted belt of a skin diver: thus deeper diving species of sealion tend to carry more ballast than the shallower diving species. In captivity this natural, fairly limited taking on of stones can go wrong. Where sealions are kept in fresh water with no access to salt, particularly if the pool is a simple one scooped out of the earth, the animal may attempt to satisfy its craving for salt in its diet by eating soil and stones. To avoid this I try to see that all the sealions and seals in my care that are not in saltwater pools have table salt added daily to their fish diet.

Unfortunately, I still see the results of stone-swallowing by sealions over a long period, as when a sealion at a safari park in England died suddenly after a lengthy spell of erratic eating. For months it had been keen to feed but quickly lost its appetite after being given one or two fish. Then, as if it had just had a Chinese meal, it would be hungry and calling for fish within half an hour. The owners had not worried unduly because the sealion seemed to be actually gaining weight. Indeed it was! When I looked at the body it had a plump rounded belly that must surely be full of fat. I began the autoposy and within seconds of slicing through the abdominal wall was faced with an amazing sight. The sealion was, in fact, skinny and free of healthy fat stores. The stomach, which is normally about the same size and shape as a human's and lies tucked neatly away under the rib cage, was horribly distended. It filled the abdomen, squeezing the liver and kidneys and intestines. It bulged everywhere, particularly back towards the tail. I could not see the end of it; it continued on into the pelvic cavity where only the bladder and associated organs should be found. Inside the stomach were stones, hundreds and hundreds of them packing every bit of available space and stretching the stomach wall until it was as thin as tissue paper. When they were all removed they filled three gallon buckets and weighed almost forty pounds. It was the worst foreign body load I had ever seen.

There were other sealions in the safari park of the same age as the poor dead individual. What about them? They were fit-looking animals who delighted in performing their skilful feats of balance before the visitors. All looked well, but I was of a mind to X-ray the lot of them to make certain that no more were carrying around stomachs like gravel pits. I asked the trainer whether there were any abnormal symptoms to report. He thought for a moment and began to shake his head.

'No, I don't think so except . . .' He frowned and then carried on. 'Except for Mimi. She's a little bit like Otto, the dead one, always hungry but very easily filled.'

I walked over to where Mimi stood elegantly on her show stand. She sniffed diffidently at me and clapped her front flippers hopefully. I could see no sign of trouble brewing. Then the trainer called Mimi off the stand and she slipped down onto the ground and hauled herself towards the fish bucket. As she passed I heard a soft and unusual sound, like the lapping of water on a shingle beach, the rush of pebbles one upon another. There was too much incidental noise from the other animals and the visitors to hear it clearly so I had Mimi taken to the quiet of the hospital. There I listened again. When she moved it was possible to hear the crunching, grinding noise of gravel. I stroked her and made friends and then carefully pressed her stomach. Scr-r-runch. It was exactly like digging into a bag of marbles. Mimi was full of rocks.

Although, along with the giraffe, the sealion is one of the more difficult animals to anaesthetise (its ability to hold its breath as if diving can cause problems with anaesthetic gas machines), I decided to operate. Opening the stomach of a dog to remove swallowed objects is a common and not very difficult operation but the sealion is somewhat trickier. A particular risk is post-operative infection from the skin, which literally teems with all sorts of nasty bacteria. For the surgeon, too, contact with sealion skin and other tissues can be risky if there are any cuts in his rubber gloves and abrasions on his hands. A germ often found living harm-lessly on sealion skin can attack pigs, dolphins and other animals dramatically, and in humans may set up the un-pleasant infection known as 'blubber finger' or 'seal hand' to generations of seal skinners and whaling men.

From Mimi's stomach one by one I retrieved 124 stones weighing almost sixteen pounds altogether. No wonder she had been hungry, with nowhere to accommodate a decent meal. When she was stitched up Mimi was a much more streamlined creature. I looked forward to seeing her eat a hearty meal of three or four pounds of herring in a few days after the stomach sutures had done their work and she could come off the post-operative diet of liquidised fish and water.

Other animals have eaten odd things as well. The elephant at Belle Vue Zoo that took an umbrella did not seem to suffer the slightest twinge of the collywobbles, although an enormous old elephant seal at Cleethorpes found a woolly cardigan too much for it and tragically choked to death. It is not always necessary to approach the stomach by operation through the abdomen, since increasingly nowadays, particularly in dolphins, the arch-swallowers of bric-à-brac, we employ an ingenious piece of equipment normally used for exploring the higher reaches of the human bowel. This is the Olympus fibre-optic gastroscope, a very expensive device which can do wonders when slipped simply and without anaesthetic down the animal's throat. It is thin and flexible and carries a powerful light source, a mobile viewing tip, a water spray, an air tube for inflating organs to be inspected, and a host of special attachments. Looking through the eyepiece we can see magnified and in full colour every nook and cranny in the stomach and even further down into the intestine or up the bile duct. The tip can be made to go round corners and to look backwards towards the viewer. By passing minute instruments down within the tube we can cauterise bleeding points, take biopsy samples of diseased tissue and grab or lasso objects. The stomach and bowels expanded by air from the gastroscope become fascinating caverns and grottoes through which by remote control we can wander in search of the bizarre and the diseased.

It was by using this machine that we took the first colour photographs ever made of the inside of a living dolphin. Since then we have begun to build up a reference library of slides of the various bacterial, fungal and other ailments that can attack the crucial three stomachs of our cetacean friends. One of the first patients on which we used the fibre-optic gastroscope was Brandy, a talented star of the dolphin show at Marineland in Palma Nova, Majorca. One day, for no apparent reason, Brandy swallowed one of the soft plastic rings, six inches across, which he played with during his performances. Down into his stomach it went and down it stayed. Nothing untoward happened at first, and Brandy continued to eat and work normally. But the powerful acids in his stomach were slowly vulcanising the plastic and turning the soft ring into something much more hard and irritant. David Mudge, the director of Marineland and an old friend in the dolphin business, became worried when the ring was not regurgitated as he had hoped. What was more, after some days Brandy began to look unwell. He became irritable, his work became erratic and his appetite disappeared. David was certain that Brandy was experiencing stomach pain.

We had talked together over the telephone when the ring was first swallowed and had decided to observe the animal and to treat him conservatively at first. Now it became obvious that we would have to intervene with strong positive measures. Andrew, my partner, flew out to Majorca with the fibre-optic gastroscope and accompanied by David Wild, the most skilled 'driver', as he calls himself, of the complex instrument in the country. Brandy certainly looked ill. He was pale, seemed tense and in pain, and his usual cheeky, vivacious temperament had changed to one of irritable misery. No longer was he cock of the male dolphins in Palma Nova, forever paying court to his harem of admiring females. Blood analysis showed strong evidence of bleeding ulcers in his stomach. Without further ado Brandy was caught, hauled out of the pool and placed on a soft rubber mattress.

Dolphins out of water produce a lot of body heat and unless they are kept wet may overheat and show dangerous cracking and peeling of the skin. A man stood by with a bucket wetting the animal down while Andrew completed his preparations. First, wet towels were wrapped round Brandy's upper and lower jaws and used to pull the mouth open and hold it open. Gently, Andrew passed the lubricated gastroscope over the back of the dolphin's tongue, to one side of the larynx and then down the gullet into the first stomach. Kneeling behind him David Wild watched through the eyepiece as the tip of the instrument moved onwards, spraying the lens with water when stomach juices threatened to cloud the vision and pushing the walls of the stomach away from the tube with air so that he could have space to look around. Through a side attachment to the eye-piece Andrew was able to monitor progress as well. Before long they both saw the first of a series of ugly bleeding ulcers in the stomach lining. Everywhere there was black blood from the ulcers, partly digested. Brandy's digestion was in a terrible state. David swung the tip of the gastroscope round, and there was the ring! They could see a segment of the red plastic lying in a black pool of blood. The natural contractions of the stomach muscles against the hardening ring were grinding one ulcer after another through the delicate velvety lining of the organ.

Now to get the ring out. A special attachment to the gastroscope allowed the introduction of a wire loop which was guided round the ring and back to the gastroscope again. When the ring was firmly snared it was pulled to the tip of the instrument and then both ring and gastroscope were withdrawn together. Brandy gave an enormous gulp as the ring travelled back up his gullet. Luckily dolphins have remarkably elastic gullets for swallowing large fish whole, otherwise there would have been a risk of rupturing the organ. With the ring gone Brandy looked much relieved, but Andrew reintroduced the gastroscope to inspect the ulcer damage. Some of the worst bleeding points were electrically cauterised and photographs were taken. Then Brandy was returned, to his great relief, to the pool and his wives, and his complete recovery was ensured by a course of tablets normally given to dyspeptic middle-aged business executives. To celebrate his sense of well-being after the poolside operation, Brandy was seen to mate long and amorously with one of the female dolphins, and eleven and a half months later, on the following Boxing Day, a little baby dolphin was born in the pool at Palma Nova.

☆☆☆☆☆☆☆☆☆☆☆☆☆☆☆☆☆☆☆☆☆☆☆

Chapter Twenty-one

☆☆☆☆☆☆☆☆☆☆☆☆☆☆☆☆☆☆☆☆☆☆

THE EYES of Kim, the Antibes killer whale, began to improve after the chloramphenicol injections and for a time my gloomy forebodings about his condition lightened. He seemed happy in the hospital pool where he was regularly visited by Martin Padley, Michael Riddell or some other member of the marineland staff throughout the day. I, too, would spend half an hour with him as often as possible, plopping into the water beside him, paddling round his great body, stroking his flippers with my toes and talking to him. When he had had enough of our company he would give us a firm knock with his nose or politely show his teeth. Then it was time to climb out of the pool and let him take up his position by the massive metal door that separated him from the main pool, close behind which Betty and her two attendant dolphins would lie most of the time communicating to him in their secret language and, I suppose, doing their best to cheer him up in 'cetaceanese'.

But the regular blood analyses were not encouraging. The level of red cells was appallingly low, the antibody proteins remained high and now suddenly a new fault was observed: the tests for kidney function showed that these vital organs were in trouble. Everything in Kim's body seemed to be breaking down and Andrew and I began to talk of the possibility of imminent multi-organ failure.

Every day, pints of French anti-anaemia liquid were injected into Kim's food fish and we made sure he had massive extra supplements of iron, trace elements, vitamin C and folic acid along with his usual vitamins. But nothing made any impression on the now thin and watery blood. As, years before, I had desperately tried to arrange a blood transfusion for Cuddles at Flamingo Park when he suffered a massive intestinal haemorrhage, so again I began to consider the possibility of taking a gallon or two from another killer whale. After all, on this occasion I had another whale to hand.

When I raised the matter with Michael he was understandably lukewarm about turning Betty into a blood donor, but typically said he'd go along with a transfusion attempt if I really thought there was a realistic chance of doing some good. 'How the hell are you going to get the gallons you need without stressing Betty by keeping her far too long out of the water?' he asked. A belligerent and excitable whale when put on the bottom of the pool, Betty was, as we knew from bitter experience, prone to overheating as well as to making dangerous sideways snaps at folks' legs. She wasn't playing either: if any of those snaps connected it wouldn't be a few nicks in one's skin through a torn wet suit but rather an instantaneous amputation. And to get blood, we'd obviously have to work as close as possible to her.

When I talked about gallons of blood, wasn't I anyway being terribly imprecise as to what was really necessary? Accurate calculations were essential. Aquatic animals have, as part of their adaptation to life in the water, much bigger blood volumes than terrestrial animals. Ducks, for example, have more blood than hens, and diving birds such as puffins more than non-diving species. The same goes for marine mammals, and radioactive iodine experiments on killer whales had shown that 10% of their body weight is blood volume compared with 8.5% in humans although some dolphins have as high as 15% and young elephant seals reach an amazing 20%. It worked out that in order to bring Kim's blood above the minimum level at which transfusions are ordered in anaemic human patients, he would need no less than sixty gallons of blood – almost exactly what I calculated Betty's total blood volume to be! So what about just giving some blood, as much as Betty could safely spare?

My next task was to consider whether the blood of the two animals was compatible. Blood groups don't only occur in man. Bottle-nosed dolphins have several groups and at least two groups have been identified in fin and sperm whales. But nothing was known about killer whales although the probability was that they existed and would therefore be of crucial significance in any transfusion attempt. I decided to do the basic test, the only one open to me, of cross-matching Kim's and Betty's blood. This simply meant observing under a microscope how drops of blood taken from each of the two whales behaved when mixed together. I took two phials of blood to the local hospital laboratory and asked for the test to be set up. It didn't take a minute. When the samples were mixed on a square of smooth white tile, the formation of large clumps of red cells was quickly apparent even to the naked eye. No doubt about it: Kim's and Betty's blood definitely did not get on together. Even a pint or two of Betty's blood injected into Kim's system would cause serious and possibly fatal effects.

So ended all thoughts of transfusion, but while it had been a live issue I had spent much time pondering on how to physically extract large quantities of blood from a whale. After the failure of the cross-matching, this eventually led to a new line of thought. I had heard of a unique form of therapy being used in Germany on human patients which entailed the withdrawal of a quantity of blood from the body, treatment of it by ozone gas and then return of the blood into the patient's circulation. This ozone therapy was being credited with excellent results in various types of infectious disease and certain blood cancers. No-one seemed clear how it worked exactly, although ozone is a powerful killer of microbes. But with the potentially poisonous ozone gas only being applied to the blood outside the body, the procedure seemed safe to me.

One of the pioneers of ozone therapy of human disease

in Germany was my friend Dr Ferdi Wurms, brother of Fritz Wurms, Director of the safari park at Stukenbrock. Dr Wurms and I had often met at Stukenbrock and discussed common areas of medical interest; brought up in a 'zoological' family, he was as much at home with the problems of sick animals as of sick people. I decided to ring him to see what he thought about trying ozone therapy on Kim. 'I've got a bull killer whale with what I believe to be a chronic focus of infection. How do you feel about coming down to Nice with the ozone machine and us having a try at washing his blood?'

'As soon as I finish my clinic this afternoon,' he replied, 'I'll be on my way. The maker of the ozone machines has a private plane, and I'll get him to fly me and all the gear down.'

Although it was April, the weather was bitterly cold on the Côte d'Azur. The wind howled down from the snow-covered Alps that seemed in the crystal-clear air of early evening to rise straight out of the orchards, cypress groves and red-tiled roofs behind the marineland. As I waited for Dr Wurms' plane to arrive, I worried again about the procedure. Perhaps I'd asked the German down on a fool's errand. Blood-sampling whales where a mere seven or ten millilitres is enough for a host of laboratory tests is one thing; pumping out litre after litre of blood and then pumping it back in again is something else. How long could I safely keep Kim dry on the bottom of a hospital pool? Would he lose patience and start flailing his tail around, dislodging the vital tubes? Could I find and connect with a big enough blood vessel that would provide a decent rate of flow? If clotting occurred in the needles, cannulas, tubes or whatever, how much damage would I inflict by multiple re-insertions? I realised that I'd have to use the tail veins. Only four of them would be big enough for the job so I would have only four chances.

Dr Wurms and Herr Felgner, the ozone machine maker, arrived on schedule with loads of equipment and, as is always my practice, we went straight to work. It was dark by the time Kim's pool was completely drained and the big whale was comfortably lying on thick pads of plastic foam

303

which Martin and his team of trainers had slipped under his body just before the last few inches of water were pumped out. Banks of specially rigged floodlights illuminated the scene. The steadily dropping temperature and frosty wind were ideal for the whale. There was no chance of him overheating in such conditions, but for us in our motley assortment of dress – wet suits, swimming trunks, old jeans and wellington boots – it was increasingly unpleasant. My hands were soon numb from the spray of icy water which was continually hosepiped over the whale's body to assist the cooling process. Placing the tubes into the veins was going to be tricky.

All the instruments were taken down into the pool: oxygen cylinders, the ozone machine itself, dozens of blood transfusion bottles, black plastic tubes of every thickness by the yard and hundreds of sterile needles, including some that looked like miniature drainpipes. 'How much blood do you think we need to draw off for treatment?' I asked Ferdi Wurms.

'Well, going by comparison with humans, I would say we should wash at least thirty litres – seven gallons.'

'Any idea how long that would take?'

'In a man, ozone washing of one litre, which is normally all we need to do, takes maybe twenty minutes. The machine draws out the blood into the flasks by suction, then the blood is shaken gently to mix it with a known volume of ozone that is produced electronically in the machine by conversion of oxygen, and then the blood is sent back into the circulation through the same tube and needle under positive pressure. Easy.'

'But thirty litres would take ten hours by that reckoning.'

The German pulled his anorak hood close around his face and smiled gently. 'Yes. And that's if the tubes and needles don't get blocked up by coagulation.'

Ten hours on the bottom – if all went smoothly! Still, La Soeur had said all that time ago that everything was going to be all right, even if nothing had happened at the hour she had specified. Maybe the ozone machine was the 'three things'. After all there was the machine itself, the oxygen cylinder and the glass flask.

I was clutching at straws. 'OK. Let's get started,' I said. 'The first thing is to plant a big needle securely into a big vein' (something that had never been done before in a killer whale). 'Put the heaviest net we have over the narrow part of the tail and have four men sit on it at each side.' The net with its chain and lead weights must have weighed about four hundred-weights. With eight men in addition, maybe, just maybe, it would be enough to stop me being smashed in the face by the tail flukes if Kim objected to being the guinea-pig in this rare experiment.

When the tail stock seemed reasonably secure, I knelt down by the flukes and signalled for Wurms to move the equipment ready for connection. I injected some local anaesthetic into the skin over the main blood vessel on the upper surface of the tail and then, shivering from the cold, I took a needle five inches long and as thick as a pencil. Sucking in my breath and gritting my teeth, ready for all hell to break loose, I stabbed it into the numbed area. Killer whale tail flesh is as tough as green wood; it has to be to form such a powerful paddle. I gave a grunt and pushed with all my strength. The thick needle moved on and suddenly I was blinded by a bright red curtain – I had struck oil. The needle had entered at first attempt the central artery.

Wiping my face and blinking through the gore, I saw a powerful jet of bright red arterial blood spurting out of the needle. 'Connect up!' I shouted.

Ferdi Wurms moved in with a plastic tube and attached it to the needle. At once blood raced up the tubing and began to fill the big glass bottle held by Martin. The ozone machine hummed. I could smell the characteristic 'seaside' smell of ozone in the chilly air. Normally veins, not arteries, are used for sampling and injection but for this technique either would do. With the circuit set up, I sat back on my haunches and watched. Kim didn't seem to have noticed a thing; he was in his most co-operative mood. I watched the piston on the machine move as it sucked air out of the receiving bottle. Herr Felgner twiddled knobs and adjusted the ozone concentration. Martin seemed mesmerised by the rising tide of red in the bottle that he held and shook gently as Ferdi Wurms instructed. I looked for signs of clotting in the plastic tubing and the filter of the bottle itself but couldn't see any. Thank God or, as Michael later suggested with a certain ecclesiastical wittiness, Saint Januarius, that whales and all other cetaceans have a prolonged blood-clotting time (the average clotting time for bottle-nosed dolphins is three-quarters of an hour).

Sure enough, we had a litre of blood within about ten minutes. When the bottle was full, ozone was pumped in and the blood/ozone mixture was gently shaken while the machine was reversed and began to push the blood back down the tube and into the artery. As soon as the bottle was empty, Wurms and Felgner began the cycle again and blood once more surged up into the bottle. From time to time samples of blood were extracted from the system and taken by one of the trainers on his motor-cycle to the hospital laboratory a couple of miles away for oxygen level analysis. The technicians and doctors there, bless their hearts, have always been happy to provide us with a round-the-clock service 365 days a year. None of the National Health Service mentality – 'Love to help you, Doc, but there'd be bloody hell to pay if the NUPE shop steward got to know we were handling animal blood' – that we have sometimes encountered in Great Britain when handling emergencies in the middle of the night and far away from our usual veterinary laboratories at Newmarket and Weybridge.

At the third filling of the bottle I noticed that the blood seemed to be flowing more reluctantly. 'Some coagulation developing in the system,' said Dr Wurms. 'Check the needle.'

I disconnected the plastic tube from the needle in Kim's tail. The gout of bright blood that pulsated up towards me was as strong as ever. 'It must be in the tubes or bottle,' I said. Wurms prepared a new unit and we changed over. Everything ran smoothly once more.

The cold intensified and, with all of us clustered round the whale being relatively immobile except for Martin who continued his bottle-shaking, cramps and numbness began to set in. 'I must get something warmer,' I muttered through chattering teeth to Michael. 'The cold is coming straight through wet suit, two sweaters and a duffle coat!'

Michael is probably the best 'fixer' in the whole of France, and he disappeared to return after a few minutes with half a dozen bottles of Vin du Var and a lady's astrakhan fur coat. 'Some old bird left this here a few weeks ago,' he said. 'Try and squeeze into it.' Somehow I managed to stretch the fur coat over all my other garments. It did the trick. 'Must be worth the best part of ten thousand francs,' said Michael, 'but she really ought to have collected it before now.' At each of the following changes of tube and bottle the exquisite astrakhan got a bloody drenching, but I was soon as warm as toast. Michael kept the Vin du Var flowing.

The hours passed by and Kim remained utterly placid. I checked his heart and respiration, felt for 'hot spots' on his forehead, flippers and flukes, smelled his breath: everything was good and stable. We changed ten litres, then fifteen, twenty and twenty-five. The pile of discarded transfusion units on the pool bottom mounted steadily.

At last, and with the original needle still firmly in place and running as freely as it had at the beginning, the final weak litre was washed in the ozone and returned to the whale's circulation. With a sigh of relief I removed the needle and slapped on a pad of cotton wool. 'Get all the gear out of the pool and begin filling up,' I said wearily.

Dawn was breaking over the Mediterranean and the caked blood on my astrakhan coat was frozen and glistening. 'You look like a damn' great Black Forest gâteau,' Martin remarked.

We breakfasted as is the custom after nightwork at Marineland Côte d'Azur on whole ungutted mackerel (the same fish that the whale and dolphins get), grilled over a wood fire set in a rusty old wheelbarrow and accompanied by fresh baguettes of bread, lemons and red Provençal wine. Then, leaving one man to watch over the whale as he floated up with the steadily rising water, we went off to snatch a few hours sleep. At least we had proved that transfusion and similar techniques involving the movements of large quantities of blood in giant mammals were technologically possible.

The ozone therapy didn't produce any ill effects on Kim. With his pool full again he even seemed a little chirpier and did some upside-down swimming, a cheerful sign in killer whales. I waited two days before taking my first blood sample after the treatment. The results of the analysis were amazing – the level of antibody protein in the blood had dropped steeply. For the first time since he fell ill, the graph that plotted his internal battle with infection showed a turn for the better. 'We must repeat the treatment,' I told Michael excitedly. 'This could be the answer to all our troubles'. Wurms and Felgner flew down from Germany again a few days later and in now much milder weather conditions we washed Kim's blood a second time.

We also made an heroic attempt at X-raying his chest with a powerful industrial set that could penetrate metal. It entailed covering the whole of one side of his body with X-ray film and the conversion of an ice-cream kiosk into a temporary dark room. Sadly, the radiographs were useless and showed nothing; the whale's dense tissues in his broad trunk scattered the X-rays in all directions.

More depressingly, in the days following the second ozone therapy, there was no further dramatic improvement in the blood sample and within a month the antibody levels started to rise once more and Kim stopped accepting fish altogether. My tests showed serious kidney failure now: a human or a chimpanzee with an analysis as bad as that would not be expected to live more than a few days unless put on to an artificial kidney machine. Michael, typically, actually made enquiries about hiring such equipment but it was hopeless – the same problem of the massive blood volume of a killer whale confronted us. Human kidney machines are capable of treating an animal containing a mere eight pints of blood in its body. Kim would have needed to be linked up to two dozen kidney machines simultaneously!

Because of the impossibility of forcibly getting anything down the whale's throat, I wondered how I might flush his system through with fresh water; stomach tubing was out of the question. A scientist in Denmark had recently proved that porpoises, contrary to what we had believed up to that time, could absorb water through their skins, a frog-like facility which was most unexpected in marine mammals. Perhaps killer whales too could 'drink' through their skins. 'Let's fill up Kim's pool with pure tap water,' I said to Michael.

He looked aghast. 'But it has always been said that dolphins and whales in fresh water get skin disease and have difficulty with buoyancy.'

'The buoyancy idea is nonsense. As for the skin, well, two or three days won't do any harm. Even if it does peel a bit, so what? We're in big trouble. Cosmetic matters can wait.'

Michael reached for the phone. 'Get the fire brigade,' he told his secretary. 'We'll need them to pump in from the hydrants. Oh, and give the Fire Chief my compliments and tell him it's the mad professor from England again. There'll be the usual free dinner and champagne for him and his crew if he can get it done this evening.'

The Chef des Pompiers in Antibes had helped out magnificently on numerous occasions in the past when we had had water problems, even providing fire engine escorts when animals were being transported from the airport to the marineland. 'I am ze 'ead of all zings to do wiz water in ze 'ole area, professor,' he told me when we first met at the opening of the marineland. 'Dolphins, whales, zay leeve in ze water so voila! It iz my job just like fires and rescues to look after zem, n'est-ce pas?'

'Oui, ah oui,' I had replied. 'And maybe, professor,' the Chief had carried on, 'you will train me some dolphins for me to 'elp bring back ze corpses of drowned people.'

'That is your province also?'

'Mais naturellement, professor – everyzing to do wiz water.'

The firemen duly arrived and Kim's salt water was changed for fresh. Within twenty-four hours the beneficial effect of the fresh water was clearly to be seen in the whale's blood. I arranged for Kim to be kept alternately in three days fresh and three days salt water from then on. The fire brigade would be eating and drinking well that spring!

The kidneys were still not functioning normally, however, and I had to find some more specific line of therapy. Pills and potions were out; Kim still wasn't eating. There was nothing among orthodox injectable drugs that I felt might be beneficial. I had already dabbled in the highly unorthodox in this case what with the Antoiniste sister and the magical ozone machine, so perhaps there would be no harm in trying herbal remedies. Many 'orthodox' drugs like digitalis, atropine, strychnine and the antibiotics are strictly of herbal origin. Although I was not familiar with the broad field of herbalism which claims to provide remedies for the whole spectrum of ailments human and veterinary, I consulted the French pharmaceutical tomes where orthodox and unorthodox medicines and their applications are listed alongside one another. Continental physicians are not as toffee-nosed as their British counterparts over so-called alternative medicine. I found an injectable liquid compounded from the fresh leaves of a plant with a Latin name, *Cynara scolymus*. At least such vegetable extracts should not do any harm, even if they did no good. I ordered two thousand bottles of the stuff – and probably made a significant contribution to the balance sheet of the little pharmaceutical company that manufactured it.

Martin and his men began injecting Kim with the herbal kidney preparation, which looked and smelled rather like Coca-Cola, every eight hours. Kim was by now very thin and his breath had become foul-smelling. And, like everything else to do with whale medicine, the unpleasant odour was big: it was detectable many yards away and this of course in the open air.

Although otherwise his breathing continued to be normal with never a sign of cough and there was nothing I could hear through his mighty chest wall with my stethoscope, I began increasingly to suspect that Kim's hidden focus of infection might lie in the lungs. I still stuck firmly to the diagnosis of a chronic thick-walled abscess in soft tissue despite increasing scepticism on the part of the

310

French vets and laboratories who opted for leukaemia, and despite La Souer with her 'grille'. There had even been a gratuitous diagnosis by a man with a 'black box' who literally stole a few drops of Kim's blood from our small laboratory in the marineland itself and phoned us to say that his wondrous machine had without a shadow of a doubt indicated a severe liver disease in the whale. For a few thousand francs he would be prepared to mix his own remedy.

Despite all the doubts as to whether my line of reasoning on Kim's illness was correct, Michael Riddell, Andrew Greenwood and Martin Padley, who had followed the grim saga every inch of the way and with whom I discussed each of the innumerable laboratory results and dissected my conclusions, gave me unwavering support and agreed with my general thesis. If only we could get at the secret fortress of germs and wipe them out! The trouble with abscesses is that even with antibiotic treatment they usually need draining ultimately. Either they burst or are lanced. But you can't lance something unless you know where it is. Anyway, open-chest surgery on whales was out of the question. We have one anaesthetic machine in Great Britain that can keep a dolphin breathing while its chest is opened but the apparatus big enough to ventilate Kim simply doesn't exist.

The strain of round-the-clock nursing of the big whale week after week and month after month showed in the faces of the marineland staff. Night work, cold water, the physical strain of pushing and pulling heavy equipment and the whale himself, the tedium of long hours standing with their arms extended, holding an intravenous bottle or an oxygen lance, the discomfort of crouching or kneeling in a fixed position holding a needle or a tube at a precise angle: all this on top of the day's regular routine work of preparing the marineland for thousands of visitors, cutting the fish and presenting the shows going on as usual seven days a week. The worst thing that insidiously sapped us all was the feeling that we were, for all the occasional minor triumphs and apparent moments of success, losing the war. Kim was fighting hard but was it hard enough?

311

Chronicling all this, as in the earlier books that I wrote, I record events as they actually occurred. The American publishers of my first autobiographical volume, *Zoovet*, asked me to 'soften' several of my stories to ensure that there were always happy endings, less gore and pain and an abundance of 'Ohh-ahhs!' as the little tiger cub or elephant or giraffe takes up its bed and walks. I have always resisted this approach. The care of wild animals isn't all dewy eyes and plaudits: it is rough, tough and so often depressingly, frustratingly a failure. It isn't all funny or easy – and it is best told as it is.

Phone calls at 3 am for me invariably mean trouble, so when I picked up the receiver one morning a week after the start of the herbal mixture, I was ready for some grim tidings of death or disaster. Michael's voice, however, was far from sombre. 'He's begun to eat again!' he announced before I could complete 'Bagshot 75. . .'. 'The night watchman tried him as usual ten minutes ago and he gobbled five kilos of mackerel and is asking for more.'

Kim was doing yet another of his displays of medical brinkmanship. 'Get Martin out of bed,' I said. 'Ask him to take blood at once and have the lab run the usual series of kidney function tests.' By breakfast time the results were in and we had the stunning reason for the whale's remarkable improvement: the kidneys were working perfectly normally again! I ordered the vegetable injections to be continued another month and telephoned the local bookshop to order a copy of *Culpeper's Compleat Manual of Herbs*.

Acupuncture in giraffes, white magic in the case of Cuddles the killer whale and now herbal remedies for Kim! 'What next?' Hanne asked as I opened the morning mail. (From one extreme to the other: there was a letter from a lady in New York who had a paralysed brown mouse. Could I please advise? I sent her a note and a tiny bottle of medicine to put in its water.) 'Chiropractic for crocodiles?'

'Why not? Or maybe a spell in the waters at Baden Baden might be just the thing for sick whales,' I replied.

Kim's kidneys never faltered again and the foul smell from his blow hole soon cleared with the spraying of anti-fungal aerosols down the nostrils when he breathed –

a tricky job. The blow hole opens and shuts quickly and is designed to keep out strong seas, let alone stuff squirted in by human beings. It needed a steady hand and good reflexes to deliver the jet into the hole which opened only at irregular and lengthy intervals.

The anaemia and high antibody levels continued as bad as ever, though, and he was down by now to half his normal weight, a sad, snake-like shadow of his former plump and glistening self. In a desperate effort to knock out the elusive bugs with something that could penetrate the less accessible areas of the body, I was now using the very expensive anti-tuberculosis antibiotic, rifampicin. It is rarely used for diseases other than TB but it can destroy a wide range of bacteria and it finds its way into the chronic well-walled nodules of tuberculosis, so perhaps it could infiltrate the stronghold of my hypothetical encapsulated abscess. One of rifampicin's common and harmless side-effects in humans is the staining red of the urine, saliva and tears. Killer whales naturally produce copious syrupy tears as a protection against the friction of movement through sea water. Kim on the rifampicin looked like some horrific monster from a Hammer film, weeping and drooling 'blood'. Despite normal kidney function the whale's appetite began to fade again by March 1982. It finally stopped completely and on 3 April I received the phone call I'd always known deep down I'd receive one day: Kim had died peacefully during the night.

The Sunday airbus to Nice was full of jolly up-market holidaymakers and the moneyed English expatriates of Monte Carlo and Juan-les-Pins. Lady Docker was sipping champagne across the aisle and I sat next to Cary Grant, who politely offered me his cheese. He wasn't hungry, but neither was I. In the rack above, among all the Gucci handbags and fur stoles, was the Bag, full of scalpels, sample bottles and sharp saws. I caught a whiff of my formalin bottle cutting through the mists of 'Opium' and 'Rive Gauche'. When a passing stewardess wrinkled her nose and looked up, trying to locate the source of the smell as usual, I never let on – as usual.

Many miles from the sea, in the quiet Provençal countryside near Gap, there lives a knackerman who has a keen amateur interest in whales and has disposed of the carcasses of many of the cetaceans washed up on the coastline of France. In his processing shed I performed the autopsy on Kim, helped to the end by Michael and Martin. There was no 'grille', nothing untoward between stomach and intestine, no leukaemia, no cancer, no diseased liver. But an abscess as big as a sack of coal, with a tough fibrous wall an inch thick, lay deep in the right lung. If I had known for sure its size or precisely where it lay, if X-rays had been possible on an animal of such a girth, if I had had a special extra-long cannula made and pierced the abscess through the chest wall and drained it, Kim could have made it. If.

I sat on the terrace of the marineland at Palma Nova in Majorca eating thin wafers of *jabugo* ham and splitting a bottle of Valdepeñas with my close friend the director, Robert Bennett. We had finished the routine two-monthly inspection of all the animals and in an hour I had to catch the one o'clock Iberia flight to London. 'By the way, I've got a little present for you,' said Robert, pulling something out of his pocket, 'the first of a new line of up-market souvenirs we've had made for the coming season.' Onto the table between us he trickled a chain carrying an exquisitely moulded pendant of a leaping dolphin in solid silver.

While I was admiring the gift, a posse of English tourists swept by, making for the bar in search of tea or Sangria and shade from the burning sun. One lady, lobster-red and perspiring, saw the shining pendant and in an unmistakable Manchester accent said to the man walking beside her, harnessed like a brewer's draught horse in a mesh of photographic equipment, 'Ay, Melvin, take a look at that. You can buy me one of those before we go back.'

'Right, luv,' replied the camera buff. 'Certainly, my dear.'

The incident at once recalled to my mind something which happened to another Melvin and his spouse six or seven years ago in the latter days of Manchester's Belle Vue Zoo.

The red-neck ostrich in Belle Vue was having one of his better days. Normally he was utterly bloody-minded and

314

anti-social. He liked nothing better than terrorising his keeper, fluffing out his apologies for wings and trying to leap high enough to stamp down on the man's head. On occasions in the past he had managed to kick the keeper in the solar plexus and flatten him. He'd broken one of the fellow's fingers and chipped a vertebra in the triumphant dance that followed, up and down the keeper's prone body. But today was indubitably one of his good days. Maybe it was the unaccustomed blue of the Manchester sky and the silver sun peeping over the Ardwick Hippodrome or the sound of the rushing roller-coaster across the park, warming up for the start of the Easter season, that mellowed him. At any rate the ostrich – he of the fearsome countenance, red-rimmed eye and iron-hard beak – was, as I insist, in a better mood. He was unarguably milder, no more than cantankerous, crotchety and quibbling. He hadn't, it would seem, had anything to quibble at all morning. No-one had looked at him in the wrong way. No-one had given him the faintest excuse for a punch-up. It was a good day. Until the lady with the pendant came along.

She was to humans a good-looking bird (I cannot speak for ostriches) and she wore a silver mink coat, silver stiletto heels and a silver necklace and pendant. Behind her trailed the probable fount of all these goodies – a small, globular, harassed-looking gentleman in a camel coat and brown 'racing man's' trilby. The ostrich didn't care for, in fact positively resented, the way in which she and then he stopped in front of his paddock and proceeded without so much as a by-your-leave to stare at him. It ruined the ostrich's erstwhile comparative euphoria. He took immediate remedial action. Advancing smartly towards the gawking couple, he did his usual: whipped out his long red neck, opened the steely beak and snapped at the lady's silver pendant. With one gulp and a 'Yawk! Friggin' 'ell, Melvin, look what's it's done to me!' the bauble was safely ensconced within the ostrich's gizzard. Honour satisfied, the ungainly bird turned away and stalked off, sniggering, I suspect, if indeed ostriches can snigger.

The encounter resulted in my being summoned by Matt Kelly, the head keeper, to do something. Silver-mink was

doing her nut, he told me over the telephone, demanding
the retrieval of her plundered pendant pronto. I drove
down to the zoo and found Matt in an embattled position.
He was standing by the ostrich paddock confronted by the
silver mink lady who was giving him hell, the camel-coated
gent who was looking even more harassed and mopping
his brow and the red-neck ostrich who was looking for
trouble. 'That effin' bird's got my pendant!' shrieked the
silver mink. 'Gerrit back or I'll sue you!'

'Darling, I keep telling you it's not platinum, it's only
silver plate. I bought it, I know. Let the bird keep it.' That
was camel-coat.

'Well now, Oi'm sure Dr Taylor can help us here,' said
Matt – passing the buck craftily as I arrived.

'I want my pendant back or I'll sue for assault, for theft,
for grievous bodily whatever, for gross incompetence!'
Silver-mink stamped her silver heels.

'Darling, cool it, my luv. I'll buy you another one, angel. It
wasn't worth the sweat. Twenty nicker, as I live.' Camel-
coat was looking as if he were about to break into tears.

'Shurrup, Melvin!' snapped silver-mink. 'You 'aven't got no effin' idea and no spunk.'

Camel-coat blew his nose and shurrup.

'I presume the red-neck snatched something,' I said diplomatically.

'Effin' right,' said silver-mink.

'It would seem so, Doctor,' said Matt in his lovely brogue. 'Taken the lady's pendant.'

'Want it back *now*!' snapped the lady.

'No go, I'm afraid,' I replied, 'but if it's not been passed by the bird within seven days, then I might operate.'

'But . . .'

'Seven days,' I repeated loudly. 'Come back then, madam and we'll have it one way or the other.'

The ostrich elected not to excrete the pendant in the usual way. A week went by and still the jewel was safely tucked away in its innards. I brought a portable mine-detector to the zoo and sure enough there was a positive pinging response over the crop area. An operation was unavoidable. With the deadline expired, I had Matt catch up the enraged bird and throw a sack over its head. Then I opened the crop under local anaesthetic. It was a simple matter to reach in and withdraw the pendant, looking surprisingly unaffected by long contact with digestive fluids. No sign of corrosion, tarnishing or verdigris. Silver-mink and camel-coat appeared on cue after I'd finished the operation. I handed her the pendant – 'With the ostrich's compliments,' I said.

'Ta very much,' replied silver-mink.

'I'm sorry that the bird has had to go through this,' muttered camel-coat. 'Really the pendant wasn't worth a light. But the wife . . .'

'Well, you've got it back now,' I butted in. 'No harm done.' The couple went out of Matt's office. 'Funny that such a cheapy didn't corrode at all,' I remarked to Matt after they had gone.

In the same instant the door opened and silver-mink darted back in. 'Psst! Melvin's gone for a pee. That pendant really is plantinum, you know. *He* thinks it's silver plate and so it was, the one that he bought me, the schlepper.

This one's identical, but in platinum – a present from a friend, a *very* good friend!' She winked, turned round and clicked out on her silver heels.

Matt and I looked at one another for once both mute as ostriches.

'Dr Taylor come quickly, *please*. She's eaten all but one of 'er childer!' The lady on the other end of the telephone was sorely distressed, as well she might have been. Living in the Lancashire cotton town of Bury, in a drab, drizzle-grey triangle that had a brook blocked by bedsteads and tin cans as its base with the gas works, a derelict Wesleyan chapel and a willow-herb-covered rubbish-tip at its corners, Mrs Stansfield had always been one for exotic pets. A diminutive, rosy-cheeked widow, she had possessed the only loris I've ever seen taking the place of a fireside cat. And where others would keep a budgie, a parrot or perhaps a mynah bird, she preferred a one-winged flamingo that had been found to everyone's surprise on a local reservoir after surviving an encounter with a high-tension cable and then went on to recover from a subsequent amputation. It occupied most of the tiny bathroom of the house and fed from a soap-holder converted to hold a mash of beetroot, dried shrimp and dog meal. The bread-bin in her kitchen, lined with hay, was the kennel of an ancient hedgehog, blind from cataracts in both eyes, and there were two free-flying plum-head parakeets in the front room who had shredded everything from wallpaper to soft furnishings, from the books on the shelves to the music sheets on the upright piano. She adored and pampered them and they were as plump as dormice and arrogant as fighting cocks.

In a greenhouse in the back yard was the object of her present concern, a female six-banded armadillo that she had bought about a month earlier from an animal dealer in Manchester's Tib Street. It seemed to thrive well in the greenhouse and possessed a prodigious appetite for eggs, milk, tomato juice, minced meat and the occasional chunk of melon: good armadillo grub. Then, only twenty-four hours ago, she had telephoned me in high excitement to say that the armadillo had produced six tiny babies out of

318

the blue! As the mother didn't seem to be caring for them very conscientiously, could I advise on a suitable milk formula for dropper feeding.

I had been surprised and delighted at the good lady's news. Armadillos often breed in captivity with up to twelve young in a litter which may all be identical dodecaduplets (if that is the correct word) of the same sex, formed by the splitting of one single fertilised ovum. Rearing them, even if their mother does her stuff, is not easy and normally few survive. As for artificial armadillo milk – I have been asked for even stranger things – I had suggested cow's milk in a two to one mixture with water plus a little glucose. Any weakly ones were to be given a few drops of neat protein hydrolysate hourly for the first day or two. I had made a note to go over to Bury as soon as I had the opportunity to see the unexpected sextuplets.

Now here she was again, utterly distraught. All had apparently gone wrong. Many animals will eat their dead or dying young, as if it were Nature's way of tidying up without wasting precious protein, but I had never come across an infanticidal armadillo; that was more like tigers, bears or wolves. Perhaps I should have advised her to separate mother and young, but armadillos are such gentle creatures – I never thought, damn it. I promised her I would go over at once and went out to my car.

It is rare enough to see armadillos in Lancashire, let alone newborn baby armadillos. I cursed our luck as I swung out of Woodhouse Lane and took the road over the moor towards Bury, lying under a mantle of smoke in the next valley. Mrs Stansfield's pink face was streaked with tears as she opened the door and led me through the hallway to the back yard. 'A reet bonny little beggar, Doctor, and so kindly. Why would she murdur all 'er childer?'

'Well, I can't say, but sometimes if a mother recognises some fault in her young, perhaps something we humans can't discern, she'll act that way.'

The armadillo, a grey rugby football, lay sleeping in a wooden box in one corner of the greenhouse. Armadillos are night people who spend most of the daylight hours dozing, and it was now early afternoon. I gently lifted out the curled-up animal and it began to wriggle in my hands as it roused. I couldn't see any armadillo baby left behind in the hay-lined box.

'Oh Doctor, she's et'n t' last one,' wailed Mrs Stansfield. 'All six babies in one day!'

'Just move the hay, Mrs Stansfield,' I said. 'Maybe it's got underneath.'

The armadillo's hard claws scrabbled irritably at my arm. Its owner bent down and began to rummage through the bedding. Almost at once she gave a shrill squeak. 'Ooh look, Doctor, you're reet. It is still here. Come on, me little bobby-dazzler.' Fiddling about with her fingers in the hay, she seemed to have some difficulty catching the infant but finally she straightened up and turned to me beaming, with the palms of her hands cupped together. 'A wick little bugger, Doctor, ah'll have to be careful not to drop it.'

Very slowly she began to open her hands and I looked in. I got a good view of the 'survivor'. Scurrying frantically over one calloused pink palm was a fat woodlouse.

There must have been dozens of such 'baby armadillos' if she'd hunted thoroughly through that greenhouse, all of them just the sort of toothsome live food that armadillos and other insectivorous mammals go searching for after dusk. Mrs Stansfield flushed with embarrassment when I explained. 'Aah well, Doctor,' she said, shuttling as she made me a cup of tea, 'I bet that's the the first insect you've ever been called to look at, eh? Aren't I a one, eh?'

'It's not an insect, Mrs Stansfield, it's a crustacean, a relative of the lobster. And I have been called to deal with those before,' I said.

Mrs Stansfield seemed much relieved at hearing that. 'Ay well then, Doctor, that's all reet then, innit. I'm not so daft after all! Any road, when you've drunk up I'd like you to come and look at these snakes that I've got that I'm keeping in the airing cupboard.'

☆☆☆☆☆☆☆☆☆☆☆☆☆☆☆☆☆☆☆☆☆☆

Chapter Twenty-two

☆☆☆☆☆☆☆☆☆☆☆☆☆☆☆☆☆☆☆☆☆☆

THE ZOO vet hasn't always got the luxury of an operating theatre and well-equipped veterinary hospital when it comes to emergencies, and often I feel like a battlefield medic having to make do and mend under fire. It's a great tribute to the fitness and natural powers of healing of wild animals that so many operations carried out in the far from ideal place with bad lighting, little or no assistance and sometimes improvised equipment do go remarkably well. Large animals such as elephants, giraffes and camels are still generally best dealt with in situ in their stables, paddocks or fields. It would rarely be possible, even if desirable, to hospitalise such a patient. But smaller creatures can usually be tranquillised in their quarters and then removed to a hospital area – if it exists. Even the smallest beasts, though, sometimes require on-the-spot surgery.

Chessington Zoo has changed immensely under its new management, with an excellent examination room and post mortem laboratory among other things having been built in recent years. Despite its image within the zoological establishment as a 'commercial' funfair-cum-small-zoo that cannot be taken seriously, Chessington has a first-class breeding record in a wide range of exotic species from sea-lions to otters to lemurs to beavers and a dedicated staff of young keepers, many of whom are as good as any you will find in European or American zoos. Its percentage incidence of disease is lower than Regents Park and it is steadily replacing old and out-moded exhibitions with effective new ones, using money it earns and not from government handouts. In the days before Chessington possessed a special veterinary clinic with hydraulic operating table and the like, I had to tackle operations in the same way that I had done at Belle Vue Zoo in Manchester twenty-odd years before, but without benefit of a fully-equipped surgery fifteen miles away as had been the case when I lived in Rochdale.

At Chessington in pre-clinic days animals had to be operated on in their own houses or else in some ersatz theatre in a food kitchen or barn or curator's office, frequently with no time to clean, disinfect and warm up the surroundings. One can argue that there were advantages in those good old days, which ended with the advent of the NHS, when the family doctor would remove an appendix on the scrubbed kitchen table, but they were outweighed by all the considerable disadvantages. With zoo veterinary work on small species the same is true, but when there is no alternative I do confess to secretly revelling in the need to fall back on the old fundamental principles of successful surgery: speed, efficient anaesthesia and a good technique. These are infinitely more valuable than gadgets and gear, shadowless operating lights, electro-cauteries, masks and gloves and a bevy of beautiful RANA nurses mopping one's brow. And a fast operation is more important than worrying about dust in the air or the lack of sterile drapes to surround the operating site; soap and water and skin disinfectant will suffice where time is of the essence. Post-operative infections are very rare in my experience and when they do occur are a nuisance rather than a serious threat to life.

Caesar, the male Capuchin monkey at Chessington, had a mate called Cleopatra, and when she became pregnant Chris, the head primate keeper, didn't expect any trouble. Monkeys usually give birth without difficulty and I find that I am only called about twice a year to give obstetric assistance to primates and need to do a Caesarean section

322

perhaps once every two years in apes or monkeys. Monkey mums-to-be keep fit and do their exercises! When her six-month gestation period approached its conclusion, Chris watched carefully for the first signs of labour in Cleopatra. An experienced primate man, he knew what to watch for: a discharge of waters, contractions and the speedy presentation of a baby looking at first like a drowned rat. It would be a brief, undramatic affair. More likely than not, it would happen at night or during the day just when he nipped to the loo. On his return Cleo would be proudly grooming the new infant, its umbilical cord chewed off by her and hanging down, a couple of inches of glistening pink cord. She might well have started scoffing the lump of placenta that quickly followed the baby.

But it didn't happen that way. Chris spotted Cleo's first contractions early one morning. She was definitely bearing down, but there was no sign of placental water loss. He waited an hour and, when there was no change, tele-phoned me.

'No sign of any discharge at all?' I asked.

'None,' came the reply.

'OK leave her another couple of hours but ring me before if there is any sign of blood without the baby making its appearance.'

Exactly two hours later Chris 'phoned again. 'No change,' he reported. 'Contractions regular every six to seven minutes. Still no signs of water or blood and she's behaving otherwise as if she hadn't a care in the world.'

I decided to wait. It is a mistake to interfere too early in the birth process of animals. 99.9 per cent of creatures, particularly wild ones, deliver their young unaided by the prying fingers, instruments or drugs of well-meaning humans. Doing nothing can often be the wisest and safest form of treatment. Precipitate action can cause innumer-able problems. The trick is spotting the one-in-a-thousand case that needs early intervention if mother and baby are to be safe. Chris's accurate observation and my knowledge of monkeys gave me confidence in acting Brer Rabbit for a while longer.

Half a day passed and Cleo progressed not one whit but

323

then she didn't decline either. By the evening I had to make another decision: to let things take their own course through the night, ask Chris to sit up with the little monkey or bring matters to a head by forcing labour to a speedy conclusion. It isn't easy 'guesstimating' Nature's intentions and while a dead baby is awful enough, a dead mother is heartbreaking. Nevertheless, enlightened zoo management requires that animals are treated as individuals, not as machines. A uterine cervix that relaxes in its own good time is usually to be preferred to one that is forcibly expanded. A natural birth that 'paces' itself gives the body time to adjust and minimises trauma. With Cleo showing no sign of pain, discomfort, illness or discharge, I told Chris to go home and 'phone me as soon as he came to the zoo next morning. The phone rang at 7.30 am. 'She's much the same as yesterday. No discharge but the contractions are very weak and widely spaced.' The primate keeper sounded upset. 'She's been at it a day now.'

There are no fixed rules in such matters but twenty-four hours in the second stage of labour is the limit as far as I am concerned in monkeys. Now I had to interfere. I breakfasted on Marmite toast sandwiches while I drove through the rush-hour traffic in Chobham and Byfleet on the twenty-mile journey to Chessington from the house near Bagshot which has been my home and the practice's southern office since I moved down from Lancashire. As is my custom, I used the travelling time to go over mentally the possibilities of what might lie ahead: courses of action, snags, how, where, which and so forth. Past difficulties with monkeys in labour. Special points concerning Capuchins. Anatomy? Physiology? Anaesthetic? A mental check-list of instruments needed. What drugs were in the zoo dispensary? What was I carrying in the Bag? By the time I turned into the zoo gates I was fully rehearsed in my head. The real thing would be just a familiar re-run.

Cleo sat calmly in a corner of the Capuchin house, hands folded across her swollen stomach. Her fur was glossy black except for a silver-white tonsure crowning the face that wore, like all Capuchins, a perpetually surprised expression. She raised her eyes and grimaced toothily at me as I watched the feeble contractions within her abdomen. She didn't push at all. The muscles of the uterus were tiring of their efforts to expel the reluctant baby. Whatever I did, she needed anaesthetising straight away. Chris caught her easily in a sort of heavy-duty butterfly net and then, taking both her arms firmly behind her back, held her securely in a full nelson while I injected half a cc of ketamine solution into her thigh. Within a couple of minutes she was unconscious and I disinfected my hands in order to perform an internal examination. As I suspected, the cervix was hardly open at all. With the tip of my little finger I could feel the intact placental 'bag of waters' pushing into it from the far side. Placing my stethoscope to Cleo's chest and stomach, I quickly located two distinct heart sounds. Mother's fast. Baby's even faster, but completely normal. Only one thing for it: a Caesarean. I would do it at once in the old quarantine room.

A little while later, Cleo was lying on a piece of plastic sheet covering a wooden food-preparation table. A keeper stood at my side holding the stainless steel bowl that contained a few basic instruments, scalpel, forceps, scissors, needles and sutures under the light from one fluorescent strip in the ceiling.

After topping up the injected anaesthetic with a further dose, I tied Cleo flat on her back with four pieces of string fixed between her limbs and the table legs. Then I washed her belly with water and povidone antiseptic. For scrubbing up I used the quarantine kitchen sink and, lacking sterile towels, prepared to operate with wet hands, shirt sleeves rolled well up. One stroke of the scalpel divided skin, muscles and silvery peritoneum. The pale blue mass of the womb rose into my incision. I chose a spot over the head of the foetus within and carefully cut the uterine wall. Taking a hold of the tiny skull between finger and thumb, I hauled the baby out and then peeled the placenta from its attachment. The womb began to shrink down at once while I massaged the infant with my hands and wiped mucus from its nose and mouth. It responded by writhing and screwing up its face. I tied off the umbilical cord, cut it and handed the baby to Chris. A round needle and a length of fine catgut were needed next. I inverted the edges of the uterine incision and put in a watertight continuous line of stitching. There hadn't been more than a saltspoonful of bleeding. I closed the muscles with more catgut. It is important to pick up the peritoneum while doing this and the last stitches are fiddly to insert – thank God for a small hand when operating on such minute creatures! Finally I placed a line of individual dacron sutures in the skin. It was all over in twelve minutes.

As Cleo began to rouse from the effects of the ketamine, the baby lay in a shoebox under an infra red lamp, squeaking lustily. It later transpired that Cleo hadn't enough milk to raise the baby who was christened, appropriately enough, Mark Antony. So the keeper reared him on Ostermilk and baby-food and eventually re-introduced him to his parents and the rest of the Capuchin colony. He is still at the zoo in Chessington, a fine specimen of his kind and none the worse for his delayed and unpromising arrival into the world.

It wasn't a difficult or unique operation and Capuchins aren't a rare species with the superstar charisma of pandas or birds of paradise, but when I see him on my weekly inspection visits pulling faces at the crowd or leaping fluidly from branch to branch with a bunch of mealworm titbits clutched in one hand, I get the feeling of secret exaltation that is the real, unsurpassable reward in being GP to wild animals.

Some exotic animals – gerbils, hamsters, budgerigars for example – make very good pets. But the majority are not suitable for keeping by private owners on the whole and in Britain the Dangerous Wild Animals Act and conservation legislation have mercifully reduced the number of people who keep lions in their gardens or crocodiles in their bathrooms to a mere handful. It isn't the same overseas, where the rich flamboyant or eccentric can still indulge their fancies for rare creatures; I recently looked at a young lion given as a gift to the King of Spain by a well-known singer, who may think he knows a thing or two about singing but can't have employed much grey matter when picking a prezzy for HM Juan Carlos. Where did he imagine the King could keep such a creature? Of course, it ended up in the zoo in Madrid where it sits in a quarantine cage while everyone (except the singer) worries over its future. How to graft it into an already established and harmonious social group? Should it be kept alone to avoid the inevitable and sometimes fatal fighting? Not a happy thought. But folk like showbiz personalities with their grand gestures and eyes on the publicity machine don't need to worry about such things. Only the lion, the zoo director and the vet are left to sort things out after the press photographers and PR mouthpieces down the last glass of champagne, gobble the last free canapé and go.

It's even worse in the Middle East. At Al Ain, unwanted, totally unexpected gifts of animals which have been received by sheiks are passed on to the zoo, usually without warning, almost every week. Tiger cubs, leopards, ostriches, monkeys, birds of prey – given by the ignorant rich to the ignorant rich – end up in makeshift accommodation behind the scenes. We never euthanase such living presents: just swear, grit our teeth and start looking for somewhere to park the bewildered creatures.

Primates are most definitely not to be recommended as private pets, although there are rare exceptions. One such is another Capuchin monkey, 'Cappy', who lives in Manchester. I first met the little fellow in 1974 when he was about two and a half years old and had just been purchased by the Bunting family. He at once became, and still remains, as well cared for and integrated a member of the family as any of the humans – or the dog. Nothing but the best for Cappy: he demanded and got everything a Capuchin who thinks he's a human might demand, and his quarters in the kitchen were a focal point of the Buntings' daily life. Cappy Bunting was very much master in his own house and he patently revelled in it.

About a year after his arrival, Mrs Bunting telephoned me to say she was worried about the little Capuchin. On the frequent occasions that he was out of his cage and roaming free, instead of as normal sitting beside the fire, watching television or grooming the dog, Cappy had taken to spending a long time in the scullery, drinking from the cold water tap. He was also vomiting frequently and losing weight. I went out to examine him. Already Cappy was quite clear as to who was one of the family and who wasn't. Vets definitely were not, and I was scolded severely as he sat on his mistress' lap while I listened to his chest and poked fingers into his abdomen. He tugged at my ophthalmoscope while I peered into his eyes which, thank goodness, were clear and healthy right through from front to back, for I had a growing suspicion as to the cause of Cappy's ailment. Taking a paper test strip, I touched it against the end of his penis. The paper at once turned blue, indicating the presence of sugar. Cappy, as I had guessed, was a diabetic.

Diabetes is not uncommon in wild animals and I have had cases in camels, kangaroos, various sorts of cats and bears. Many cases in captive animals, I believe, are due to a dietary fault, particularly where they are being hand-reared on artificial milk. It may be too much or the wrong sort of sugar in the milk or in some cases excessive protein. Whatever the exact cause, it can produce disastrous effects including irreversible cataracts in the lenses of the eyes. In early life Cappy had suffered a bone weakness and had been persuaded to accept the appropriate medicine each day for many weeks by mixing sugar with it. I wonder sometimes if too much of this sweetener was the cause of his later diabetes.

So how to tackle a monkey with diabetes? Particularly a monkey who adored sweet things, who consumed great quantities of grapes, sultanas and peaches and for whom Mrs Bunting baked little cakes, saved the finest first cut of golden-brown skin of the family's baked rice pudding and bought a quarter of a pound of jelly babies or some Toblerone as a Saturday treat? Insulin injections work as effectively in animals as in man but it wasn't likely that Cappy would take very kindly to once-daily pricks with a needle. At two and a half years old he already possessed a muscular body and dangerous teeth, and he ruled the roost in the kitchen. No-one was disposed to argue if he decided he didn't like something. Quite a martinet, Cappy was nevertheless deeply loved by everyone else in the family, except perhaps the long-suffering dog; they were deeply alarmed by my diagnosis but equally utterly determined to do everything necessary to combat the diabetes.

Many owners of animals simply haven't got the will power to put their pets on to strictly prescribed diets. They 'forget' the chocolate drops that an obese pooch with heart disease and on half a tin of reducing diet and a raw carrot per day is slipped every evening before going to bed. They cannot see any harm in the parrot with diarrhoea and the bland diet of yogurt and pobs (which it obviously hates, the way he's giving them filthy looks) being given a secret sliver of tangerine in order to get into his good books. We don't have any trouble of this sort among the professionals in zoos, I might add. The Bunting family surprisingly proved also to be very professional in rigorously applying the diet I at once outlined for Cappy. No sweet fruits, no chocolates or sweetmeats, no sugar. Cappy would have to eat meat, tinned dog food, egg, cheese and vegetables. The only fruit I would permit was a little tomato. I don't think the Buntings ever 'cheated' once.

There are anti-diabetic drugs such as tolbutamide which are taken by mouth instead of injection and work well in many human diabetics but they don't generally reduce the blood sugar of other diabetic species. An exception, as one might imagine, are the non-human primates. I decided to try Cappy on tolbutamide. I needed to arrive at a dose which in conjunction with the low-sugar diet was just enough to keep Cappy's urine free of sugar. I supplied Mrs Bunting with a bottle of test strips and got her to dip one into a puddle of Cappy's urine twice a day. She was to adjust the tolbutamide tablet dosage until there was no blue colour produced. Within a week Mrs Bunting had found the optimum dose of the drug and I arranged for her to continue thereafter doing weekly checks in case, as was likely, the monkey's requirement of tolbutamide altered.

The change in Cappy after beginning the treatment was dramatic. His thirst and vomiting vanished and he began to put on weight. His family faithfully kept up the urine screening, drug dosage and careful diet and he grew into an otherwise normal, powerful, adult male Capuchin. Now, nine years on, he's still going strong and free of any apparent side-effects from the diabetes. Mrs Bunting probably knows more about nursing a diabetic monkey than anyone else in England and Cappy certainly knows he's head of the house in the best of homes.

It was in Manchester a few years before Cappy came on the scene that I met another exotic pet kept in quite different surroundings. It was the property of a Professor of Medicine at Manchester University Medical School. Why he kept the beast I shall never know, for one day the Professor had a heart attack and died and the police called me to go as soon as I could and do something about a 'bloody great ape' that was locked in an upstairs room of the deceased's house and terrorising the undertakers who were laying out the body. Apparently it was beating on the walls and bringing down the plaster.

The Professor had lived alone in Fallowfield, and the Victorian house of smoke-black and stone with ledges and windowsills frilled white with pigeon droppings was gloomy inside, full of dusty bookcases and worn velvet chairs. It smelled of damp, Vick lozenges and pipe tobacco, and in a glass jar on a table in the hall was the pickled breast of a negress erupting with a grotesque carcinoma. The faded sepia of its label said 'Gabon 7/1/19'.

The undertaker's assistant met me in the hall and took me up. I could hear the racket even as I began to climb the stairs. There was a riot, a mutiny in full swing, a bear-garden somewhere up there. The howling, banging and crashing of objects was incessant. On the landing, which was lit by a dim bulb in a be-cobwebbed red glass lamp-shade, I looked at the door behind which pandemonium reigned. In the threshold of a nearby doorway stood the undertaker in his working overall, smelling of formaldehyde and looking as if he had seen a ghost. 'It's going to break out, I'm sure,' he said, waving a pair of rusty tweezers at me. 'You'd better do something quick, friend, or it'll be out and no mistake.'

'Has he – the dead man – no relatives?' I asked. The

'thing' was beating on the door now and dust was puffing in little spurts from around the frame.

'None. All alone he was, the Prof. Except for that thing.'

'Any idea what it is?'

'Bloody great gorilla, I believe.'

I frowned as the hairs on the back of my neck sprang to attention; 'it' certainly made as much noise as a big silver-back, but I was going to have to open the door to get a shot at it with the dart gun. 'You get on with your work,' I said to the funeral pair. 'I'll be OK taking things quietly on my own.'

The undertaker and his assistant retreated, closing their door and leaving me feeling like a character in *The Murders in the Rue Morgue*. The door behind which 'it' lay, or rather sounded distinctly to be laying into things, had no key in the lock. I crouched down to look through the keyhole. I could see nothing but a patch of peeling wallpaper on a far wall. Gingerly I turned the door knob and pushed a little – definitely locked. I had to assume that 'the thing' could not have bolted itself in. The key must be somewhere on this side. It was nowhere to be found on the landing. I tapped on the other door. 'Any sign of a key in there?' I shouted over the din.

'No, not here,' came the faint reply, almost drowned by what now sounded like 'it' beating a billet of wood against the floorboards and, what was more, precisely to the stately beat of the Dead March from *Saul*. Or so I imagined.

From the kind of noise its feet made on the floorboards and the vocal sounds, I was fairly certain it wasn't anything as big as a gorilla, but it could have been a chimp or maybe a baboon – both very dangerous animals if roused. A chimp is as strong as six grown men and has a bite as bad as a mastiff's. A baboon can take on a lion and has been known to keep advancing even against shotgun fire. Oh dear, I thought as I went downstairs and back to the car to fetch the Bag and something to open the door with, no wonder there isn't a copper around. If it had been a hoodlum or a maniac with a knife holed up in the house the place would have been stiff with constabulary. As it was, Sergeant Bumble had passed the buck to me and now I was on my own, feeling like Oliver Twist in a house with a corpse. Mr Sowerberry and Noah Claypole – and King Kong on the side for good measure!

My car boot contained several handy objects including the stainless steel chisels and a mallet with which years earlier I had removed the great tooth from Mary the elephant at Belle Vue. They should make mincemeat of breaking a lock. In fact, looking at the collection of extraordinary veterinary gear – stainless steel wire with handles that could whistle through dense bone and amputate a leg in seconds, a balling gun for delivering giant pills down large animals' throats that looked like a baseball bat with a metal-filled end, and a collection of evil-looking knives, files and pincers for trimming overgrown hooves – one could forgive an inquisitive policeman should he ever stop me at dead of night on the way back from an emergency (with blood on my clothing, undoubtedly) for gazing with considerable interest at this little lot: ''Allo, 'allo, 'allo. What 'ave we 'ere? Garrottes, clubs, instruments of mayhem and burglarious tools?' 'Well, officer, not exactly. These, for instance, are for taking teeth out of elephants.' 'Ho, ho, ho, ho – then do you mind blowing into this bag, sir?'

I loaded a syringe with the fastest-acting paralytic drug I had – suxamethonium – a big dose just in case of a surprise. Professors of Medicine who'd been to Gabon before the war just might have brought back a missing link! Walking back to the house, I looked up at the window which must have belonged to the room in question. It was completely covered on the inside of the glass with rusty iron mesh. Back on the landing, the door to the room where the corpse lay opened a crack and two pairs of eyes stared out. 'Have you done it yet?'

'Not yet. Get back in. I've been to get my stuff.'

The door was hurriedly closed. I do not have illusions about myself in a Starsky and Hutch rôle, nor do I fantasise (even as I begin to go bald) of having anything of Kojak in me, but it did seem to me that the approved American detective way of kicking in the door and dropping to a crouch, legs apart and gun held in both hands, was at least

332

worth trying first. It had the element of surprise which would be lacking if I started chiselling. As 'it' came charging out I would let it have the flying dart straight in the chest or belly (I had selected a short needle which wouldn't do much physical injury but with a barb to ensure that it held on).

I treble-checked the dart gun, made sure the safety catch was off and practised the movements in slow motion a few times. I was now ready for an SAS-style entry. I positioned the gun dead centre and held the trigger lightly. Okay, you guys! So far so good. The sweat dripped off my brow and it wasn't because it was hot. I didn't feel very SAS – more like the Royal Army Veterinary Corps, but then they don't go round kicking doors in. I breathed in, lifted my right foot and smashed it forward so that the heel of my shoe hit the door just below the knob. The door shuddered, the knob dropped off, but the door did not fly open. I repeated the attack – nothing doing.

So much for Starsky and Hutch. The heavy wooden door possessed a very solid lock. The noise in the room was continuing unabated. Irritated, I picked up the door knob, fiddled with it and eventually managed to fit it back on to its spindle. Right, it had to be chisels. I jammed my longest chisel into the gap between door and frame close to the lock and began hitting it as hard as I could with the mallet. The creature on the other side joined in. Between blows I could feel it pounding back at me. Well, with two of us working at it this should be a doddle! With a splintering crack the lock suddenly gave, and I heard it crash to the floor inside. There was a metallic scraping noise as 'it' picked it up and then a thud as I visualised the creature hurling it against a wall. The door, mercifully still held by the catch below, should now be free. I tested, heart thumping, by turning the knob and pushing just a millimetre. It was open.

I pulled it tight shut and hung on to the knob like grim death while I re-ran through my memory all the old Elliot Ness and FBI films I had watched, rather in the way that a drowning man is said to see his whole life flash before him in an instant. How did it go? Open door by means of knob, fling it wide with left hand and flatten myself against

333

landing wall with gun in right hand. Peep round door and let 'it' have it.

I squeezed the gun-butt tightly, turned the door knob and shoved it inwards with all my might. The door flew back as I pressed myself against the wall. At once a brown mass of fur came shooting out onto the landing. Screaming diabolically, the mass sprouted arms and legs and leapt up onto the banisters at the head of the stair-well. I swung the gun round and pointed it at the creature.

Before me squatted a travesty of a pig-tailed macaque monkey. One eye bulged blind and orange-coloured from its socket, the mouth snarling agape showed long, brown, deformed teeth, the belly was swollen and hairless and the toenails were so overgrown that they were curling into corkscrews. Despite all this it was still an immensely strong-looking animal – almost a cube of muscle as it crouched, glaring at me with a mixture of fear and hatred. I moved to one side to avoid a ricochet if the syringe bounced back, breaking the barb at such close range, and squeezed the trigger. At the same instant the monkey gave a great scream and hurled itself at the door behind which the undertakers were at work. Wrenching the knob, it burst inside. My syringe buried itself in the landing wall, showering plaster down the staircase. Now the howls were human ones. Out of the room of death the undertaker and his assistant came hurtling as if pursued by the Grim Reaper himself. 'Good God, it's after us!' yelled the undertaker. 'What the bloody hell went wrong?' He shot down the stairs with the assistant at his heels. There was no sign of the monkey following them.

Aghast, I dashed to the door of the room from which they had fled and slammed it shut. I listened breathlessly. The monkey had stopped its noise on entering the place where his master lay. Corpse and monkey – I couldn't hear a peep out of either of them. I loaded another syringe back at the car, where the undertaker and his mate were standing on the pavement, nervously puffing at cigarettes. 'Get it right this time, friend,' said Mr Sowerberry lugubriously. 'Damn' right,' added Claypole.

There was still no sound when I returned to the landing for the third time. I threw open the door and stood back. Nothing came out. Cautiously, ever so cautiously, with the barrel of the gun poised like a metal extension to my nose, I put my head round the door. It was the Professor's bedroom. A brass bedstead with yellowing sheets, a marble wash-stand with porcelain ewer, a side-table stacked high with old copies of *The Lancet* and a heavy mahogany wardrobe. At the foot of the bed on a trestle lay a coffin. In the coffin was stretched the body of an old man, his face blue-grey above a long linen shift. Sitting on the corpse's ankles and blinking indifferently at me was the macaque. Very gently, with two fingers, he stroked his master's cold knees. All anger and fear had vanished from the animal's face. I raised the gun and fired. The dart hit him in the thigh, he gave a whimper, snatched briefly at the embedded dart and then quickly returned to stroking the corpse. Ten seconds later he collapsed without any fuss and I went over and lifted him out of the coffin. *Requiescat in pace*, I thought – both of you.

The macaque was in a terrible condition, with a tumour in the eye socket, vitamin deficiencies, a hernia, tooth and gum disease. He was also very old. There was nothing to be done for him and no-one who would want him. I injected him with an overdose of barbiturate.

Before I left the house I went into the room where the macaque had been living. It was an appalling sight. What had once been a bedroom was in utter ruin. A bed stripped to the springs, a cupboard torn to pieces, wallpaper shredded and plaster ulcerous with gaping holes, a dressing table with its mirror gone and covered with dusty shards of glass and years, not just days, of excrement and filth. Bits of wood, rusty metal and food – dried, decayed, mouldy and maggot-ridden – were strewn everywhere. I had never seen nor smelled so foul a habitation. It could not have been cleaned in a quarter of a century. Why a learned medical man should keep an animal like that for so long I will never understand. He probably loved it. It loved him, I am sure. But. . . . The answers are buried with both of them.

When I walked out of the house carrying the body of the macaque, the undertakers backed off. 'God, what a bleeding monster!' exclaimed the undertaker, wrinkling his nose.

'Serve it bloody well right,' opined the assistant.

They were both utterly wrong – and I felt curiously sad about the whole business.

Chapter
Twenty-three

T HERE WERE only three more days before I was due to fly out to Seattle to see how the Americans went about shipping the killer whale. It was breakfast-time again when Shelagh answered the phone and said it was Matt from Belle Vue. My appetite vanished as I pushed back my chair to take the receiver.

'What now?' I asked tersely, steeling myself for further catastrophes. Not more giraffe problems, I prayed.

'A woipe out. Not a survoivor,' came the Irishman's voice. Yet he sounded remarkably cheerful for a bearer of sad tidings.

'How many of what?' I barked.

'Oh, the lot. Around three dozen, they say.'

The man must have cracked under the shock, I thought. He was quite clearly chuckling.

'Three dozen dead what?' I bellowed.

Matt paused for maximum dramatic effect and then said quietly, 'Fleas, Doctor, the whole bally lot of 'em, the performin' fleas.'

Belle Vue possessed the last surviving example of that Victorian curiosity, the flea circus. In a small round kiosk in the centre of the zoo, the flea trainer would crouch over a miniature ring set on a table-top and put a troupe of shiny brown fleas through their repertoire. The circle of paying customers huddled round him would see two of the minute creatures fence with swords made out of fuse-wire, another couple pull Lilliputian chariots and a supposedly female star do a high-wire act along a filament of cotton whilst clasping a diminutive parasol. The fleas worked well. They submitted gamely to being harnessed with the aid of a magnifying glass and tweezers, they pushed and pulled and lifted in demonstrations of their relatively enormous strength, and the show went on. It was not actually true to say that the fleas were trained; they did what they were supposed to do quite naturally. Put a well-fed flea on a thread and he (or she) will walk along it. Give him a little parasol to grab and he will grab it for sure in one pair of legs and still walk happily along on the remaining two pairs. Place two fleas face to face, give them each a bit of fuse-wire and they will wave the useless things in front of them (what else should a flea find to do with fuse-wire?), looking for all the world like a pair of miniature Errol Flynns.

If that makes it sound too simple, let me hasten to point out the pitfalls before you tell your boss what he can do with his job, shake the cat in search of an off-the-peg and out-of-work company of artistes and take a one-way ticket to Broadway. First, there are fleas and fleas. To put it another way, there are Thespian fleas, fleas that have greasepaint and the roar of the crowd in their yellow blood, that are invigorated by the limelight, that dream dreams of playing Hamlet or Macbeth, and then there are the common herd, the fleas lacking in pizzazz. It goes without saying that flea circuses depend on a plentiful supply of the former variety, plentiful because of the brevity, if brilliance, of their lives and because of the tendency, so well known among flighty show-biz types, to be unreliable, miss rehearsals, elope. Experience has shown that only *Pulex irritans*, the human flea, has got what it takes to make the grade in flea circuses.

The second necessity, common to all performers whether they be Laurence Olivier or a six-legged blood-sucker one-eighth of an inch long, is nourishment, and where Lord O. might make do with a cold cutlet or fish and chips, fleas demand meals of blood. Human fleas prefer human blood and take other brews with reluctance. The provider of the meals, usually by baring his forearm, is the long-suffering trainer who owns the flea circus.

Now I come to the bit that will bring tears to the eyes of every dedicated animal conservationist: along with the blue whale, the Javan rhinoceros and the okapi, the human flea faces the sombre possibility of extinction, at least in the West. The plain fact that the species is becoming increasingly difficult to find is no doubt the principal reason why flea circuses, those bizarre backwaters of show business, are no longer around. The decline of *Pulex irritans* was brought on by increased standards of hygiene in the human population and especially by the universal use of DDT and other pesticides and fly-sprays around the house. What applies to the human flea, however, does not seem to have worried unduly the hundred or more other species of flea that make their homes on almost all kinds of mammals and birds throughout the world. They thrive, but the trouble is that their histrionic abilities are said to be abysmal.

'The feller runnin' the flea circus is as sick as a parrot,' Matt was saying. 'Some joker squirted Flit in the room where he keeps his insects. He thinks it was his woife after they'd had a bit of a barney. Anyway, he comes in this morning and foinds the lot with their legs in the air, croaked.' He chuckled louder than ever.

'Can't he get replacements easily enough?' I asked. My knowledge of the flea business at that time was zero. I assumed that a quick dash down to the nearest Salvation Army doss-house would have a full complement of performers on cue for the afternoon performance.

'No chance,' said Matt. 'Human fleas are loike gold nowadays. His last batch he had sent in from a scientist in Wales at two pounds apiece. But apparently that source has petered out.'

'And they must be human fleas?'

'So he says. It's traditional. Apparently if they're content and well fed they'll march about and not indulge in too much jumpin'. Other fleas object to marchin'.'

'Surely some other species of animal flea would do as a substitute, at least temporarily?'

339

'Well, that's whoiy oi'm ringin' you. The flea circus man doubts it'll work but he thinks it's worth a go. Perhaps some of the zoo animals have their fleas on them, fleas mebbe with a little bit of talent. Dog and cat fleas he says are an absolute dead loss. They clear off before you can say Finn McCool.'

'So?' I queried.

'Well, if you could spare half an hour, he'd be most obloiged if we could look through some of our animals.'

'To round up candidates for audition?'

'Correct, Doctor.'

I went to the zoo. Apart from the reptile house, where block-sucking ticks on snakes and lizards were carefully controlled, our defence against external parasites was simply to powder, bath or spray any bird or mammal on which ticks or mites had begun to cause skin disease or itching. Newly arrived animals were inspected for fellow-travellers and dealt with as necessary. Fleas, of all the various types of creature that pass their days browsing beneath the fur or feather of their hosts, are rarely seen.

Matt and the mournful flea trainer, whose name was Alf, met me and we set off round the gardens, carrying with us a handful of small, waxed pill-boxes. There was no question of picking over some of our beasts, and we passed by the big cats, the wolves, the gorillas and such. A selection of monkeys was clean as a whistle. (People often think that these creatures can be seen picking fleas from one another's coats but it is not so: what they see is mutual grooming, with the groomer taking skin scales and grains of salt from the other animal's body). We parted the lush wool of the llamas and alpacas, grabbed a Barbary sheep or two and frisked an amazed group of kangaroos. They had not got a single flea among them. On we went, like the School Inspectors who came once a year and scratched around our heads in search of 'nits' when I was a little boy.

Then we made our first capture. A little black fellow fumbled his take-off leap from the belly fur of an Arctic fox and was collared by Matt. Soon we bagged a rather somnolent brace of bigger reddish ones which were napping on a parrot. Within a couple of hours we had almost twenty fleas of various sorts safely incarcerated in our pill-boxes. We went back to the flea circus kiosk to see them auditioned. When we were inside and securely battened down, Alf illuminated the table-top where all the action took place, set up his props and laid out the pill-boxes in front of him. Each box had been labelled with the name of the host species. If by any chance there was a minuscule Richard Burton waiting to be discovered in one of the containers, we needed to know where more like him might be obtained.

One by one the pill-boxes were opened and the inmates removed with tweezers. Alf first examined them through the magnifying glass. Some he thought were far too small, as apart from the difficulty of putting on the cotton harnesses, the audience would have difficulty seeing them. He tried the bigger ones in the ring. The first three of these, from a coatimundi, took one look at the Big Top and vanished, never to be seen again. The next, a solitary, mahogany-coloured individual plucked whilst still sucking brunch from the neck of an ostrich, was found to have expired in the pill-box. So it went on. Some jumped straight out of the ring, others keeled over, legs bicycling furiously in the air, when urged to walk. The few that Alf actually managed to encumber with parasol, fuse-wire or harness seemed to be struck with instant stage fright and froze up, feigning death.

'Just like I thought,' muttered Alf. 'We've always said in the profession that there's no substitute for yer grand old 'uman variety.' He shook his head sadly, recalling the gracious, flea-ridden days gone by.

My part in the attempt to save the death of another little bit of theatre ended there, and although Alf eventually obtained a small troupe from somewhere, the growing difficulties of supply did finally bring down the curtain on Britain's last flea circus.

The news of Alf's misfortune had got into the early edition of the evening paper, I found later that day, and before I had finished reading my copy, there was a phone call.

'My name's Andrew Greenwood,' said the voice. 'I'm a

341

veterinary student at Cambridge. I live over the hills from you and read in the paper about the flea circus at Belle Vue. I wondered if I could be of any help.'

It was the chap who had been chasing me up about lobsters, I suddenly remembered.

'I've collected some of the biggest fleas in Britain, if you'd like them,' continued the voice earnestly. 'They're mole fleas, a quarter of an inch long. I'd be delighted to bring them along.'

The mole flea certainly is a giant of its kind, though still not as enormous as the pea-sized monster of a flea once seen in the nest of an American beaver.

'Thanks anyway,' I said, 'but I don't think we're in the market for any more fleas today.'

Less than a week later, I was sitting in a restaurant on the Seattle seafront, chewing whopping great pieces of broiled lobster and outsize oysters. Like so much American seafood, they looked delicious and were temptingly served, but had somehow outgrown their subtle, flavourful birthright, sacrificing delicacy and taste for sheer size. Oh for a Cornish lobster or a dozen Whitstable natives, I thought, as my jaws began to ache with the effort and I washed the rubbery chunks down with a dispiriting beverage that claimed to be wine and went under the enigmatic name of 'Cold Duck'.

Through the window I could see below me the round metal pools of the Seattle Aquarium. Floating motionless in the one nearest to me, like an inflated plastic bath toy, eleven feet long with oil-smooth, jet black skin and crisp, snow-white markings, was the young killer whale I had come for. He was a perfect specimen, about two-and-a-half years old, with the teeth at the front of his jaws only just beginning to push through the gums. I was stoking up for the two-day journey to Flamingo Park. He was fasting; whales and dolphins never travel on full stomachs.

Don Goldsberry and Ted Griffin, the two owners of the Aquarium, were the pioneers of killer whale catching. Using a mile of immensely heavy and unwieldy stainless steel netting, they trapped the powerful and sharp-witted

342

whales in Puget Sound. Goldsberry, Griffin and their veterinarian, Bill Klontz, were the experts at what was a fairly new game. All I was supposed to do was watch and listen and learn.

The first of their killers had been given the Eskimo name of 'Namu'. Later animals were christened 'Shamu', 'Ramu' and so on. They had a few appropriate, noble-sounding suggestions for my little fellow.

'Sorry,' I said, 'Pentland Hick has already decided what he is to be called. His name is Cuddles.'

The Americans did not like it. I hated it. But Hick was a shrewd entrepreneur with an eye to publicity: 'A fierce hunter of the oceans with a soft and winsome name. It's a good gimmick that will catch the imagination of the media men,' he reasoned. He was right.

Goldsberry and Griffin gave me a long list of do's and don'ts concerning the whale, all of which I meticulously noted down. This was the gospel to be followed – any infringement and Cuddles would undoubtedly run into trouble. 'If his dorsal fin flops over he's short of sweet water'; 'Use a three-inch needle if you have to inject him'; 'The only safe vaccine is 5 cc of such and such'; 'A shot of penicillin before he travels is all he needs'; 'Eggs are bad for him'; 'Sugar and glucose aren't absorbed by his gut and may do him harm'; 'If he falls ill give him a quart of Maalox and fly us over'.

It sounded daunting, but who was I to judge? The practical study of larger cetaceans in captivity may have been in its infancy in the United States, but it had not even been born in Britain. It was prudent to go along with the instructions that accompanied the goods, not least because Pentland Hick had paid fifteen thousand dollars for Cuddles and was in no mood to quibble. It would be two years or more before we realised that the Seattle team knew little more about the care and treatment of these complicated marine animals than we did.

Next day Cuddles' long journey began. A padded hammock with holes for his eyes, flippers and vent was slipped under him as he floated in three feet of water. He did not fight or complain as a crane picked him, dripping, out of the pool and lowered him gently into a framework of tubular steel in which the hammock was to be slung. At last I got a chance to touch him. It was a wonderful experience. As I leaned over the placid beast after clambering up the bars surrounding him, he exhaled with a soft roar. A blast of hot air, carrying a not unpleasant, cow-like smell, hit me in the face. I revelled in the sensuous delight of passing my fingers over the skin. It was polished, very finely grooved and had the consistency of hard india rubber. It was soft and cool under his axillas, like sheet-steel across the blade of his tail fluke and warm as toast on his forehead, or melon. I climbed down and looked through the holes in the hammock. I waggled the paddle-like flippers and tried to trace the outlines of the bones within, bones that are identical to those in the fingers of human beings. Then I peered close to one large round brown eye. It was streaming with transparent tears as thick as syrup. The eye with its pleated, chocolate-coloured iris rolled slightly and fixed on me. He was looking at me. I stroked the nearby flipper and whistled.

To my utter delight, the eye remained gazing at me and a squeaky, high-pitched chirruping was squeezed out of the blow-hole on top of Cuddles' head. I whistled again. The whale chirp-chirped in turn. He was answering me. Cats answer back, Henry, my goat, willingly exchanges bleats, dogs do it and tigers have a lovely habit of replying to a low 'prrh-prrh' with a similar welcoming sound that never fails to excite me, but this was something unique and it touched me deeply. It was to become a regular feature of my relationship with Cuddles, but that first moment when I came eyeball to eyeball and conversed with a Lord of the Sea, as the Eskimos call these magnificent beasts, was one of the most moving of my life, a vivid instant of sentiment, not sentimentality. Quite inexplicably, a bond had been forged between the whale and me. Whales, and particularly this one, were going to be something extra-special from now on.

As a greenhorn with whales, I was allowed to help in coating every inch of Cuddles' body with thick lanolin grease. This would stop the delicate skin drying out and cracking. Next, towels were spread along his back and smoothed to get rid of air-bubbles that could 'burn' the skin during the long journey. After that, hundredweights of crushed ice were sprinkled on and around the whale. The entire framework was shrouded in plastic sheeting and a water-spraying system of pipes, pumps and electric batteries was set up. The animal would go all the way sticky, wet and cold to avoid the killer's principal enemy, the risk of internal overheating.

We set out for the airport by road, on the back of a long low-loader. In the freight hold of the TWA jet freighter purposely kept at 1°C to help keep the whale cool, it was no fun clambering over his framework for a solid twelve hours. Don Goldsberry, Ted Griffin and I had to keep a constant watch for 'bed-sores' that can end weeks later in death from toxic gangrene, for blobs of lanolin melting and running into the blow-hole, for shifting towels that could be sucked in by one powerful inhalation of the whale's breath. The water sprays had to be kept going, batteries replaced, the system cleared of blocking particles of faecal matter re-circulated with the water. Most important of all, the whale must be constantly reassured. Stroking his forehead, whistling to him or just talking nonsense into his pinhead-sized but highly sensitive ear – it did not matter what, as long as we kept doing it, hour after hour. I had brought my *Collected Poems* of John Betjeman with me, a constant companion on my travels, and I passed the time on my spells of duty at the head end by reading aloud from the book. Apart from the comforting murmur of my voice, I wonder if Cuddles got anything more from such Betjemania as the delightful, awful Miss Joan Hunter Dunn.

Arriving at London Airport, we passed smoothly through Customs, then came the inspection by the Government vet. He had never even seen a whale before and would not have been any the wiser if our boy had been lying there in the terminal stages of rabies complicated by bubonic plague. His main function, he said, was to count incoming animals. To my amazement, he climbed up onto the whale container, looked down and said, 'One'. This he wrote in his notebook before jumping down and bidding us good evening.

After a six-hour road journey up into the north-east of England, where Flamingo Park lies in the sleepy village of Kirkby Misperton, the whale was unloaded from his truck and hoisted above the floodlit figure-of-eight pool that was to be his new home. Gently he was lowered into the icy cold water where several of us were waiting in wet-suits to release him from his hammock. The cold water and my tiredness were forgotten as the canvas fell away. Heart in mouth I waited, bobbing by Cuddles' side. If he had become stiff and could not flex his tail flukes, if he sank out of control, or if he listed because of a congested lung, we would have little chance of manhandling his great bulk in the deep pool. I saw that two Americans who were conducting the releasing operation were looking tense, too.

For a second Cuddles hung in the water. Lazily he raised his great tail. Its deceptively powerful upbeat thrust the water into foaming furrows and his torpedo body glided gently forwards into the centre of the pool. We paddled after him – not that he needed us, but with all the photographer's flash-bulbs popping we wanted to look useful. Goldsberry called for a mackerel and threw it a couple of yards ahead of the whale. It sank in a flickering spiral through the blue water. Instantly Cuddles saw it, blew out a broad plume of water droplets and dived. Half-turning gracefully ten feet down, he opened his mouth a mere inch or two, sucked and the mackerel shot in. To the cheers of the crowd Cuddles rose to the surface, floated vertically with his head well clear of the water and opened his jaws wide. For the first time I saw the salmon-pink expanse of Cuddles' unmistakable grin.

Half an hour later this untrained animal that had roamed the north Pacific only one month before, that had raided fishing nets, murdered great whales, out-run and out-thought sharks and sealions and dolphins, this grinning cuddly Cuddles with the appealing chirrup, was seen to begin playing with a floating beach-ball.

During the following weeks the killer whale settled down

admirably in his new home. Every few days I made the 200-mile round trip over the hills, through the cities of Leeds and York and across the fertile farmland of the vale of Pickering that stretches east to the coast, to see that all was going well. This usually entailed swimming with Cuddles in his pool of artificial sea water. In a wet-suit and face mask I inspected his ventral surface under water; it would be several months before he was trained to roll over on command so that his tummy could be viewed and prodded from dry land. Underwater, too, I had a chance of catching for parasite analysis a sample of his elusive, near-liquid faecal matter before it dispersed irretrievably in his wake. Even so humble a task as collecting droppings from these remarkable creatures presented quite special complications, as the whale, ever curious about the submarine antics of this ungainly caricature of a drunken walrus, buffeted me with his rounded nose.

Giving injections was another poser. Asian 'flu swept through the human population of Britain shortly after Cuddles' arrival and, on learning that Sea World in San Diego had evidence that the influenza virus could attack cetaceans, I had to think of some way of jabbing Cuddles with the current strains of 'flu vaccine. In the early days we had no special slinging device for 'dry-docking' the whale, and emptying the 300,000-gallon pool except for serious emergencies just was not on. For one thing, artificial sea water is expensive to make up. For another, the local river authority did not take kindly to so vast a quantity of brine passing via the drains into their waterways. The salt injured freshwater river life and could poison vegetation along the banks. I had already seen the effect of brine discharge into a stream near the Marineland on the Côte d'Azur: every one of the three dozen majestic palm trees in the gardens of villas running down to the stream was dead as a dodo in a couple of weeks and had to be given fake crowns of branches cut from other trees. The villa owners played hell. On top of these problems, pools like the one at Flamingo Park, built in sandy soil with a high water table, often object to being emptied by collapsing inwards when the enormous outward pressure of their contents is removed.

Cuddles had behaved like a playful, amenable child so far. He doted on humans, craved their attention and was impeccably well-mannered. Pondering the problem of the 'flu vaccination, I decided to try simply swimming up to him in the water and slapping a needle in. I was a dab hand at doing this sort of thing with large land animals. Take an elephant: thump his buttocks hard with your clenched fist one, two, three times so that he knows you are there and is accustomed to what is, to him, a friendly pat on his inch-thick skin. Then, O wily elephant doctor, still keeping up the regular rhythm, with the fourth thump flick forward the wide-bore hypodermic needle that you have concealed in the palm of your hand. Slap goes your fist for the fifth time and the needle zooms to the hilt right through the tough grey leather. The elephant does not feel a thing and consequently has no nasty memories to never forget. This technique is used on horses, cattle and pigs by James Herriots all over the world.

I looked at the whale contentedly basking on the surface after a snack of twenty pounds of mackerel and I reckoned there was a good chance of doing it the same way with him. The press were going to take pictures of the novel inoculation, and I came forth from the dressing room looking like Dustin Hoffman in *The Graduate*. Apart from the frogman outfit I carried a disinfectant aerosol in one hand and a syringe fitted with a ten-inch needle in the other. With the panache of a commando off to plant limpet mines on the *Tirpitz*, I somersaulted backwards into the pool. This flashy entrance was then followed by a more feeble dog-paddle towards my prey. As I arrived at Cuddles' glistening hull, steam was rising from his forehead where it was drying while he basked. He tolerantly rolled a liquid brown eye at me and gave me the salmon-pink grin. The sloping rows of conical white teeth sparkled.

I selected a spot on the top of the killer's back at the base of the dorsal fin. Supporting myself by throwing one arm over his loins, I sprayed the area with disinfectant and then threw the can away from me. Cuddles was most intrigued. Only his big eye moved, following my every movement.

I balanced myself in the water and raised the syringe and

needle high in the air. Cuddles watched it go. Then with my free hand I slapped at the disinfected spot. One, two, three. 'What *is* the lad up to?' I could imagine the whale musing good-humouredly. Four, five – down came the syringe, straight as an arrow, and at exactly the same instant I had the impression that someone had dropped an atom bomb on the *Tirpitz*, prematurely aborting my mission. The pool water beneath me seemed to levitate itself. I was in no doubt that the entire three million pounds of liquid was unexpectedly on its way up towards the ceiling. Certainly I was proceeding in the opposite direction. Somehow I had been transported into a giant washing machine. Arms and legs flailing, I was sucked down, tumbled, rolled, swept and swirled in a maelstrom of foaming water. What looked like a nuclear submarine with a full-open throttle was tearing round me. My lungs were bursting. I had swallowed what felt like a hogshead of salt water du maison. My syringe and needle had vanished,

and my shins had received an excruciating blow from something that could only have been Neptune's iron trident.

A half-drowned veterinarian was hauled miserably over the edge of the pool and lay, puking salt water, in a very un-commando-like fashion at the feet of the pressmen, who found it all very interesting.

Apparently, as soon as the needle had touched the whale, he had launched himself forward with full, fast beats of his flukes. The entire muscle strength of a cetacean's body is concentrated on the focal point at the hinge of the tail. The energy contained in this highly efficient propeller is enough to storm-toss incredible volumes of water in the twinkling of an eye. I had been the centre of such an instant storm and the painful bruising of my shins had been caused by the tip of a flipper grazing by.

Half an hour and a stiff shot of brandy later, I felt ready to try again. I was loath to use the dart-gun, since its longest needle measured only three inches and anyway I was afraid that the wide bore might carry unsterile water into the tissues. I would not have been able to disinfect the skin and there was the problem of retrieving the spent flying syringe.

The question of needle length interested me. It was generally assumed that a long one that could reach beyond the thick blubber layer was essential: everyone talked as if the blubber was inert stuff, without blood vessels that could pick up and circulate drugs and vaccines. But even fatty tissue must have blood to remain alive, and I decided to try a foolproof but shallow injection method on Cuddles. I telephoned a friend at a Leeds University dental clinic, and a car was sent over with what I wanted: the needle-less gun that fires liquids at high velocity into human gums or skin. It was the instrument being developed for mass vaccination against cholera, typhoid, polio and so on.

The dose of vaccine for a killer whale was my next problem. With most vaccines it is by no means true or safe to give, say, six times the amount of vaccine to an individual who weighs six times the average for any particular dosage. Vaccines do not work like that. Nevertheless it was possible to use too small a dose – in Seattle Cuddles had been given what was thought to be an adequate shot of a vaccine against germs of the lockjaw family, but tests I had done on his blood when he first arrived showed virtually no antibodies to lockjaw circulating in his system. He was not protected as everyone thought. In the end, I decided to give Cuddles three times the human dose of 'flu vaccine and then take blood after a couple of weeks, by when, I hoped, a dry dock would be ready. I would check the level of 'flu antibodies and give bigger booster shots if necessary.

The intrepid frogman re-entered the water carrying the vaccine-gun. Once more Cuddles was resting and gave no sign as I approached that only a couple of hours before I had tried to harpoon him and had been summarily demolished. Again he grinned disarmingly. A trainer on the pool-side threw a mackerel into the gaping jaw. Cuddles sucked it down with smooth ease and ogled me. I raised the gun and drew in a big breath. If the typhoon struck, I was determined to keep my mouth shut this time, no matter what.

I pulled the trigger. There was a sharp crack. I got ready for drowning.

Cuddles grinned benevolently again and did not move an inch. He was vaccinated and had not felt a thing. Now all I had to do was wait and hope that the inoculation was effective.

I was quite pleased as I struggled out of the pool for the second time that day. One way or another, I had injected my first real live killer. By the time I had showered, admired the blue and red protuberances on my shins and got into warm clothing once more, everyone had gone from the dolphinarium except one fellow. He stood at the water's edge, looking down intently at the whale, a camera slung from his neck and his pockets bristling with notebooks. I took him to be the last of the press, or possibly the usual late arriver from the local rag who always gets upset when you politely explain, 'No, it isn't possible to do it all again just for you. No, not even mocking it up. No, even though I appreciate how bloody-minded your editor's going to be if you return without the hoped for pictures of Dr Taylor being eaten by a killer whale or stomped by a rhinoceros.'

'Get what you want?' I asked the mousy-haired young man with the faintest resemblance to Robert Redford.

'Oh yes, very much so,' came the reply. 'By the way, I'm Andrew Greenwood. I spoke to you a few months back. Lobsters, fleas – remember?'

'Come and have a spot of lunch and tell me all about your lobsters,' I said.

Andrew barely touched the meal, he spent so much time enthusing over his determination to practise with zoo animals once he had qualified from Cambridge.

'How did you know I was working on the whale today?' I asked.

He grinned. 'I drop a keeper in the bird section a packet of fags every week or two to keep me informed.'

His chutzpah appealed to me. 'And the lobsters?'

Earnestly, he explained. 'You may well know of the significance of lobster blood serum in identifying a certain type of haemophilia in humans. It's a very rare condition, and only about eight cases have been reported so far, but Manchester Royal Infirmary are working on a test for the disease. That test relies on a supply of lobster serum.'

'Quite. To detect the missing clotting factor in the human blood,' I said, nodding sagely but not knowing the faintest thing about the rôle in such obscure areas of medicine of a crustacean that until then had been useful to me only when coated with a mixture of cream, parmesan cheese, white wine and garlic, and lightly broiled.

The intent young student appeared to think that I knew all about the matter. 'So I've been asked to supply the laboratory at Manchester with lobster serum and I came to you, Dr Taylor, for advice on taking blood from lobsters.'

It was flattering, of course, but I had no idea where to begin finding veins on such an armour-plated creature.

'I'm afraid I can't help you,' I confessed. 'Lobsters don't fall sick very often these days.' (In fact, within a couple of years Reg Bloom, a zoologist friend, started flying plane-loads of Canadian lobsters over the Atlantic to stock his 'lobster farm' at Clacton, and I discovered then that the species can be expected to feel poorly with monotonous regularity.)

Andrew Greenwood seemed disappointed that I could not shed any light on how to persuade the shellfish to enrol as blood donors, but I had the feeling that he was not the type to let it rest at that. When we parted he asked if he could contact me and keep me informed of his progress.

'There must be a way of sampling a lobster without doing it like the Dutch scientists do – simply chopping off a claw and letting the poor thing bleed into a jar,' he said.

I liked that. Andrew seemed a promising sort of bloke.

I was further impressed when, three or four weeks later, he proudly appeared at my home in Rochdale carrying a little tube of pale blue liquid. He had studied the architecture of the crusty old lobster and had found a particular soft spot where a needle can be inserted and blood drawn off easily without hurting or damaging the lowly creature in any way. It was his unusual début in the world of wild animal surgery.

☆☆☆☆☆☆☆☆☆☆☆☆☆☆☆☆☆☆☆☆☆☆☆☆

Chapter
Twenty-four

☆☆☆☆☆☆☆☆☆☆☆☆☆☆☆☆☆☆☆☆☆☆☆☆

WHEN THE whale trainer walked into the dolphin-arium at Flamingo Park early one morning he could not believe his eyes. The deep, hour-glass-shaped pool in which the killer whale, Cuddles, had lived for three years was no longer brimming with clear blue artificial sea water. Instead the entire pool was filled with murky scarlet liquid. He felt a sickening contraction of his stomach. Something terrible had happened to the whale. Surely the sixteen-foot-long animal must be lying dis-embowelled on the bottom of the pool. But no – with the usual blast of steaming breath, Cuddles' shining black head suddenly emerged from the red soup. He was alive. The trainer dashed down to the basement and peered through the underwater windows. It was like looking into a crimson fog, a pea-souper with less than six inches visibility.

When I received the frantic telephone call I set off for the zoo immediately. Obviously, I thought, someone is ex-aggerating rather in the heat of the moment. Whales bleed like any other animal when injured, but to turn 250,000 gallons completely red? Impossible! OK, whales are big creatures and Cuddles weighed over two and a half tons, but how much blood did they think such an animal could carry in his circulation system? Horror erased such thoughts the instant I saw the pool. It was actually true. The

354

water looked like somewhat anaemic blood. We all know that blood stains easily and that a little goes a long way: every veterinary surgeon has been called to see a dog with a cut foot where the scene of the accident or the house in which it is being attended looks as if a dozen pigs had been slaughtered there. But this was something unbelievable.

Cuddles floated quietly in the middle of the pool. His deep black body colour had taken on more of a dark grey shade. When I called him over to the side he responded slowly. This was not the perky, mischievous creature that I knew so well, who would call to me with his high-pitched piggy squeal whenever I passed through the crowd of spectators. He was torpid and depressed. His gums and the membrane round his eye, normally a deep pink colour, were now a death-like white. I enquired about his appetite. Zero. For the first time since he had arrived in Yorkshire, Cuddles' enormous appetite for herring and mackerel had vanished. He would not face even a single fish.

I was highly alarmed. Of all the animals with which I have worked I have been closer to none than to Cuddles. Despite the species' fearsome-sounding name, and although in the wild state they are voracious and deadly hunters, killer whales in captivity are generally amenable and gentle to the humans who look after them. I had been with Cuddles when he arrived one frosty winter night, a plump and genial baby with teeth just cutting through his gums. Through the summers we had played daily together in the water. He loved to hug you with his flippers while he floated vertically and you tickled his smooth round belly with your toes. Tug-of-war with an old car tyre, carrying a rider round on his back either in front of his dorsal fin or behind, on what I called the rumble seat where the ride was bumpy and exhilarating; he had played eagerly all day. As a patient he had been impeccable. Martin Padley, his trainer, and I had designed a special examination sling that ran out over Cuddles' pool on telescopic girders. Not only was he easy to get into it for routine blood sampling or vaccination but he was positively reluctant to leave this aquatic examination couch! Martin always had to entice him out rather than in. There had been the awful time when he swallowed a child's plastic trumpet and submitted placidly to stomach pumping, and he had been highly co-operative as a donor in a unique attempt at long-distance artificial insemination of another whale in Cleethorpes. I had learnt most of my techniques of whale handling and medication on this fellow. Now it seemed that I was about to lose him through some mysterious calamity.

The first priority was to find out where the blood was coming from. There was no sign of a wound on his upper surface as he bobbed in the water. I put on a wet-suit and jumped into the pool. The crimson water smelt dank and unpleasant. I paddled across to my friend and hugged his head. Cuddles gazed at me with his round dark eyes but made no move to cuddle up to me as he usually did. Ominously, the healthy syrupy tears no longer flowed from his eyelids. Cuddles was dehydrating somehow, bleeding to death.

I went all over his back and tail flukes: no sign of any injury. Then, using his paddle-like left flipper as a lever, I laboriously rolled him over in the water. His gleaming white abdomen broke the water surface. Not a trace of a wound could I see. There were now only two possibilities: the blood was coming out either with his urine or in his stools. Suddenly, as he floated like a great capsized plastic boat, a massive welter of what seemed to be almost pure blood gushed out of his anus. That was it. Cuddles was bleeding massively somewhere in his intestines.

Climbing out of the pool, I gave instructions for it to be emptied immediately. Whatever the problem was, it had struck rapidly out of the blue. Cuddles had been normal up to the previous evening when all the dolphinarium staff went home. It seemed to be affecting the lower bowel: if the bleeding source was in the stomach or high in the bowel the blood would have been partly digested and changed to a much darker brown or black colour on its way through the intestinal tract. I suspected bacterial or virus infection producing rapid ulceration of the bowel lining. If it was a bacterium, perhaps the culprit was the evil salmonella, a food poisoning germ which causes diarrhoea and the

356

passing of blood in other animals. Whatever the cause, my first priority now was to get Cuddles down onto the dry bottom of the pool, examine him thoroughly and take blood samples to see how bad the damage was. Next I had to stop the bleeding and replace some of the liquid that his circulation had lost. When the volume of circulating blood becomes too small to carry enough oxygen and other vital supplies to key organs, shock and death speedily set in. How to expand Cuddles' blood volume? I decided that in any event I had to make preparations for some sort of transfusion. Ideally I wanted many pints of killer whale blood, not quite the sort of stuff that is usually available at the local blood bank! We knew that there were certainly three major blood groups in bottle-nosed dolphins, but no-one knew anything about the blood groups of whales. The nearest captive killers were in America. Perhaps some of my colleagues out there had some suitable blood stored.

I telephoned all the major marinelands in the United States and explained my predicament. No-one had any killer whale blood stored and no-one had come across a similar problem. My friend Dr White at Miami Seaquarium had had a case of severe bleeding in a whale that had crashed through an underwater viewing window. It had needed lots of surgery and supportive medical therapy but no blood transfusions had been given. Would anyone fancy volunteering one of their whales as a donor of a dozen or two pints? I could easily get the stuff shipped over express on the next Pan-Am or TWA flight. The answer was always the same. Highly valuable animals. The difficulty of having to drain pools in the middle of the show season in order to take blood. Anyway, how were we to be sure without wasting days testing samples whether any particular whale's blood would be compatible with Cuddles'? Whole blood transfusion was out.

The fire brigade arrived. Whenever we needed to speed up the emptying of the pools they were called in. Half an hour later, an unusually dark grey and very white whale was lying passively on the concrete bottom of the pool while hoses and buckets were used to keep his skin moist. I went down and took blood from the big blood vessel in his

357

tail. Even to the naked eye the sample appeared watery and thin. The crucial analyses were quickly done in the laboratory at the pool side. As I had feared, Cuddles had lost a great deal of blood into the intestines. Normally he carried a regular seventeen grammes of haemoglobin, the red oxygen-carrying constituent, in every hundred c.c.s of his blood. Now it was down to only ten grammes. The total number of red blood cells had also dropped precipitously. Other tests showed no sign of active bacterial infection or liver or kidney damage.

A trainer came into the laboratory carrying what looked like a fragment of wet white paper. 'He's just passed another load of blood,' he reported, 'and there was this in it.'

The specimen was sticky and fragile. I dropped it into a beaker of cold water and teased it out with a needle. It unfolded into a delicate white film as big as a postage stamp. The film was not completely intact for at three or four points there were round holes ringed distinctly by reddish-brown material. It was a piece of intestinal lining membrane and the holes were ulcers surrounded by blood pigment, a valuable find but a depressing one. Cuddles had actively bleeding multiple ulcers in his bowels. If there were so many on this small fragment, how many thousands more might there be if the entire hundred feet of his intestines were similarly involved?

The bit of bowel lining and some swabs went to the bacteriology laboratory for urgent examination and I then returned to the problem of replacing Cuddles' lost blood volume. I had to take second best. Although it had no oxygen-carrying power, transfusions of artificial plasma would combat many of the shock-producing factors and would stop the blood vessels from literally collapsing. It was going to mean putting Cuddles on an intravenous drip, and I estimated that at least forty pints would be required. An urgent call for help was sent out to Leeds General Hospital. They readily agreed to supply us with a hundred bottles of the life-saving liquid and it was despatched by fast car under police escort. Meanwhile I filled Cuddles with other important drugs to tackle the sadly abused bowels. Through the giant one-foot-long needle I injected things like vitamins, anti-inflammatory drugs and antibiotics. Although it would take ten to fourteen days for it to be assembled into the essential haemoglobin, I gave big shots of iron liquid. He would need the iron reserves if he recovered.

When the cases of artifical plasma arrived I started work on the transfusion. I used a special needle-like tube of the sort we had employed when doing electrocardiographic investigations on Cuddles some weeks before. The tube had to be inserted accurately into a tail vein. In both dolphins and killer whales, veins and arteries near the surface are closely intermingled for heat-exchange purposes, and if any of the liquid from an intravenous injection goes into an artery there can be nasty repercussions including profound sloughing and death of a large area of tail skin. Kneeling with Cuddles' great tail held above my head I inserted the tube and checked and double-checked that the blood oozing from it was coming only from a vein. When I was satisfied that all was well I connected the plastic tubes to the plasma bottle and adjusted the dosage regulator. A keeper stood on a chair holding the bottle high in the air so that the flow of liquid was not counteracted by Cuddles' massive heart pressure.

Slowly the golden fluid seeped into the whale's system. After ten minutes I switched to the second bottle. Although whale blood does not clot easily, I had anticipated trouble with the tube in the vein and had used a chemical to inhibit clotting and consequent blockage, but I felt sure that frequent changes of the tube would be necessary. In fact, as the hours passed slowly by, the keepers holding the bottles and the bottles themselves were the only things to be changed. The tube remained unblocked throughout the whole ten hours of the transfusion. Cuddles was as good as gold. Not once did he protest or wriggle.

The man holding the tail up during all this time refused to be relieved. He, too, was deeply involved with the animal and wanted to do everything in his power to help. It was cold and damp in the pool bottom so I sent for a bottle of rum to ward off inner chills. From time to time I insisted on the tail holder taking a good pull from the rum bottle. So solicitous was I for the man's health that I did not realise how many tots he had taken during the long hours of waiting. When it was all finished we discovered the good man to be totally drunk and incapable and had to hoist him out of the pool in a dolphin sling.

We refilled the pool. To my delight, when it was up to the six-foot mark Cuddles accepted a few fish. It was terrible to see the chalk-white back of his throat when he opened his jaws to take them but at least the boy was eating again! I stopped the refilling at eight feet. It was good to see clear blue water again but what if he continued to bleed?

Next morning I held my breath as I went into the dolphinarium. My heart sank like an express lift when I saw the glum expressions on the faces of the trainers. The pool water was deep scarlet again. We drained immediately and once more I took a blood sample. The haemoglobin and red cell counts were lower than before, below the point at which, in humans, a blood transfusion becomes imperative. I transfused the plasma again, gave more injections and passed a stomach tube. Cuddles took it all philosophically. Through the stomach tube I pumped in a peculiar pink mixture which I had concocted in a large unused plastic dustbin. It contained water and honey, mineral salts to replace those lost in the bleeding, glucose, rose-hip syrup, invalid food, kaolin to soothe the inflamed bowel, and Guinness. As it by-passed his taste buds I do not suppose Cuddles relished it or otherwise. The next day things looked much brighter – Cuddles had not bled overnight and showed an improved appetite. The following day dawn broke for the third time on a scene of gory water, but analysis showed the blood loss to have been much reduced and the haemoglobin level, though still below the critical minimum, was levelling out. Still seriously worried, but no longer in complete despair, I repeated my injections and the dustbin mixture.

By now the laboratory results were all back. No bacteria were involved. The cause of the ulcers remained a mystery, as it does to this day, although I strongly believe a virus to have been the culprit. Cuddles continued to eat quite well and even agreed to play gently. He did not haemorrhage on the day after the third bleeding, nor on the next day or the one after that. I became increasingly hopeful. The whale was still very pale but steadily growing stronger and I fortified his fish by packing them with chunks of cooked Lancashire black puddings, rare delicacies made from blood and fat.

Cuddles never bled again. His recovery was fast and free from further incident. Two weeks after the first attack his blood analysis was halfway back to normal and in a further three weeks it was completely satisfactory. By this time he was greedily gulping down whole undisguised black puddings by the dozen and opening his now salmon-pink mouth with alacrity to have foaming quarts of Guinness poured straight into his gullet.

Many things about Cuddles' bleeding disease I do not understand, and which if any of my lines of treatment helped to save the day will never be known. Certainly the transfusions only averted death from shock and tackled some of the circulatory complications. Perhaps it was the kaolin or the anti-inflammatory drugs or the black puddings that turned the tide against the ulcers. Perhaps if a virus was involved Cuddles developed a rapid immunity which effectively combated the attack. A Devonshire woman working at Flamingo Park as personal secretary to the director had a different view on the affair. When it was all over we were talking and she told me what she had done to help the dying killer whale.

'When he bled the third time I went and phoned a wise woman in my home village in the West Country,' she told me. 'She's a person who uses white magic on warts and styes and rheumatism. Marvellous reputation. Never known to fail.'

'What did you say to her?' I asked.

'I told her briefly what was wrong at the dolphinarium and she just said that everything would be all right, and that the bleeding would stop when I put the receiver down.'

It sounded like the most ridiculous humbug to me, but I respected the director's secretary as an astute and intelligent woman.

'Well,' I said, 'can you remember the time when you finished speaking to your wise woman acquaintance?'

'Of course I can,' she replied with an odd smile. 'It was eight-thirty in the morning.'

I walked down to the dolphinarium and looked in the record book. Every minute item concerning the whale and dolphins in health and sickness is logged there day by day, year in and year out. On the morning of the third and final episode of Cuddles' bleeding a trainer had recorded the last occasion on which the whale was seen to pass blood. The time was entered as 8.31 a.m.

Chapter
Twenty-five

I N MY office at Flamingo Park I was going through
Andrew's dung list. While I was in Spain he had
collected samples of droppings from every animal in
the collection. With a microscope he had painstakingly
searched for parasite eggs, identified them and calculated
the actual number contained in every gramme of dung.
Now complete and neatly tabulated, Andrew's figures gave
a valuable run-down on the present status of everything
from elephants to egrets. The complicated cycles of parasites passing through a variety of hosts, the ingenious
methods they use to protect themselves and to find and
enter their prey, their amazing reproduction rate and the
subtle damage they can inflict deep inside the body are of
crucial importance to zoo veterinarians. Andrew was
providing valuable intelligence.

The telephone rang. It was the main gate. 'Someone to
see you. Big car. Posh,' said the cashier. 'Urgent, they say.'

'Send them over, please.'

As I walked outside, a pre-war Daimler limousine,
gleaming black with headlamps like frogs' eyes, drew up. A
uniformed chauffeur leapt out, opened the rear door and
stood smartly to attention. After some seconds a lady
emerged. The chauffeur saluted crisply and closed the door
behind her. My visitor was a tall, skinny woman of at least
seventy years. She did not stoop, nor was her back

hunched, but she somehow tilted the whole of her body forwards as if supported by invisible wires. I wondered why she did not fall flat on her face. The way she slanted, together with her scrawny long neck and aquiline features, reminded me strongly of an Egyptian vulture. She was wearing a big black straw hat and a long green velvet dress that smelled of camphor, eau de Cologne and mentholated vapour rub. Deep-set behind curtains and palisades of waxy flesh, two lizard eyes fixed me.

'Dr Taylor? How do you do. I'm Philomena Rind, from Harrogate.' Harrogate is the spa town near Leeds where the woollen merchants and others who, as they say in the North, 'think they're no cat muck' dwell in stone mansions behind thick privet and rhododendrons.

As I showed the old lady into my room, I wondered what animal she had got wrapped in a blanket on the floor of the Daimler. Animals resemble owners in my experience, and I weighed up the possibilities. Hardly a vulture or condor, despite the strong resemblance. Macaw? A strong possibility. Monkey? No, Miss Rind was not one of the distinctive monkey-owning types. Hawk or falcon? No: once upon a time maybe, but not now with her powdered throat and fingernails as long as a mandarin's. Her vibrations were of something quite different. Reptilian? Yes, that was it. She was going to send for the chauffeur in a moment and he would bear in a dyspeptic alligator or some such.

'An urgent matter, I believe, Miss Rind,' I said.

She sat clutching a large velvet handbag and scrutinising me intently with the lizard eyes. 'Yes, indeed, Doctor. It's Hugo.' She unclasped the handbag and put a hand inside. 'Hugo, my dear old friend.' Her hand emerged from the bag and carefully set something on my desk top.

It was a terrapin, as big as a saucer and with handsome striped head and red flashes behind the eyes. It began to row its way clumsily over the surface of my blotter.

Hugo's owner leaned even further towards me and spoke again in confidential tones. 'Do you see his eyes, Doctor, how they're becoming sore? And he's not eating a thing. That's why I've come to see you.' Her voice became a whisper. 'Mr Lawrence sent me.'

I picked the terrapin up and looked at it closely. The under-shell was softer than normal, yielding easily to finger pressure. The eyes were indeed inflamed and oozing cloudy tears. It was typical terrapin trouble – a deficiency of vitamin A and probably vitamin D and minerals too, most likely brought on by a diet of too much raw meat and no nourishing pond snails with their livers rich in the essential vitamins. Under that dark green shell there would be a pair of kidneys starting to pack up. An injection of vitamin A in oil might be just in time. It is an irreversible and lethal disease once it is well established.

'Mr Lawrence?' I remarked. The name was not familiar to me. 'Is he your vet in Harrogate?'

Miss Rind sat back and looked miffed. 'Dear me, no. Certainly not.' She seemed to soften slightly and leaned forwards once more. 'Doctor, do you know D. H. Lawrence?'

'D. H. Lawrence? The writer? *Sons and Lovers*, you mean? I thought he died years ago.'

'Yes, passed on. Have you never read his poetry? He wrote beautiful poems about tortoises.'

Oh Lord, I thought, a time-wasting crank. Poetry – what next? Anyway I never realised that Lawrence wrote poetry, let alone anything about tortoises. This must be a batty old bird with more money than she knows what to do with.

'I'm afraid I haven't,' I said coldly. 'I thought sexy gamekeepers were more in his line. Now, about this terrapin, the problem undoubtedly is . . .'

Miss Rind stood up abruptly and loomed over me. 'I haven't come for a diagnosis on Hugo, Doctor,' she interrupted with a boom. 'All I want is what Mr Lawrence instructs – Balm of Micomicon.'

I was totally at a loss. I had better start from the beginning, slowly. 'Please do sit down, Miss Rind. Just tell me the whole story.'

She lowered herself into the chair and started whispering again. 'Are you a believer, Doctor? In the after-life, the world beyond?'

'Well, er, yes. I suppose so.'

'Good. You wouldn't be one of us, I suppose – a spiritualist?'

'Afraid not.'

Hugo was snuffling about the plastic sachets containing Andrew's dung samples. He did not appear to be paying any attention to the conversation. Was he supposed to be a spiritualist, I wondered.

'Well, I am a believer, Doctor,' Miss Rind went on. 'I'm not fortunate enough to have been gifted with clairvoyant powers myself, but I have been greatly helped and uplifted by Mr Pickersgill.'

'Mr Pickersgill?'

'Our wonderful leader at Otley Road Spiritualist Church. A most talented medium.'

'And Hugo?' I interposed quickly.

Hugo had just recklessly launched himself over the edge of my desk when Miss Rind shot out an arm that looked like a flamingo's leg and took the catch in mid-air.

'Hugo here became ill, like he is now, about two weeks ago,' continued the old lady placidly, as though nothing

366

happened. 'Mr Pickersgill held a wonderful séance shortly after Hugo stopped eating, and that's when Mr Lawrence came through.'

'Came through?'

'He's on the other side now but still interested in animals – tortoises and things. He wrote so beautifully about tortoises when he was among us. "You draw your head forward, slowly, from your little wimple . . ." That's from his poem, "Baby Tortoise". Odd you've never read it, someone like you.'

I was losing the thread again. 'I'm sorry, Miss Rind, but I still don't understand.'

For the first time, the old lady smiled. 'No, of course, Doctor. Anyway, Mr Pickersgill suddenly found that Mr Lawrence was coming through, trying to communicate a message. And it was for me. I'd spoken on previous occasions to my father and to a Red Indian chief called Fire Mountain, but here was a famous writer concerning himself with me!'

It was interesting, but I must get back to being a zoo vet. Again I said, 'And Hugo?'

'That's who the message was about. Mr Lawrence said he knew Hugo was ill, that his eyes were diseased and that there would be no difficulty in curing him if I annointed them with – and he was quite clear about the name – Balm of Micomicon.'

'I'm afraid I've never heard of the stuff,' I said.

Miss Rind sighed heavily and flapped her arms. 'Just what the vets and doctors and chemists in Harrogate and Leeds all say. They've never heard of it and have no suggestions to make. That's why I came to you, knowing you have so many reptiles under your care.'

'But perhaps the name's wrong, garbled. If it's not in the drug lists, maybe it doesn't exist, unless it's some obscure old herbal remedy.'

'Dr Taylor!' She stood up again. 'I hope you're not suggesting that one who's passed into the Greater Awareness would lie. Mr Lawrence was quite specific. What's more, we used the ouija board afterwards and it spelled out Balm of Micomicon for all to see!'

I fetched a dictionary. There was no mention of Micomicon or anything like it.

'I'm sorry,' I said finally. 'I can't help with this balm, but I do know what's wrong with the terrapin. An injection is needed. Eye drops and ointments aren't the way to treat what is in fact a general deficiency.'

There was a long silence. Miss Rind sat motionless with her eyes glued on the reptile in her lap. Bubbles of liquid came out of Hugo's nostrils. He looked as if he had a rotten head cold, but he was far sicker than that.

'I don't know what Mr Lawrence will say, nor how Mr Pickersgill will take it,' she murmured eventually. 'They were so adamant, and said nothing about injecting the little mite.'

'It would be wise, I can assure you. If you like, I'll make you up a balm to apply to his eyes. It's the best I can do. Not this Micomicon, of course, but something soothing.' Then, like a sycophantic prig, I heard myself add, 'Mr Lawrence might understand the substitution in the light of our failure to locate the precise thing he prescribed.' Lord, I'll be spouting ectoplasm before long, I thought.

That did it. The old lady nodded. I prepared an injection and mixed a little chloramphenicol cream with a teaspoonful of colloidal silver. I jabbed Hugo in his groin and showed his owner how to apply the quasi-Balm of Micomicon.

Then, with the terrapin back in her handbag, Miss Rind thanked me, said she would let me know how Mr Pickersgill and others took things, stuffed a ten-pound note in my top pocket and swept out to the limousine.

Ten days later there came a phone call from Harrogate. Hugo was fighting fit, eating again and no longer having trouble with his eyes. 'Mr Lawrence says he's very pleased with you, Doctor,' Miss Rind purred. 'He came through again last Sunday. He thought your concoction was an admirable second-best.'

I put the receiver down and had an interesting thought: maybe if I ever got to Heaven I could swap my harp for a microscope and syringe and find plenty of work as a zoo vet?

Cuddles, the corsair of the oceans with a computer for a brain and the lethal power of a wolf-pack submarine, was like a lamb, as gushily soft as a Liberace with water wings. Martin Padley and I and the others working in the dolphinarium knew that; the public did not. The very name, killer whale, the vague recollection of stories by polar explorers of how these creatures had lunged up onto ice floes in pursuit of human prey, the way whaling fleets detested marauders who blatantly freebooted among the coveted blue and fin whale herds, memories of old sea-farers who had seen the sea turn red as packs of the distinctively marked assassins slaughtered whole dolphin schools just for the hell of it; all this patchwork of myth and reminiscence and folk memory made a reputation for his kind of which Cuddles, as he basked in his pool with love in his heart and his belly full of prime herring, was quite unaware. He liked people and seemed to try to reach out mentally towards them. People got delicious goose-pimples as they looked down at him. They thrilled and admired and shrank back. There was a chasm of incomprehension between the whale in the water and the primates with smaller brains that gibbered on the pool-side.

Martin and I did not include ourselves among these landlubbers. With much delight and more than a touch of exhibitionism we continued to swim daily with the whale. The crowds thought us ever so daring. In fact, I had never felt safer. Not noted for intrepid acts of derring-do, a fair to middling swimmer only, and with a concern to preserve my own skin from the attentions of nature red in tooth and claw, I nevertheless felt at home with the whale from the very beginning. I had been frightened by horses that lashed out with both hind feet at the slightest touch – not to mention a mad onager – cornered by hysterical Alsatians that made me sweat, and forced to back down by bloody-minded alligators. But Cuddles I knew instinctively to be benevolent. It was in his eyes, the carefully measured pressure of his jaws on my hand or leg, the squeeze of his flippers round my trunk, his very presence. We had our lingua franca of squeaks and whistles. Like making love to a girl from Venus, it was the way things were said and done rather than the actual meaning of the words exchanged that mattered. Looking through the literature, I could find no authenticated cases where killer whales had been proved to attack humans. The polar explorers' story of the animals breaking a pathway through ice to reach them did not end in actual assault and was, I believe, more probably just sheer curiosity on the whales' part. Americans had already swum among schools of wild killers and come to no harm. Eskimo lore contained no hard evidence, only tales of hunters paddling their kayaks into a fog-bank, never to be seen again and presumed taken by one of the 'Lords of the Sea'.

Scientifically, we were convinced that unlike the dim-witted and primitive shark which will snap at anything, even its own entrails after being disembowelled, the highly sophisticated whale does not do anything without thinking first with fine precision. It is equipped with sonar that can not only judge ranges but identify the nature of objects with a precision far beyond the capabilities of man-made devices: in pitch-black water it can distinguish between one kind of fish and another and even read the emotions of another of its species by 'looking' into the skull sinuses to detect internal blushing. It has an intricate communications system that uses unjammable codes so far uncracked, and eyes that see well above and below the surface. It seizes only what it wants to seize, never attacks blindly. And whereas it counts dolphins, seals, walruses, fish, diving birds, jellyfish, squid and, no doubt, ships as familiar inhabitants of its environment to be eaten, hunted, ignored or avoided in the natural order of things, free-swimming, awkward humans are outsiders, objects merely of curiosity and of less significance than a clump of floating seaweed. Killer whales do not waste time on seaweed, so we romped with Cuddles in the water during his first year without qualms. My own children did it. Nude model girls did it. The whale treated each and every playmate considerately and benignly.

I had overlooked one very important fact. Bright as they are, killer whales are not omniscient. Wise in the ways of the deep waters, of hurricanes that madden the breakers above and of the fire-jewelled shrimps that troll the abyss below, they know nothing of fellow mammals who stayed on land when they, aeons ago, went back to the seas. They assume that creatures plying their trade in the ocean can survive in a liquid world. Watching, touching, tasting me, Cuddles must have assumed too much. I imagine he was amused by my inelegant paddling around and impressed by the way in which so clumsy a beast could evidently hunt. This flailing pink ape had a knack of somehow coming up with an inexhaustible supply of fast-running fish like herring and mackerel. In my bathing trunks I showed no sign of possessing much in the way of weapons and my feet seemed very inferior to flippers and flukes. Still, the proof of the pudding was in the eating, and I appeared good at catching fish.

The crunch came when Cuddles assumed that I was good at something else. Killers can hold their breath underwater for more than a quarter of an hour. While it is true that a man has stayed under without special gear for $13\frac{3}{4}$ minutes, most homo sapiens, including pearl divers, have a far lower limit of endurance. Cuddles could not be expected to know such statistics when we began a new game one rainy morning in late summer after I had dived into his pool for our regular daily mixture of fun and veterinary checks while Martin and his trainers prepared the whale's food downstairs in the fish kitchen.

It all developed out of something we had enjoyed many times before. Cuddles would push me round his pool with the point of his snout stuck in my navel. I was expected to tickle his throat with my toes as he propelled me backwards through the water. Sometimes he would angle me down a bit and we would take a quick swoop towards the pool bottom, then up he would soar, balancing me perfectly as I crashed through the surface in a welter of foam. This morning Cuddles decided on a further variation. He would push me as usual, then he would stop abruptly. I quickly caught on that I was supposed to flounder away, escape him even, and when I was a few yards off he would come after me and gently pick me up once more on the tip of his snout. It was a sort of tag. Cuddles enjoyed the competitive

371

aspect of the new game immensely. He would roll slightly to one side and, with one syrupy eye held well above the water, watch me make off. There was the glint of an excited puppy in the eye.

I did quite well and on the odd occasion almost managed to sideslip when he took up the pursuit, which is not to be sniffed at when you realise that killers can turn on a sixpence and use their great tail-flukes to brake to a dead halt from sixty miles per hour in a second. I tried rolling under him; that worked quite often. The pink ape was learning. Cuddles thought it was all a marvellous wheeze but unlike a dog or cat, that will repeatedly make the same error at ball-games where humans are involved such as 'pig-in-the-middle', Cuddles used his vast expanse of grey matter to neutralise my evasion tactics. He began to come in twisting like a snake so that I could not see him for foam, or climbing up like a fighter plane to intercept me at my blind spot, below and behind. Always his final attack was gentle; I felt the round, warm smoothness of his muzzle press into me and I knew I had been caught again.

Next I tried deflecting his muzzle at the last moment rugby-style by pushing him off with a hand so that he cruised by me. Full marks to me. That, and a kick back with one foot pressed against his side, and I was away. Cuddles squealed contentedly and turned to follow me. I raised a hand to deflect him again. Before my fingers could touch him, he stopped dead, sank vertically a few inches and zoomed in for my stomach. With consummate ease he made contact, and to secure his hold dived slowly at a shallow angle. Holding my breath I went down, expecting any second to be taken up to the surface as usual for the next round.

But no. With a soft thwack, my back was flattened against the wall of the pool. Not painfully – Cuddles was far too careful with folk to act roughly, even in the heat of a good game. He simply pressed me against the concrete. I could almost hear him clicking through the water, 'Now, old friend, gotcha! Get out of this one if you can!' All of which was fine, good, clean, healthy fun – except that we were four feet under water. He could hold his breath for fifteen minutes and I knew it. I might manage no more than two at a pinch, and he did *not* know it.

I pushed. Cuddles increased the pressure just enough by the minutest vibration of his tail fluke. I wriggled, tried to squeeze sideways, thumped on his fat-filled forehead. Cuddles did just enough to make sure I was fixed. My wriggles and thumps no doubt showed how much I was enjoying myself. Cuddles liked being thumped.

Fear swept through me. My lungs were ready to explode. I must breathe, even if it was only one last inhalation of sparkling blue water. I remember the resentment I felt at dying accidentally, the ridiculousness of it all. It seemed absurd to be drowning in fun instead of dying in a rational, professional manner under the fury of a badly tranquillised polar bear, lanced unexpectedly by an oryx or even from some virus picked up at an autopsy. As my fear turned to terror and my resentment to despair, Cuddles remained motionless but transfixing me as surely as a pin holds a butterfly in its glass case.

The haze of green and blue, the dancing white bubbles, the black fuzz of the whale's head were beginning to spin when I heard through the rising roar in my ears a far-off whistle. Instantly the pressure on my stomach disappeared and I felt my hair grabbed and pulled painfully. The next moment my head was above water and I was pulling in chest-fulls of precious air. Martin was kneeling on the pool-side, holding me up by my hair while the rest of me dangled like a string of frog-spawn. Cuddles was floating a few feet away with his mouth open and his eyes fixed on the gleaming bucket by Martin's side. By good fortune the head trainer had come up with the first fish of the day at exactly the right moment. He had taken in the situation immediately and blown his whistle to give the 'come and get it' signal to the whale, who had at once left our deadly game and gone to breakfast.

Martin helped me out. When I had got my nerves under control I issued an instruction that no-one was to swim alone with Cuddles ever again. Killers may not attack human beings but I knew now how easily they could kill accidentally.

Things were never the same again. Children and model girls were no longer invited to have a dip with the genial giant. When we went in, there was always someone on the side with a whistle and a bucket of fish, just in case. About that time we found out that some of the American marinelands always had a baseball bat on hand when their killers were being ridden. They did not like talking about it, but it was plain that other folk had had their doubts about the safety of these whales.

Before long it was Martin's turn to revise his ideas about our cuddly Cuddles. 'I can't put my finger on it,' he said to me one day after a session swimming with the whale, 'but I don't feel as secure with him any more.'

We discussed it, but could not arrive at any precise reason for his apprehension. Perhaps it was Martin's knowledge of my experience. Certainly Cuddles was playing games with greater gusto than ever, but he was still good-natured and cheerful all day long.

Then Cuddles developed a fetish for rubber flippers.

374

First he started refusing to release the grip of his teeth on the black, webbed footwear of a diver in his pool. Quickly this worsened to the point where he was obsessed with the things and, with a jerk of his head, would wrench the flipper off the wearer's foot. A pink and white unclad human foot, complete with toes, was of no interest; Cuddles was just kinky about frogman's gear. His pursuit of a man wearing the flippers became doubly keen to the point where he would surge up and snatch them off as the swimmer scrambled over the pool edge. The first Achilles tendon sprains appeared. Martin's fears deepened, but we decided to continue swimming with the whale whenever necessary for veterinary inspections and for cleaning and maintaining the pool.

The next stage was more serious. Like an underwater commando, Cuddles would neatly break the air-pipe of a diver's scuba gear, forcing him to surface rapidly. The latter was not so easy if the attack then turned, as usual, to the flippers. We stopped the use of scuba gear unless absolutely essential and made do with masks and snorkels. Cuddles soon found he could rip the masks off, breaking the rubber retaining bands with ease.

Finally, Martin walked dripping into my office with his wet-suit in tatters. There were blue weals on his skin below long tears that had shredded the rubber in half a dozen places. He looked pale and grim.

'I went in to seal a leaking window,' he said, shivering. 'Cuddles came up like an express train and tried to rip my suit off. His teeth bruised me for the first time. I can tell you, I was bloody scared.'

So our salad days were over and swimming with Cuddles came to an end. On special occasions when we had to go into the water, we wore bathing trunks and hung protective nylon netting between us and him. I believe that the wet-suits were the key to the problem. In them men became sealions. Sleek and shiny, with a changed outline and a different, more facile movement through the water, maybe these mermen awakened memories in Cuddles' subconscious of those fin-footed creatures like seals which, while of the ocean, have not totally forsaken their ancient home on land and which, while able to dart like arrows through the dark water, are not able to out-think or out-manoeuvre the killers who find them such tasty morsels.